HOMEBUILDING
&RENOVATING
M A G A Z I N E
BOOK OF

HOUSE
PLANS

an
ovolo
book

1

Ovolo Publishing Ltd, I The Granary, Brook Farm, Ellington, Huntingdon, Cambridgeshire PE28 0AE

This edition © 2007 Ovolo Publishing Ltd, I The Granary, Brook Farm, Ellington, Cambridgeshire PE28 0AE.
Original text and illustrations © 2002-2006 Ascent Publishing Ltd, St Giles House, 50 Poland Street, London W1F 7AX

ISBN: 978 0 9548674 54

The publishers make no representation, express or implied, with regard to the accuracy of the information
contained in this publication and cannot accept any responsibility in law for any errors or omissions. The information
in this publication contains general guidelines only and does not represent to be advice on any particular matter or
project. No reader, purchaser or other third party should act on the basis of material or information contained in
this publication without first taking professional advice appropriate to their particular circumstances.

The plans in this book have previously appeared in Homebuilding & Renovating magazine –
Britain's best selling monthly for self-builders and renovators (www.homebuilding.co.uk).

This edition first published in the UK by Ovolo Publishing Ltd. Printed in China

To purchase books about property and home interest please visit:
www.buildingbooksdirect.co.uk
or call: 01480 891595 (24 hours)
For information about Ovolo publications please visit:
www.ovolobooks.co.uk

How to get the best from this book

All of the houses and bungalows are sorted first by the number of bedrooms and then by volume (as shown by square meterage)

Traditional style

HOUSE TYPE
Icons show the exterior style of each building, either: barn; traditional or contemporary.

Barn style

Traditional style

Contemporary style

Floor area

$242m^2$
$2605ft^2$

FLOOR AREA
The size of the house is quoted in square metres and square feet. Figures are rounded up or down to the nearest square metre. The square foot figure is converted from the square metre figure and rounded to the nearest square foot.

Bedrooms

4

NUMBER OF BEDROOMS
The number of bedrooms is not always clear cut as some rooms have an optional use. Where a bedroom is shown as having an alternative use on the plan such as bedroom/study, we have made a subjective choice. In some cases you could change room use to have more or less bedrooms.

Bathrooms

2

Floors

2

NUMBER OF BATHROOMS
All rooms with washing facilities are included in this figure – including downstairs shower rooms, but toilets without a shower or bath are not included.

NUMBER OF FLOORS
This lists all the floors in a house including basements and attics with rooms designed for habitation.

Key features
Kitchen/dining room
Study
Utility room
Double-height hall
Galleried landing

KEY FEATURES
A quick guide designed to help you choose which plans to look at.

Garaging for
2 cars

GARAGING
Lists how many garage places there are on the plan but excludes car port spaces.

Design
Great House Co

DESIGNER AND CONTACT DETAILS
Web site, e-mail address and/or phone number (where available) for the designer or building company who own the plans.

www.ovolopublishing.co.uk
01480 891777

BUILD COST
This figure is an estimate based on three factors: house size; location (which assumes an average price); and quality/type of build (which is based on a figure between that for an excellent quality build using a builder and subbies and that for a standard quality build using a main contractor). Guide figures to work out the build cost of a home in different areas of the UK and using a wider range of different construction routes are shown on page 10.

COPYRIGHT
Each plan in thiis edition is copyright as indicated here. This means that you cannot use the plan without permission.

Build cost
£217,000

Design © Great House Co

Getting started

Your essential introduction to Homebuilding and Renovating

Undertaking a homebuilding or renovating project gives you the opportunity to create a home built to your chosen design and specification in the location of your choice, at a cost that is likely to be considerably less than the market value of the completed project.

Each year around 15,000 new one-off homes are built by private individuals, and a further 3-5,000 are created through the change of use of an existing building, e.g. a barn or school conversion. All of these projects are treated by HM Customs & Excise as new dwellings and, as such, the building work involved is largely free of VAT (see section on VAT and Self-build).

In addition to these 'self-builders', there are thousands more who undertake a renovation project: modernising, extending, or remodelling an existing house to create an individual home. There are no official figures for these projects, but estimates suggest that there are around 20-30,000 major renovations every year, with tens of thousands more undertaking smaller extension or remodelling schemes. Work to existing houses is almost always subject to VAT at the standard rate, unless they are listed or have been empty for three or more years (see section on VAT.)

A home designed for your needs

The external design of a new house or renovation project will be controlled to a greater or lesser degree by local planning policies (see section on Planning Permission) — however, this still leaves considerable scope to create a unique house.

Providing you choose the right plot in the right location, you can build in almost any style you choose, from a cutting edge contemporary style property in glass and steel, to a traditional cottage. (For archive H&R case studies visit www.homebuilding. co.uk.) Even where planning controls place limitations on the external appearance of a development, the internal layout can be configured in almost any way you choose, constrained only by the statutory Building Regulations and the limits of available materials. You can create a floorplan with any number, size, shape and interrelationship of rooms you desire, arranged to suit the individual living requirements of your household. You can also choose to create

inspirational living spaces with features such as double height rooms, galleries and vaulted ceilings.

Freedom of design also extends to the selection of all of the fixtures and fittings throughout the house, so from the outset you can choose the right flooring, doors, windows, staircase, kitchen, bathrooms, showers, fireplaces and lighting. You can incorporate at first fix stage other modern features such as underfloor heating, air conditioning, smart house technology and modern plumbing, as well as choose the specification of the construction itself to create a home that is designed to be, for example, highly energy efficient.

How the savings are made

Very few self-builders or renovators spend more on their new home than it is worth when completed. Self-build and conversion is generally more cost effective than renovation, as it is largely free of VAT. Average savings are 15-25% when comparing the market value of a completed property with total development costs. This saving reflects the effort and risk involved in undertaking the development, and the time and resources invested. Self-builders are effectively buying their property at cost price, i.e. the net cost of land, labour and materials. How much is saved depends on the quality of design (i.e. building the optimum house for the plot), and the efficiency of the build process.

HOW TO SELECT A DESIGNER

Hiring an experienced designer with a good track record in one-off housebuilding is essential, both in terms of ensuring the house is appropriate for the site, and that it can be built cost effectively. Design has two main stages: Concept/Planning and Detailed Design. Some designers also offer project management services (see below).

Experienced house designers will include chartered architects, architectural technologists, surveyors and engineers, and also partly- or non-qualified house designers. Experience and flair are just as important as qualifications when it comes to house design, so make sure that you meet several designers, visit their projects and talk to their clients before making any decisions. You can find an architect via the RIBA Client Advisory service; 0207 580 5533. Be aware that designers may have different strengths in different areas and that you do not necessarily have to use the same designer for all of the work.

Who should project manage?

Effective project management is the key to delivering the finished house on time and on budget. Project management services are offered by architects, surveyors and professional project managers. Fees for managing the build will typically range from 3-10%. If you choose to use a project manager, their track record is everything, so speak to several of their previous clients.

If you are using an experienced contractor who is on site every day, you may decide that you do not require a project manager, but will oversee the work yourself instead. This works for many.

Other self-builders choose to take on the role of both project manager and contractor themselves, hiring individual tradespeople (see section on Build Routes). Project management is not a task to be taken on lightly, but can result in significant savings if carried out efficiently.

Raising the money

Providing you have a regular income and a reasonable credit history, you should have no difficulty in obtaining a loan to build your own home or to undertake a renovation or conversion project.

For details of lenders that offer mortgages for homebuilding projects see the H&R finance table below. For full details of mortgage stage payments, terms and conditions, contact individual lenders direct. In addition to the lenders in the table, there are others, such as Halifax HBoS, who will finance conversions, but will not lend on land.

It is also possible to finance your project using a bridging loan secured against equity in your current home, either in conjunction with, or instead of, a stage payment mortgage secured against the building project. This kind of funding, often charged at a small

THE H&R GUIDE TO STAGE PAYMENT MORTGAGES FOR SELF-BUILDERS

Lender	Contact No	Web Address	Advance on Land	Advance for for Building	Stage Payment Details for a Two Storey House	Maximum Loan on Completion
Amber Homeloans (Self-cert)	0870 870 9991	buildstore.co.uk	Max 95%	Max 95%	Flexible stages, released in advance	Max 90%
Bank of Ireland (N.Ireland only)	02890 241155	bank-of-ireland.co.uk	Max 100%	Max 100%	Flexible stages, released in arrears	Max 95%
Barclays Bank - via branches	0800 000929	barclays.co.uk	Max 80%	Max 80%	Five flexible stages, in arrears	Max 95%
Capital Bank	0845 7253 253	bankofscotland.co.uk	Max 75%	Max 80%	Flexible stages, released in arrears	Max 95%
Cheshire BS	0800 243278	cheshirebs.co.uk	Max 60%	Max 75%	Four set stages, released in arrears	Max 95%
Clay Cross BS (England and Wales)	0800 834497	claycrossbs.co.uk	Max 75%	Max 75%	Four flexible stages, released in arrears	Max 95%
Ecology BS (Eco projects only)	0845 6745566	ecology.co.uk	Max 90%	Max 90%	Flexible stages, released in arrears	Max 90%
Ecology BS (Accelerator)	0870 870 9991	buildstore.co.uk	Max 95%	Max 95%	Flexible, released in advance	Max 95%
Furness BS	0800 834312	furnessbs.co.uk	Max 75%	Max 75%	Five set stages, released in arrears	Max 95%
Kent Reliance BS	01634 848944	krbs.co.uk	Max 25%	Max 75%	Four set stages, released in arrears	Max 95%
Leeds BS	08450 502230	leedsbuildingsociety.co.uk	Max 85%	Max 85%	Five set stages, released in arrears	Max 90%
Lloyds TSB Scotland (Scotland only)	via branches	lloydstsb.com	Max 95%	Max 95%	Flexible, released in arrears	Max 95%
Lloyds TSB Scotland (all of UK)	01259 726650	afsbm.co.uk	Max 95%	Max 95%	Flexible stages, released in advance	Max 90%
Lloyds TSB Scotland (Accelerator)	0870 870 9991	buildstore.co.uk	Max 95%	Max 95%	Flexible stages, released in advance	Max 90%
Monmouthshire BS	01633 840454	monbsoc.co.uk	Max 75%	Max 75%	Four stages, released in arrears	Max 85%
Nationwide BS	0800 302010	nationwide.co.uk	Max 75%	Max 75%	Four set stages, released in arrears	Max 95%
Newcastle BS	0191 244 2468	newcastle.co.uk	Max 75%	Negotiable	Negotiable, released in arrears	Max 85%
Norwich and Peterborough BS	0800 883322	npbs.co.uk	Max 85%	Max 85%	Four stages, released in arrears	Max 95%
Progressive BS (N.Ireland only)	02890 244926	theprogressive.com	Max 80%	Max 75%	Four stages of 25%, in arrears	Max 90%
Saffron Walden BS	01799 522211	swhebs.co.uk	Max 70%	Max 70%	Min. £5,000 a time, in arrears	Max 90%
Scottish Building Society	0131 313 7700	scottishbs.co.uk	Max 80%	Max 100%	Flexible stages, released in advance	Max 95%
Shepshed BS	01509 822000	theshepshed.co.uk	Max 66%	Max 80%	Negotiable, released in arrears	Max 80%
Skipton BS (Accelerator)	0870 870 9991	buildstore.co.uk	Max 95%	Max 95%	Flexible stages, released in advance	Max 95%
Standard Life	0845 609 0257	freestylemortgages.com	n/a	Max 90%	Three stages, released in arrears	Max 90%
Stroud and Swindon BS	0800 616112	stroudandswindon.co.uk	Max 50%	Max 65%	Four stages, released in arrears	Max 65%
The Woolwich	020 8338 6020	woolwich.co.uk	Max 80%	Max 80%	Negotiable, released in arrears	Max 95%
TMB (self-certification)	0870 870 9991	buildstore.co.uk	Max 95%	Max 95%	Flexible stages, released in advance	Max 85%
Yorkshire BS	0845 120 0100	ybs.co.uk	Max 75%	Max 75%	Three stages, released in arrears	Max 75%

premium above mortgage rates, is offered primarily by banks. Lending is not usually restricted by the standard income multipliers that apply to mortgages but such a facility usually carries an arrangement fee, typically 1-1.5% of the advance.

As bridging finance is more expensive than mortgage finance, it is best suited to those who do not want or need a mortgage once they have sold their current home, or those who want to raise funds in addition to taking out a stage payment mortgage to help fund the project without having to sell their current home.

How much can you borrow?

The maximum amount you can borrow on a conventional mortgage is usually calculated using income multipliers to assess afford-ability. These are typically 2.5 x joint income, 3 x a higher income plus 1 x a second income or, for sole earners, 3–4 x income. Existing commitments, e.g. mortgage payments on your current home, may be taken into account when assessing affordability. Some lenders may consider offering a stage payment mortgage alongside an existing home loan, allowing you to remain in your current home during construction.

As part of your application, some proof of income will be required, typically in the form of three months' payslips and your latest P60. Self-employed applicants will usually have to provide two years' audited accounts or approach lenders, such as Skipton BS, Barclays, and HSBC who will consider offering funding on a self-certified basis.

Borrowing to buy land

Advances on land or existing buildings for renovation/conversion are usually available up to a maximum of 95% of valuation or purchase price, whichever is the lower. In most cases some form of planning consent must be in place for the development of a plot or conversion opportunity before a lender will release funds.

Borrowing for construction

Funding for construction is usually released in arrears on completion of key stages in the building work, after it has been signed off by either the lender's valuer or a supervising professional. Two specialist self-build mortgage arrangers, Buildstore and Riley Associates, offer an indemnity policy which allows some lenders to release funds in advance of the build stages. This can help cashflow and eliminate the need for bridging finance. The stages, and the percentage of the total advance released, will vary according to the number of storeys being built and the type of construction employed. Exact stage payment details should always be

MORTGAGE COST CALCULATOR

Monthly payment per £1,000 of borrowing at various rates of interest

0.75	£3.67	£0.63	2.75	£4.65	£2.29	4.75	£5.77	£3.96
1.00	£3.78	£0.83	3.00	£4.79	£2.50	5.00	£5.91	£4.17
1.25	£3.90	£1.04	3.25	£4.92	£2.71	5.25	£6.06	£4.38
1.50	£4.02	£1.25	3.50	£5.06	£2.92	5.50	£6.21	£4.58
1.75	£4.14	£1.46	3.75	£5.19	£3.13	5.75	£6.36	£4.79
2.00	£4.27	£1.67	4.00	£5.33	£3.33	6.00	£6.52	£5.00
2.25	£4.39	£1.88	4.25	£5.48	£3.54	6.25	£6.67	£5.21
2.50	£4.52	£2.08	4.50	£5.62	£3.75	6.50	£6.83	£5.42

discussed and agreed with your lender. You need to make certain you have sufficient funds to cover the initial fees.

Raising a deposit

Capital of at least 10-15% of the total project cost is usually needed to get a homebuilding project going. Although it is possible to get a self-build mortgage without selling your current home, most people choose to sell up in order to release capital. If you choose this route, do not forget to budget for somewhere to live and for storage — bear in mind that rental can be at least as expensive as a mortgage. The most common option for temporary accommodation is rental, although many people stay with family or in a mobile home on site.

Borrowing costs

Fees vary from lender to lender. Lenders may charge a mortgage application fee, typically £2–300. There will also be a valuation fee payable which will vary according to the value of your plot, typically £160–400. There may also be a separate fee for specialist products such as a fixed rate or capped rate mortgage.

Further fees are usually payable for the reinspection of building work prior to the release of each stage payment. This charge is typically £30–50 for each of four or more stage payments — check with your lender for further details. This role can also be undertaken by a supervising professional, such as a chartered surveyor, architect or approved warranty inspector (e.g. NHBC or Zurich), in which case there will not be an additional fee.

Interest will be charged at the agreed interest rate – usually the lender's current variable rate – from the moment funds are released, but only on the amount that has been borrowed/drawn down to date. Interest payments therefore start low and increase towards completion.

How to estimate your build costs

Construction costs for a new home vary, depending on the quality of the specification, the size, the number of storeys and your own level of involvement, either in managing the build or in undertaking some of the building work. You can gain a quick estimate of the likely cost per square metre ($£/m^2$) for your project by using the H&R Average Build Cost Guide. The Guide is based on figures researched by the Building Cost Information Service of The Royal Institution of Chartered Surveyors (RICS) for the purpose of estimating rebuilding costs. The Guide to Rebuilding Costs should be available from RICS (0207 222 7000). The H&R figures are adjusted to remove professional fees and demolition costs which are not always applicable to homebuilding projects.

To get an estimate of the likely cost of your project, take the three steps in the following pages or alternatively use the calculator online at www.homebuilding.co.uk.

The average build cost figures provided are based on houses built using standard brick and block or timber frame construction methods. They are not applicable to: unusual ground conditions requiring specialist foundations; steeply sloping sites; special design features, eg. oak frame, large areas of glazing; houses of very high quality specification; renovation or conversion projects.

Step One

Select the average build cost per square metre from the H&R Build Cost Guide (on page 10) by reference to your chosen build route, number of storeys, the area in which you are building and the quality of your specification.

VAT & SELF-BUILD

One advantage of building a new house, as opposed to renovating or extending, is that all of the building work is free of Value Added Tax (VAT), which means a saving of 17.5% at the current rate. If you are using a VAT registered contractor, then all of their invoices for labour and materials should be zero rated to exclude VAT. If you are managing the project yourself and buying materials, you will have to pay the VAT but will be able to claim it back on completion of the project by applying to your local Customs & Excise VAT office. Full details of the refund scheme are available from your local VAT Enquiries Office (listed under Customs & Excise in the phone book). A leaflet entitled VAT refunds for 'do-it-yourself' builders and converters (or VAT Notice 719) will be sent to you on request.

The main considerations of the scheme are:

- You are only entitled to claim back VAT if your house is a new building and not an extension and was not constructed in relation to any business activity.
- Your house must be built with the intention of residing in it and not for the purposes of selling or leasing.
- Where you are buying your own materials you should keep all receipts for submission with your claim.
- Where a builder is employed for the supply of materials and/or labour you should not be charged VAT for either. (If you are, contact your local VAT Enquiries Office before you make any payment.) Being registered for VAT, the builder will be able to claim back the VAT on their own return.
- You will not be able to claim back VAT for professional services, eg. architect, surveyor, engineer etc.
- You will not be able to claim back VAT on hire of equipment e.g. JCB, scaffold, power tools etc. However, you may be able to claim if a labour element is involved, eg. JCB and driver.
- You can only make one claim for a VAT refund and it must be made within three months of completion (receipt of a completion certificate from your local authority). Make sure that all invoices, the planning permission and proof of completion are sent to the VAT office with the claim form.

- You should receive a refund within 30 days of receipt of your claim.
- You do not have to do any of the building work yourself except as the organiser of the construction. You can employ any specialist help you need.

VAT & CONVERSIONS

Work involved in creating a 'new dwelling' through the conversion of an existing building is also largely free of VAT. VAT registered builders must charge the reduced rate of 5% on the supply of labour and materials which you can later reclaim on completion of the project via your local Customs & Excise office. Details are outlined in the leaflet entitled VAT refunds for 'do-it-yourself' builders and converters (VAT Notice 719). Renovation projects are not considered to be 'new dwellings' and are therefore fully rated for VAT unless the property has been empty for 3 years or more, or if you are changing the number of units, in which case a reduced rate of 5% is applied. Properties abandoned for 10 years or more are treated as conversions (largely free of VAT).

VAT & LISTED BUILDINGS

Work involved in carrying out 'approved alterations' to listed buildings can be zero rated by VAT registered contractors, providing the work has been granted listed building consent and is neither a repair or maintenance. Details are available from Customs & Excise and are detailed in VAT — Buildings and Construction (VAT Notice 708).

CAPITAL GAINS TAX

Capital Gains Tax is not levied on the sale of your 'principal private residence', so the profits from a homebuilding or renovating project are usually totally free of this tax, regardless of the sum involved. There is no published guidance but a period of 12 months is broadly accepted as the period that a dwelling must be occupied before its sale in order to distinguish private homebuilders from commercial developers who might seek to avoid taxation by briefly occupying their developments before selling.

Choose your build route

Your own level of involvement in the project will influence the build costs. For simplicity, the four most common build routes have been identified below.

Build Route A: The costs for building on a largely DIY basis, substituting around a third of labour costs with your own labour, employing local tradespeople to help with the rest of the building work. Materials purchased directly from suppliers/merchants.

Build Route B: The costs for building using local tradespeople hired on a direct labour basis. Minimal DIY involvement. Most materials purchased directly from suppliers/merchants.

Build Route C: Costs for building using a main contractor (builder) or package supplier to complete the structure to a weathertight stage, with the remaining work being undertaken by subcontractors with most materials purchased by self-builder direct from suppliers.

Build Route D: Building using a main contractor, typically a small regional building firm, or a design and build package supplier. Building in this way requires the least involvement from the self-builder.

Choose the number of storeys

Are you building with one or more storeys? The design of your home, and in particular the number of storeys, will influence the build cost (£/m²). A bungalow has a larger footprint and roof area than a two storey house of the same internal floor area. As foundations and roofs are two of the most expensive elements, a bungalow will be more expensive to build than a house of the same area over two storeys.

Choose the size of your home

The size of the property you build will influence the build cost. A larger property will tend to have larger rooms and proportionally fewer internal walls, fixtures and fittings. The economies of scale in building a larger property are incremental but for the purposes of estimation, three categories have been selected: small, medium and large.

Choose your region

There are considerable cost differences from region to region and within the same geographical area, eg. between town and country. For the purposes of estimation, however, the country has been divided up into four main regions. Urban areas are likely to be more expensive.

Choose the Level of Build Quality

The standard of specification that you choose will have an enormous influence on your build cost. For the sake of estimating purposes, three general categories of quality have been identified:-

Standard: This represents a basic build quality equivalent to that

---

CALCULATING GROSS INTERNAL FLOOR AREA

Calculate the gross internal floor area of your plans in m². This is the area measured to the internal face of the external walls and should include all floors (in most cases you can measure the ground floor area and double it or allow around 60% again for usable roof space, depending on the shape and pitch). If you have calculated the area in square feet then multiply it by 0.0929 to give the area in m².

---

offered by most speculative developers/housebuilders. Cavity walls: facing bricks (£250/1000 or £45/m² laid), insulation, 100mm blockwork; concrete interlocking tiles (£28/m² laid); off the shelf softwood joinery; studwork partition walls; basic range contract kitchen; basic range white sanitaryware; radiator central heating.

Good: This represents a superior level of quality equivalent to that offered by quality developers. Cavity walls: facing bricks (£450/1000 or £56/m² laid) insulation, 100mm blockwork; clay machine made interlocking tiles (£36/m² laid); high performance off the shelf softwood joinery; blockwork partition walls; top of the range contract quality kitchen; quality sanitaryware; underfloor heating.

Excellent: This represents a very high standard of build quality. Cavity walls: facing bricks (£650/1000 or £67/m² laid), insulation, 100mm blockwork; plain clay tiles (£45/m² laid); hardwood joinery; blockwork partition walls; bespoke kitchen; quality sanitaryware; underfloor heating.

Step Two

Having found the appropriate rate (£/m²) from the H&R Average Build Cost Guide, make any adjustment for quality or unusual materials, such as stone, natural slate, thatch etc. that may be necessary (see below) and then multiply the adjusted £/m² by the gross internal floor area of your design in m² to calculate a build cost estimate.

Calculate any adjustments

Using Roofspace: Using roofspace to provide accommodation is less expensive than adding a full extra storey. For estimating purposes, calculate the cost separately by multiplying the additional useable gross floor area by 70% of the average £/m² for the house.

Basements: The cost of constructing a basement varies according to ground conditions. For estimating purposes, treat basements as above ground space and include them as part of your measurement of gross internal floor area.

External Facing Materials: Alternative facing materials, e.g. hand-made bricks, natural stone, flint panels, timber or render will have a direct influence on overall build costs. To adjust for this you need to add or subtract an allowance/m² for your chosen wall cladding from the sum allowed for cladding within your chosen specification. Eg. for render on blockwork allow £25/m². For timber cladding allow £25/m². For handmade weathertiling allow £54/m². For plain clay weathertiling allow £32/m². For rubble walling/flint allow £90/m². For reconstituted stone allow £48/m². For natural stone allow £75/m². For Ashlar allow £130/m².

Roofing Materials: Alternative roofing materials, eg. slate, stone, hand-made clay tiles and thatch will have a direct effect on your overall build costs. To adjust for this, add or subtract an allowance/m² for your chosen roofing material from the figure allowed for roofing in your chosen Level of Build Quality (Eg. allow £45/m² for plain clay tiles. For new Welsh Slate allow £60/m². For second-hand slates allow £35/m². For handmade plain clay tiles allow £65/m². For reed thatch allow £80/m².

Specialist Foundations: The build costs indicated in the Average Build Cost Guide are for conventional concrete foundations of up to 0.5m depth. The cost of developing a site with unusual ground conditions, eg. clay, can add considerably to your build costs. Always ask your engineer or designer to investigate the ground conditions early on.

Sloping Sites: For estimating purposes, allow an additional £10/m² for every degree of slope, eg. for a 5° slope, add approximately £50/m².

THE H&R AVERAGE BUILD COST GUIDE (£/M² FOR GROSS INTERNAL FLOOR AREA)

Build Quality		Build Route A (DIY & Subcontractors)			Build Route B (Subcontractors)			Build Route C (Builder + Subbies)			Build Route D (Main Contractor)		
		Standard	Good	Excellent	Standard	Good	Excellent	Standard	Good	Excellent	Standard	Good	Excellent
SINGLE STOREY HOUSES													
Small 59m²–90m²	Greater London	940	1088	1308	996	1152	1385	1051	1216	1462	1106	1280	1539
	South East	824	954	1148	873	1010	1215	921	1067	1283	970	1123	1350
	NW, SW, East & Scotland	750	868	1044	794	919	1105	838	971	1167	882	1022	1228
	Mids, Yorks, NE & Wales	717	830	998	759	879	1057	801	928	1116	844	977	1174
Medium 91m²-160m²	Greater London	861	1045	1358	912	1106	1438	962	1168	1517	1013	1229	1597
	South East	755	916	1191	800	970	1261	844	1024	1331	889	1078	1401
	NW, SW, East & Scotland	687	834	1084	728	883	1148	768	932	1212	809	981	1275
	Mids, Yorks, NE & Wales	657	797	1036	696	844	1097	735	891	1158	773	938	1219
Large 161m²+	Greater London	767	1006	1261	812	1065	1336	857	1124	1410	902	1183	1484
	South East	672	881	1106	712	932	1172	751	985	1237	791	1037	1302
	NW, SW, East & Scotland	612	802	1008	648	849	1067	684	896	1126	720	944	1185
	Mids, Yorks, NE & Wales	585	768	963	619	813	1019	653	858	1076	688	903	1133
TWO STOREY HOUSES													
Small 90m²–130m²	Greater London	905	1047	1286	958	1108	1361	1011	1170	1437	1064	1231	1513
	South East	794	918	1128	840	972	1194	887	1026	1261	934	1080	1327
	NW, SW, East & Scotland	722	836	1027	764	885	1088	807	934	1148	849	983	1208
	Mids, Yorks, NE & Wales	690	799	981	731	846	1039	771	893	1097	812	940	1155
Medium 131m²–220m²	Greater London	762	923	1170	807	977	1239	852	1031	1308	896	1085	1376
	South East	669	810	1026	708	857	1087	747	905	1147	787	952	1207
	NW, SW, East & Scotland	608	735	932	644	780	989	679	823	1044	715	867	1099
	Mids, Yorks, NE & Wales	582	704	893	616	744	945	650	787	998	684	828	1050
Large 221m²+	Greater London	703	900	1130	744	953	1196	786	1006	1263	827	1059	1329
	South East	617	789	992	654	835	1050	690	882	1108	726	928	1167
	NW, SW, East & Scotland	561	718	902	594	760	955	627	803	1008	660	845	1061
	Mids, Yorks, NE & Wales	537	686	863	568	727	914	600	767	964	632	807	1015

These figures were updated on May 10th 2005. They are for estimating purposes only and must be used in conjunction with the guidance notes. If you live in Northern Ireland, the cost of building work is considerably lower than in the rest of the UK and you should seek local advice. As an indication, use the figures for Mids, Yorks, NE & Wales and deduct 10%. If you live in the Channel Islands, London is the most appropriate comparison but local conditions affect building costs and you should seek local advice.

Bespoke Joinery: To adjust for bespoke handmade windows and doors, add the joinery quote (excluding VAT) to your estimated build cost, less the allowance already in the costs of £40/m².

Bespoke Kitchen: To adjust for a bespoke kitchen in a good or standard quality spec. house add the quote for your kitchen (excl. VAT) to your estimated build cost, less an allowance of £20/m² for a standard or good specification or £40/m² for excellent.

Ceiling Heights: For every 0.1m of additional ceiling height (on top of the standard 2.4m) add 1% to your £/m².

Garages & Outbuildings: Although an integral garage is unlikely to be completed to the same standard of finish as the rest of the property, for cost estimation purposes include the area of integral garages within your measurements of the gross internal living area.

Step Three

To get an estimate of your total project costs you also need to take into account all other costs, e.g. plot, professional fees etc. Calculate these and add the total to your build cost estimate for a total project estimate.

Calculate your additional costs

Land Cost: Consult the www.plotfinder.net directory to get an idea of local prices.

Legal Fees: Conveyancing fees, Land Registry fees and local searches will typically cost in the region of £500-1,000. Speak to a solicitor.

Stamp Duty and Land Tax: SDLT will be levied on the purchase of any plot over £120,000. The tax is currently levied at one per cent for plots valued from £120,001-£250,000, three per cent for plots valued from £250,001 to £500,000 and four per cent for plots over £500,000. You will need to complete a land transaction return and file it with the Inland Revenue within 30 days of completion.

Topographical Site Survey: By surveyor or architect. Typical cost £350-500.

Design Fees: Architects' fees can range from 7-15% of the total build cost for a full service involving design, tender and contract administration. Plan drawing services only are also available from architects and other professionals such as architectural technologists, surveyors, engineers and non-qualified house designers. For planning drawings expect to pay from £2,500-3,500 plus VAT, plus a similar figure for Building Regulation drawings.

Structural Engineers' Fees: Design calculations required for construction details (usually foundations and roof) and as required by building regulations. Typical costs are £400-500. Speak to your designer or a surveyor. Contact RICS 020 7222 7000.

Planning Application Fees: Detailed application fee is currently £220.

Speak to your local authority planning department.

Building Regulations Fees: Budget £4-500 upwards for the plan fee and inspection fees. Fees for renovation and conversion work may be higher. Check with your local authority for exact cost details as each authority is free to set its own fees. The NHBC are also able to make the statutory inspections for Building Control purposes. Contact NHBC Solo for Self Build (01494 735363) for details.

Warranty: You need structural defects liability insurance. Typical cost is around one per cent of contract value (construction costs). Read *Insurances* in the boxed finance section.

All Risks Self-build Insurance: You will need public liability, employers liability and site risk insurance. £500-800. See section on insurances.

Services: Connection of water, gas, electricity, telecom and drainage typically total £3,500-6,000. Costs will depend on distance from the highway, and the location of mains services. Contact your local utility suppliers. For off-mains drainage costs contact specialist suppliers.

Demolition Costs: In the case of a replacement dwelling, the cost of demolition needs to be taken into account. Typical cost is £5,000-10,000 excluding the value of any items that have salvage value.

External Works: Typical expenditure on outbuildings and landscaping is around 15% of build costs.

STRUCTURAL DEFECTS INSURANCE

Structural Indemnity Insurance/Building Guarantees: Lenders will usually insist that some form of building guarantee is arranged on your new property to insure against latent structural defects. Typical cover will ensure that any problems that arise are remedied both during construction and then at any time up to 10 years after completion. It may be difficult to re-sell your new property without a building guarantee. There are currently seven types of cover against structural defects that are accepted by most self-build lenders.

- Architect's (or other recognised professionals) Certificates. Issued by inspecting professionals. RIBA 020 7580 5533
- NHBC's (National House Building Council's) 'Buildmark Warranty'. Issued by NHBC registered contractors only.
- NHBC 'Solo for Self Build'. Contact NHBC Solo for Self Build: 01494 735363
- Zurich Municipal's 'Custombuild Guarantee'. Contact Zurich: 01252 377474
- The Premier Guarantee (Liberty Syndicates). Contact: 0151 625 3883
- Project Builder (Liberty Syndicates). Contact Sterling Hamilton Wright: 020 7716 5050
- Self-build Zone. Contact: 0845 230 9874

For renovations, remodelling and conversion projects, structural defects cover is available from Zurich. Contact Zurich on 01252 377474

How to get Planning Permission

When you have carried out your design and are satisfied that it meets both your own requirements and those of your local authority, it is time to put forward an application for planning approval.

Most self-builders find this to be a frustrating and drawn out process which can cause delay and disruption to your plans. Having a professional on board – an architect, building surveyor, designer or planning consultant to take care of matters or guide you through this process – is often essential to gaining a successful outcome.

- Planning ensures the regulation of development and land use for the public interest. If you want to build a new house you will need planning permission.
- Planning permission is very much a sub-jective matter which, unless dealt with carefully, can lead to disputes. Unless you have sufficient experience, leave the negotiating to your consultant (who should have a successful track record) and be prepared to be co-operative.
- Even if your involvement is minimal it is important to have an understanding of the planning process.

Types of planning permission

There are four main types of planning consent.

Outline Planning Consent: Most building plots are sold with outline planning consent. This gives a rough indication of permitted development, such as the extent of accommodation and the height of the building, and includes a simple drawing showing the footprint of the proposed development. Outline planning permission is only a preliminary form of consent and is subject to a condition that full details will need to be approved in order for building to commence. Outline consent is valid for up to five years but you have only three years to apply for Approval of Reserved Matters.

Approval of Reserved Matters (Detailed Planning Permission): If a site already has outline consent, you will then have to submit detailed designs in order to gain approval to build. Building must then commence within two years.

Full Planning Permission: Is a combination of outline consent and reserved matters where all detailed information is submitted in one application. This is common where the proposed development is contentious. Plots in Conservation Areas or next to listed buildings are usually sold with full planning permission, as are an increasing proportion of conversion opportunities. Approval may be granted with conditions attached and is valid for five years

from the date of consent. NB: Existing planning permissions are not superseded by new consents, so making a fresh application for the dwelling you wish to build will not in any way jeopardise any existing consents.

Listed Building Consent: Is required in addition to planning consent before any alteration works can be undertaken to a protected (listed) building or for any new buildings within its curtilage. There is no fee.

Making a Planning Application

- An application form should be completed and submitted to your local authority, together with comprehensive plans and elevations, a copy of an Ordnance Survey site location plan and a site layout plan. You should also list, either separately or on the drawings, the external materials to be used. It is also a good idea to draft a covering letter, describing the implications of development, listing the documents you have provided and confirming the fee paid. A standard application fee of around £220 is payable.
- Your planning officer will make an assessment of your application before putting his recommendation to a committee of councillors (the planning committee) who will then make a determination.

ESSENTIALS BEFORE STARTING ON SITE

As it often takes some weeks to organise temporary supplies it is advisable to contact the relevant authorities well in advance of commencing construction. If you are running the site yourself, this will be up to you to arrange. The site will require temporary services, such as power supply for tools and lighting, and water supply for use when mixing materials and for cleaning and washing purposes. The site must also have WC facilities and somewhere protected from the elements for workmen to eat and take breaks. It is also a good idea to arrange to have a site office.

Authorities to contact

- Local Electricity Board
- Telephone Company
- Local Water Company
- Environment Agency (if you are unable to construct soakaways). Alternatively, you could avoid contacting the first three service authorities by replacing them with:
  - A chemical toilet
  - A generator
  - A mobile phone

However, you will almost certainly need a fresh running water supply.

- The local authority will register your application within around three working days of receipt. They are obliged to inform you how long they will require before making a decision (normally within eight weeks of receipt). However, the council could request an extension to this date. It is in your interests to co-operate; confrontation will get you nowhere.
- A decision notice will be sent out within around two days of a decision being made.
- Once you have submitted an application, it is important to keep in touch with your planning officer to see how things are progressing. They may be able to give you an indication of the likely outcome.
- If they propose to recommend a refusal you could wait for the final decision then appeal or choose to arrest the situation by either asking to defer the consideration so that appropriate changes can be made, or withdrawing your application and making a new one. NB: An initial refusal will be on record when, and if, a further application is made. It is possible, however, to avoid a refusal being recorded in the first place. Decisions do not become legal until they are sent out in the post, so if you get word of a refusal before the council contact you, write to them first declaring that you wish to withdraw your application.

Approval: If you gain approval it may be subject to certain conditions. Nevertheless, you are free to continue with construction.

Refusal: If the decision is one of refusal you basically have three options:
- Give up and find another site.
- Resubmit. You have up to 12 months to alter your proposals and resubmit at no extra charge.
- Appeal. If you are not happy with the decision and think you have a

case to reverse it, you have the right of appeal to the Secretary of State (whether it be for England or Wales).

However, you will need legal advice and you can expect to wait around 5-9 months for a decision, so it is not an advisable route — resubmission is far easier. Also, if unsuccessful, an appeal will almost certainly put an end to your scheme.

If you decide to proceed, request a guide to appeals from your planning officer and the appropriate forms.

Building regulations, like planning conditions, are statutory requirements that must be satisfied in order for construction to be carried out. They are laid down by Parliament and are aimed at ensuring adequate standards of building work are met, mainly concerning the health and safety of those in and around the building both during construction and for future occupancy.

- The legal requirements are detailed in The Building Regulations 2001. Technical guidance on how to meet the requirements of the regulations are given in the Approved Documents. The Building Regulations are available for purchase from The Stationary Office (0870 600 5522) or can be researched, along with other building regulations information, at reference libraries or your local authority offices. You can also download them at www.odpm.gov.uk.
- You should submit a building regulations application prior to the commencement of construction. A Building Control Surveyor will then assess your proposals and, if they conform, issue an approval notice.
- Following approval, the Building Control Surveyor will carry out a number of site inspections at various stages of construction – subject to notification – through to completion whereupon they will issue a completion certificate (see table of inspections).
- If you wish to occupy a self-build property prior to practical completion you may need to arrange for a habitation inspection.

Making a Building Regs application

- A Full Plans Application should be submitted to your local authority before you start building.

The application should include:
- Application form
- Plan fee (see section on costs — contact your council for fees).
- Drawings — two sets of detailed scale drawings with relevant notes showing service locations plus site location/block plan.
- Structural calculations/site investigations, depending on design and condition of site. Check with your local authority.
- The council will acknowledge receipt of your application and assign a Building Control Surveyor to your case. They will have up to two

TYPICAL BUILDING REGULATIONS INSPECTION STAGES

Stage of Work	Notice Required
Commencement	2 days prior to inspection
Excavation of foundations	1 day prior to inspection
Concrete foundations	1 day prior to inspection
Damp proof course	1 day prior to inspection
Hardcore oversite	1 day prior to inspection
Drain connection with sewer	1 day prior to inspection
Drains inspection	1 day prior to inspection
Drain backfilled and ready for test	within 5 days
Final Completion or occupation before completion	5 days prior to inspection

months (subject to agreement) in which to assess your proposals and issue either an approval or refusal notice.

- If your application conforms to building regulations standards you will be issued an approval notice. In most cases where defects are identified a conditional approval is granted, together with a schedule of amendments which must be complied with.

Refusal:

- If your plans do not comply, you may be given a Refusal Notice. The reasons for rejection will be stated. This gives you a chance to put things right and resubmit. The refusal will not go on record (unlike a planning rejection) and resubmission is at no extra charge.
- If you do not accept that refusal is justified you can seek a dispensation from the local authority. If you are still refused consent, you can seek a determination from the Secretary of State. Speak to your Building Control Surveyor for details.
- Legally, you can start work before an approval notice has been issued (apart from in Scotland), as long as you give the local authority notice of at least two clear working days.
- On issue of an approval notice many local authorities will also send a set of inspection request cards, which state the various stages of construction at which a Building Control Surveyor will want to carry out inspections (see table of typical inspection stages for a new dwelling). The notice required prior to inspection will also be specified. Note: Inspection requirements will vary with each local authority.
- Subject to notification of readiness for inspection, a Building Control Surveyor will visit the site to offer advice and carry out inspections at the various key construction stages determined by each local authority. If they feel in any way that they are not satisfied, they have the power to make you correct the situation. If you fail to co-operate you are liable for prosecution and costs.

A TYPICAL SELF-BUILD SCHEDULE STEP-BY-STEP

- Arrange a Mortgage In Principle
- Find Potential Plots
- Assess Development Potential
- Plan Budget
- Arrange Valuation of the Plot
- Arrange a Site Survey
- Purchase Site
- Arrange Site Insurance
- Choose Designer and Builders
- Create Your Design
- Get Planning Permission
- Apply for Water and Electricity
- Prepare Detailed Drawings
- Obtain Building Regs Approval
- Put Contract Out to Tender
- Select Builder/Tradesmen
- Arrange Warranty and Insurances
- Clear Site/Create Access
- Set Out and Dig Trenches
- Pour Concrete/Prepare Oversite
- Build Structure/Timber Frame Erecting Scaffold as Required.
- Build Roof Structure and Tile
- Make Weathertight
- Fix Rainwater Goods/External Decoration, Remove Scaffold
- First Fix Carpentry, Plumbing and Electrics
- Plaster Out Walls and Ceilings
- Lay Hard Floor Finishes
- Connect House to Mains Services
- Second Fix Carpentry, Plumbing and Electrics
- Decoration and Ceramic Tiling
- Landscaping, Driveway, Paths etc.
- Arrange for Final Inspection
- Completion/Moving In
- Correcting any defects

Contemporary style

Floor area
46m²
495ft²

Bedrooms
1

Bathrooms
1

Floors
1

Key features
Open-plan living area

Garaging for
0 cars

Design
**John Braid
(at Leslie R Hutt)**

lhuttarchitect@btinternet.com
01463 235566

Build cost
£50,000

Design © Leslie R Hutt

Plan no. **BHP 310314**

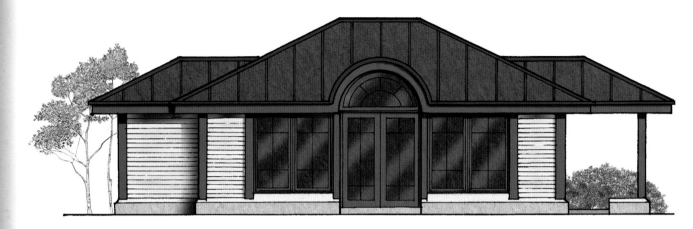

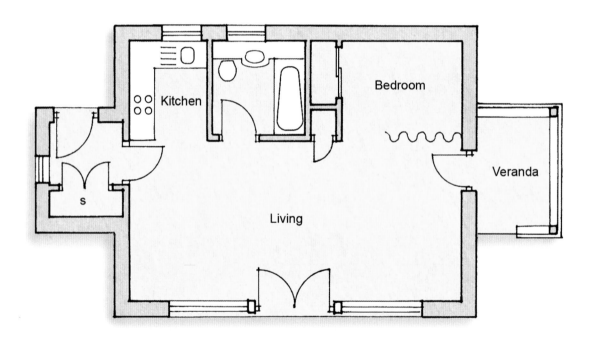

Ideal for a small plot with good views. This layout
allows maximum use of the available floor space - like
an individual loft apartment!

Plan no. **BHP**

01789 459148

There are some clever features in this compact design including the glazed end wall of the bedroom, which itself is galleried.

Bath

Kitchen

Breakfast Patio

Log Burner

Boot Room & Log Store

Living & Dining Space

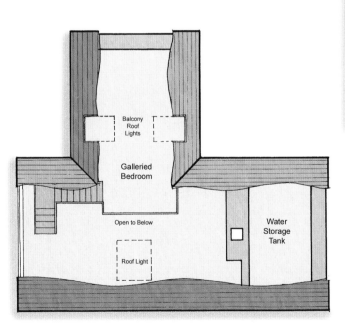

Balcony Roof Lights

Galleried Bedroom

Open to Below

Water Storage Tank

Roof Light

Traditional style

Floor area
65m²
700ft²

Bedrooms
1

Bathrooms
1

Floors
2

Key features
Galleried bedroom
Boot room/log store

Garaging for
0 cars

Design
Chaddock Design

www.dreamspelldesign.co.uk
info@dreamspelldesign.co.uk

Build cost
£70,000

Design © Chaddock Design

Contemporary style

Floor area
85.6m²
921ft²

Bedrooms
1

Bathrooms
2

Floors
2

Key features
Full height living room
Sleeping loft en-suite

Garaging for
0 cars

Design
**John Braid
(at Leslie R Hutt)**

lhuttarchitect@btinternet.com
01463 235566

Build cost
£90,000

Design © Leslie R Hutt

Plan no. **BHP 310407**

Putting a single en-suite sleeping loft into this space makes room for a lovely double-height living room that leads into a generous dining area. The kitchen could be extended with a conservatory-type breakfast room by making use of the space left by the L-shaped design.

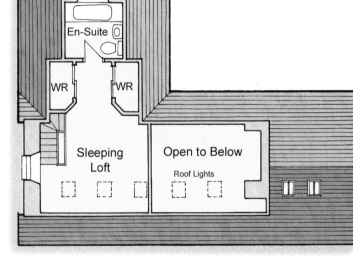

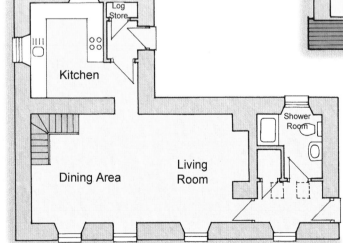

Plan no. **BHP 310740**

This house features a double-height ceiling over the kitchen and the feeling of ample space is increased by the downstairs rooms which flow into each other without interruption by walls.

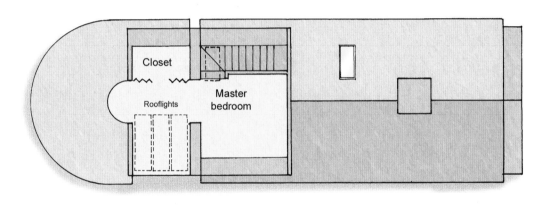

Closet

Rooflights

Master bedroom

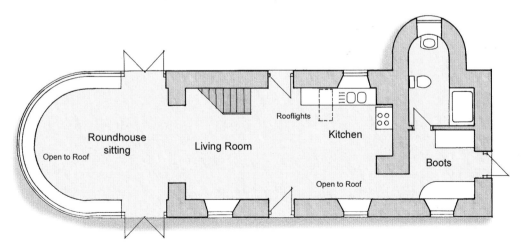

Roundhouse sitting

Open to Roof

Living Room

Rooflights

Kitchen

Boots

Open to Roof

Barn style

Floor area
110m^2
1184ft^2

Bedrooms
1

Bathrooms
1

Floors
2

Key features
Open-plan living area
Vaulted roundhouse

Garaging for
0 cars

Design
Jeremy Rawlings

www.periodhome.net
01884 266444

Build cost
£114,000

Design © Jeremy Rawlings

Contemporary style

Floor area
110m²
1184ft²

Bedrooms
1

Bathrooms
1

Floors
2

Key features
Open-plan living area
'Green' concept

Garaging for
0 cars

Design
**John Shida
(Morningtide
Developments)**

www.morningtide.fsnet.co.uk
johnshida@morningtide.
fsnet.co.uk
01621 815485

Build cost
£114,000

Design © John Shida

Plan no. **BHP 310446**

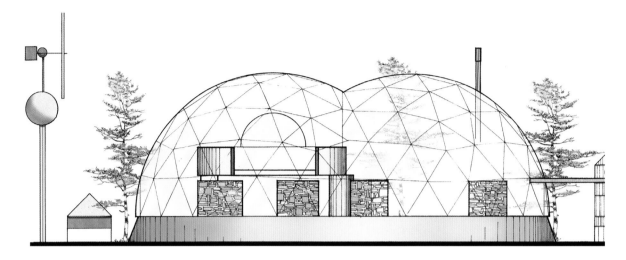

Like a scaled down Eden Project
John Shida's twin-domed house
allows all-round views of the
surrounding area from an open-
plan layout. A spiral staircase gives
access to the single bedroom
upstairs.

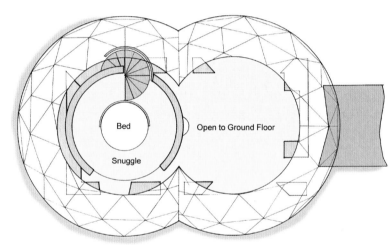

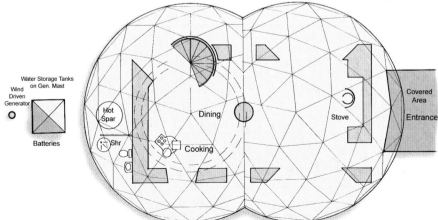

Plan no. **BHP 310767**

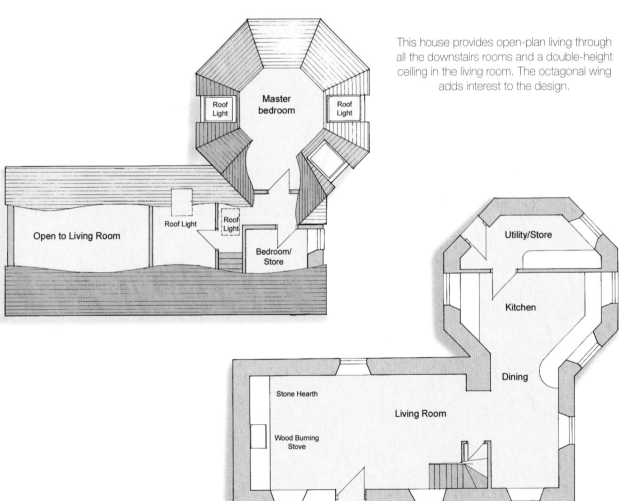

This house provides open-plan living through all the downstairs rooms and a double-height ceiling in the living room. The octagonal wing adds interest to the design.

Master bedroom

Roof Light

Roof Light

Open to Living Room

Roof Light

Roof Light

Bedroom/ Store

Utility/Store

Kitchen

Dining

Stone Hearth

Living Room

Wood Burning Stove

Traditional style

Floor area
110m²
1184ft²

Bedrooms
2

Bathrooms
1

Floors
2

Key features
Open-plan living area

Garaging for
0 cars

Design
JS Building Consultancy

www.ukbuildingconsultancy. co.uk
jsharples@ricsonline.org
0113 250 1303

Build cost
£114,000

Design © John Sharples

Contemplorary style

Floor area

64m²

689ft²

Bedrooms

2

Bathrooms

1

Floors

1

Key features
Open-plan living area
Shared bathroom

Garaging for
0 cars

Design
Architecture Plus

www.architecture-plus.co.uk
01934 416416

Build cost
£69,000

Design © Architecture Plus

Plan no. **BHP 310020**

A fully-glazed frontage allows great views from this single-storey house with its open-plan kitchen and living area. The two bedrooms look onto an internal courtyard making this design ideal for locations where there is no view at the back of the property. A rooflight brings natural light to the bathroom

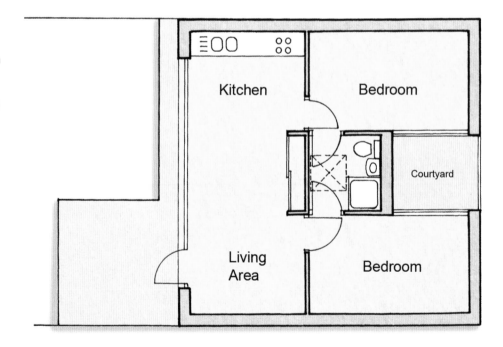

Plan no. **BHP 310059**

The stairs have their own semi circlular well so they don't intrude into the open- plan ground floor and allow maximum use of space on the first floor.

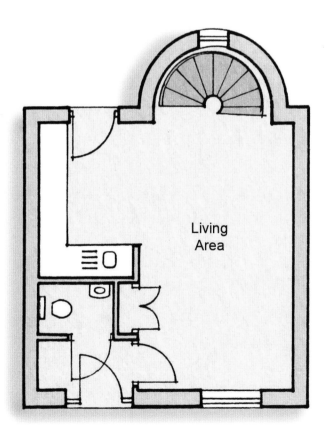

Living Area

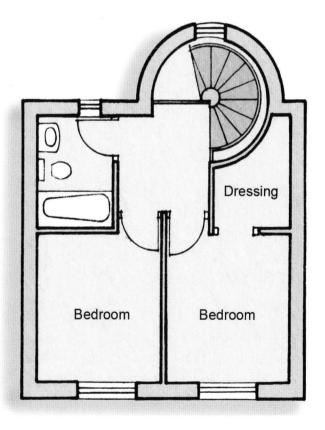

Dressing

Bedroom

Bedroom

Plan no. **BHP 310347**

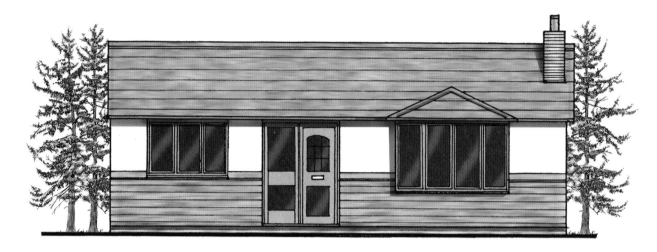

This is a fairly standard two-bed bungalow but with the added twist of an en-suite shower room for the master bedroom and fitted wardrobes in both bedrooms.

Plan no. **BHP 310999**

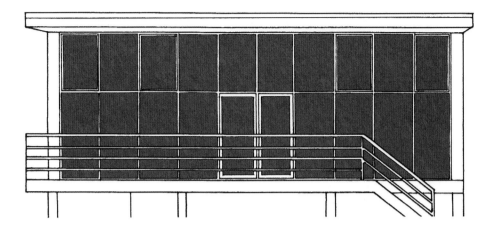

Both bedrooms and the main living area of this futuristic single-storey house have direct access to the outdoors. The fully-glazed frontage makes for a well-lit kitchen while the stilt-elevated floors lift the whole house out of the ordinary in more ways than one.

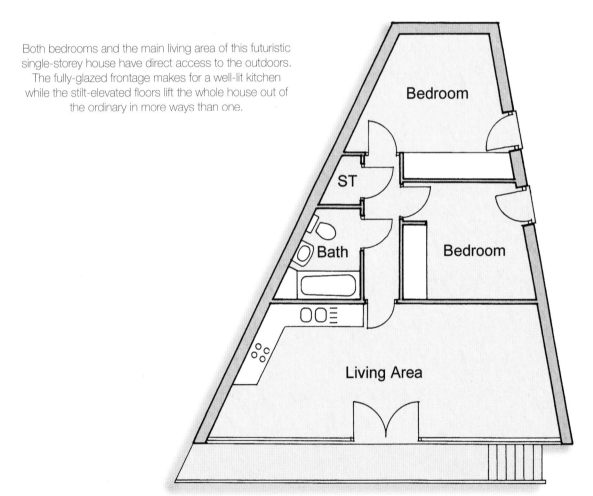

Bedroom

ST

Bath

Bedroom

Living Area

Contemporary style

Floor area
84m²
904ft²

Bedrooms
2

Bathrooms
1

Floors
1

Key features
Vaulted living rooms
Kitchen/dining room
Porch

Garaging for
0 cars

Design
**John Braid
(at Leslie R Hutt)**

lhuttarchitect@btinternet.com
01463 235566

Build cost
£90,000

Design © Leslie R Hutt

Plan no. **BHP 310416**

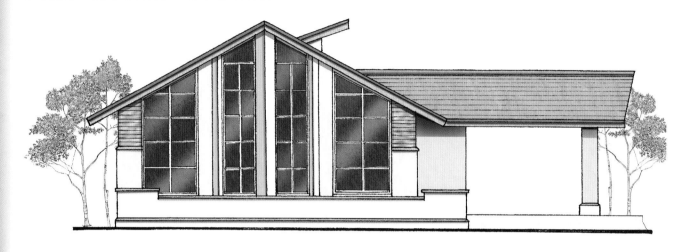

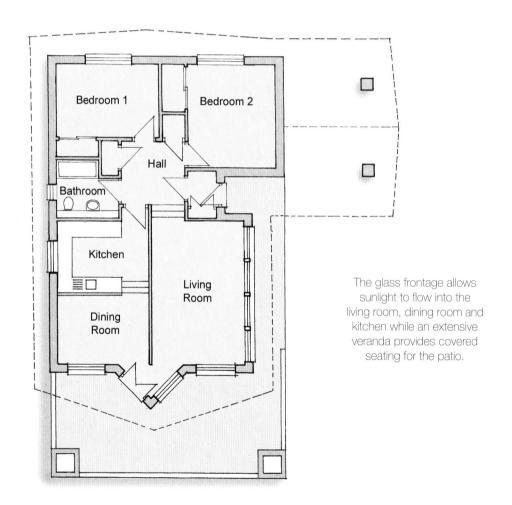

The glass frontage allows
sunlight to flow into the
living room, dining room and
kitchen while an extensive
veranda provides covered
seating for the patio.

Plan no. **BHP 310830**

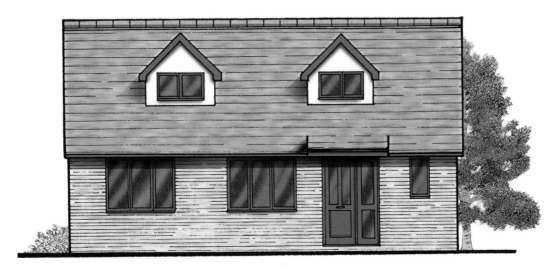

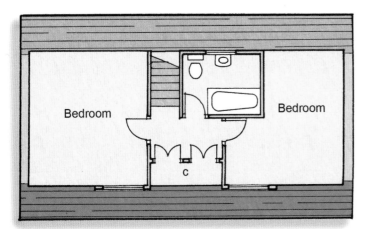

Bedroom

Bedroom

c

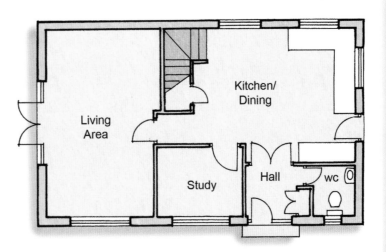

Living Area

Kitchen/ Dining

Study

Hall

wc

This is the perfect solution if you have a small plot that has height restriction problems. Dormer windows allow two bedrooms and a bathroom into the first floor while the combined kitchen and dining room make the best use of space downstairs.

Traditional style

Floor area
88m²
947ft²

Bedrooms
2

Bathrooms
1

Floors
2

Key features
Compact design
Kitchen/dining area
Study
Hall

Garaging for
0 cars

Design
Churchill Design

www.churchilldesign.co.uk
info@churchilldesign.co.uk
01252 325701

Build cost
£91,000

Design © Churchill Design

Contemporary style

Floor area
89m²
958ft²

Bedrooms
2

Bathrooms
1

Floors
1

Key features
Kitchen/dining area
Roof lights

Garaging for
0 cars

Design
John Braid
(at Leslie R Hutt)

lhuttarchitect@btinternet.com
01463 235566

Build cost
£92,000

Design © John Braid

Plan no. **BHP 310404**

Putting a clerestory window
into a single-storey house
creates loads of extra light
into the living rooms.

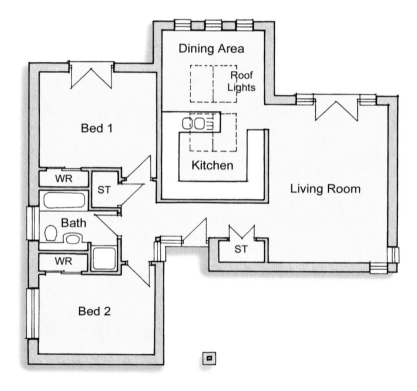

Dining Area

Roof Lights

Bed 1

Kitchen

WR

ST

Bath

Living Room

WR

ST

Bed 2

Carport

Plan no. **BHP 310026**

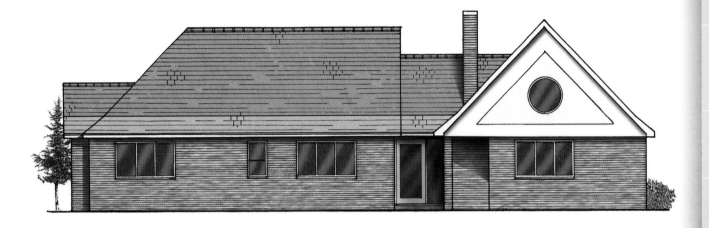

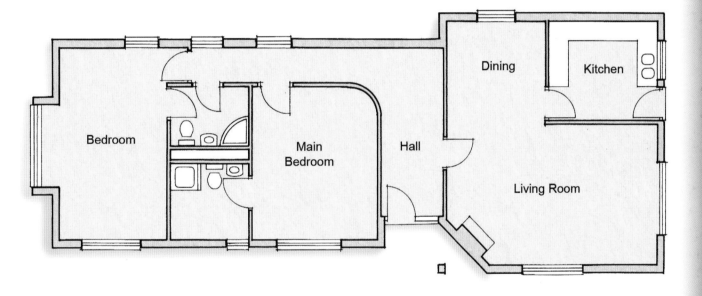

Bedroom

Main Bedroom

Hall

Dining

Kitchen

Living Room

Clever use of a curved interior wall increases the size
of the entrance hall, The living/dining room has triple
aspect windows for maximum light and both bedrooms
have en-suite facilities.

Traditional style

Floor area

92m²

990ft²

Bedrooms

2

Bathrooms

2

Floors

1

Key features
Living/dining area
Both bedrooms en-suite
Hall

Garaging for
0 cars

Design
**John Shida
(Morningtide
Developments)**
www.morningtide.fsnet.co.uk
johnshida@morningtide.
fsnet.co.uk
01621 815485

Build cost
£95,000

Traditional style

Floor area
96m²
1033ft²

Bedrooms
2

Bathrooms
2

Floors
2

Key features
Kitchen/diner
Real fire in lounge
Master en-suite
Playroom
Study

Garaging for
0 cars

Design
Architecture Plus

www.architecture-plus.co.uk
01934 416416

Build cost
£100,000

Design © Architecture Plus

Plan no. **BHP 310353**

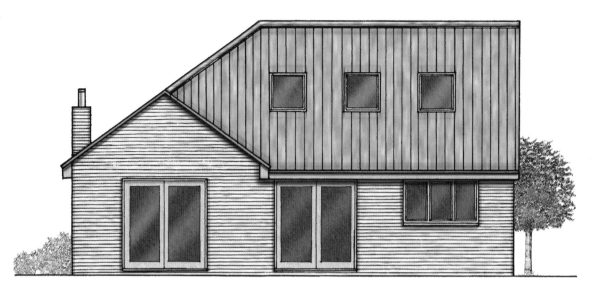

Lots of light and a great use of space are the two key factors
in this design. There's flexibility too – the first floor rooms could
easily become an extra bedroom and en-suite bathroom – great
for guests and permanent residents alike.

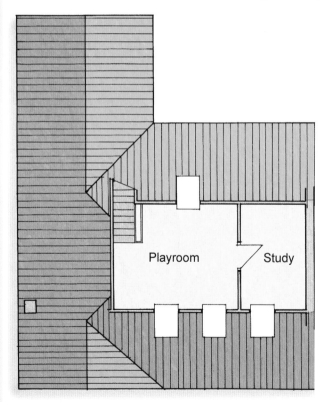

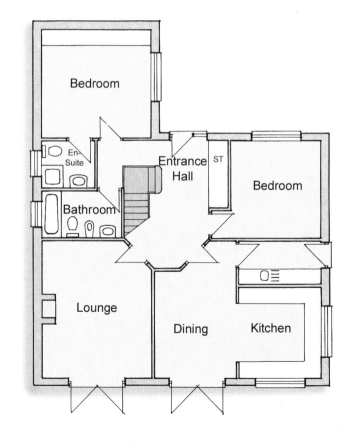

Plan no. **BHP 310350**

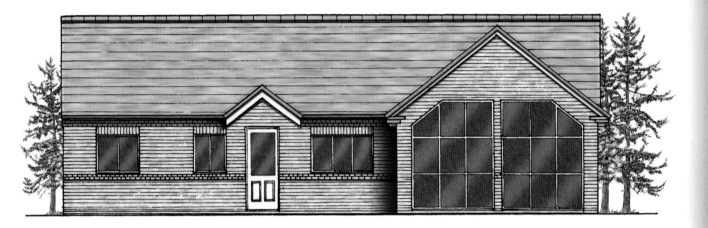

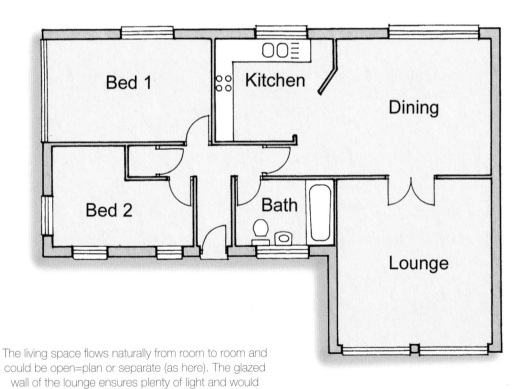

Bed 1

Kitchen

Dining

Bed 2

Bath

Lounge

The living space flows naturally from room to room and could be open=plan or separate (as here). The glazed wall of the lounge ensures plenty of light and would allow great views – if available.

Traditional style

Floor area
118m²
1270ft²

Bedrooms
2

Bathrooms
1

Floors
1

Key features
Linked living rooms
Full height lounge

Garaging for
0 cars

Design
Eclipse Design

www.eclipsedesign.
copperstream.co.uk
enquiries@eclipsedesignuk.net
0845 460 4758

Build cost
£123,000

Design © Eclipse Design

Traditional style

Floor area
126m²
1356ft²

Bedrooms
3

Bathrooms
1

Floors
2

Key features
Upside-down living
Full-width balcony
Veranda

Garaging for
1 car

Design
Architecture Plus

www.architecture-plus.co.uk
01934 416416

Build cost
£131,500

Design © Architecture Plus

Plan no. **BHP 310623**

This house offers upside-down living with bedrooms on the ground floor – great if you have views accessible from first floor height – as in many coastal locations.

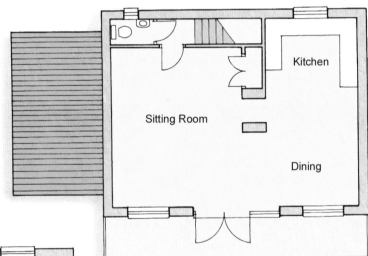

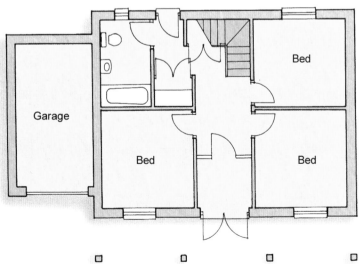

Plan no. **BHP 310458**

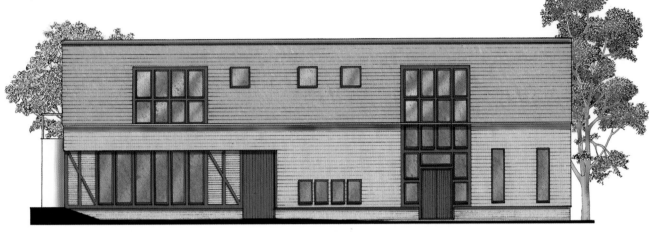

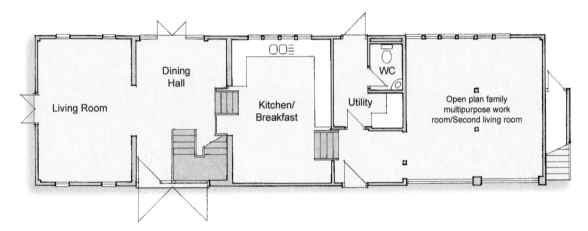

Living Room

Dining Hall

Kitchen/ Breakfast

Utility

WC

Open plan family multipurpose work room/Second living room

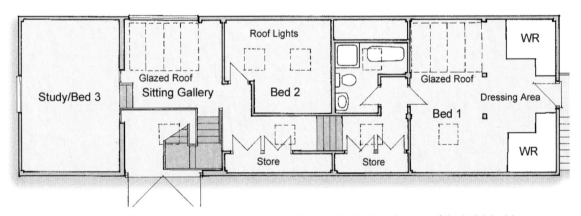

Study/Bed 3

Glazed Roof
Sitting Gallery

Roof Lights

Bed 2

Store

Store

Glazed Roof

Bed 1

Dressing Area

WR

WR

The beauty of barn-style living is the opportunity to install full-height windows in parts of the build. In this Chaddock design the windows flood light into the dining hall and the open-plan layout makes sure that both the kitchen and living room benefit too. Upstairs expansive glazed areas over the sitting gallery and bedroom 1 help to bring the outside in.

Barn style

Floor area
127m²
1367ft²

Bedrooms
3

Bathrooms
1

Floors
2

Key features
Kitchen/breakfast room
Dining Hall
Large family room
Utility room
Sitting gallery

Garaging for
0 cars

Design
Chaddock Design

www.dreamspelldesign.co.uk
info@dreamspelldesign.
co.uk
01789 459148

Build cost
£132,500

Barn style

Floor area
127m²
1367ft²

Bedrooms
2

Bathrooms
1

Floors
2

Key features
Kitchen/breakfast area
Dining room
Snug
Studio
Family room

Garaging for
0 cars

Design
James Campbell Associates

01706 354888

Build cost
£132,500

Design © James Campbell

Plan no. **BHP 310761**

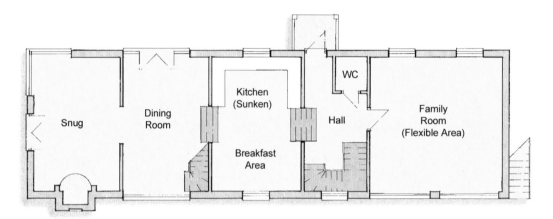

This house is all about wow factors. There's the link bridge over an atrium leading to a well-lit sitting room upstairs. Downstairs a sunken kitchen creates an interesting feature while the snug, dining room and family room provide loads of living space.

Plan no. **BHP 310491**

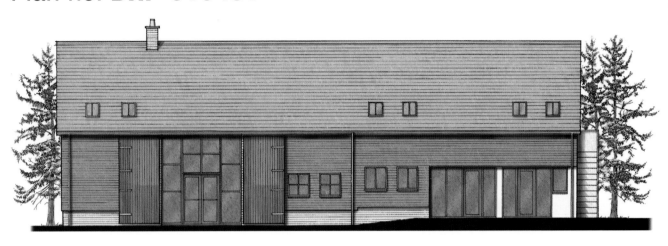

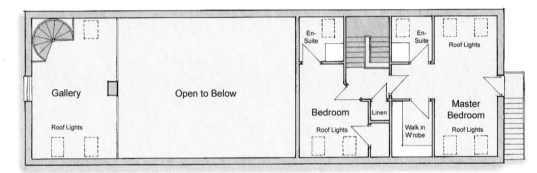

Gallery

Roof Lights

Open to Below

En-Suite

En-Suite

Roof Lights

Bedroom

Linen

Master Bedroom

Roof Lights

Walk in Wrobe

Roof Lights

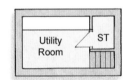

Utility Room

ST

The first floor of this design is open above the main living areas making these spaces light and airy. This design also allows for a mezzanine deck above the kitchen area. The first floor is split into two levels with an attractive gallery at one end. The guest wing can be accessed at first floor height from an external staircase. Finally, there is a semi-basement utility room accessed from the mezzanine floor.

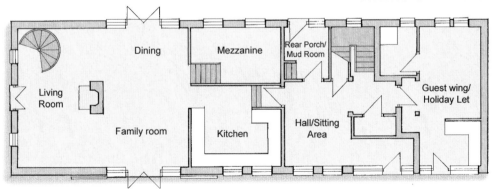

Dining

Mezzanine

Rear Porch/ Mud Room

Living Room

Guest wing/ Holiday Let

Family room

Kitchen

Hall/Sitting Area

Barn style

Floor area
127m²
1367ft²

Bedrooms
2

Bathrooms
3

Floors
3

Key features
Basement utility room
Double height living area
Guest wing
Gallery
Mud room

Garaging for
0 cars

Design
**John Braid
(at Leslie R Hutt)**

lhuttarchitect@btinternet.com
01463 235566

Build cost
£132,500

Design © Leslie R Hutt

Barn style

Floor area
127m²
1367ft²

Bedrooms
2

Bathrooms
1

Floors
2

Key features
Open-plan living area
Kitchen/dining area
Utility room
Office
Gallery/sitting area

Garaging for
0 cars

Design
Planahome

www.planahome.uk.com
plans@planahome.uk.com
01326 373600

Build cost
£132,500

Design © Planahome

Plan no. **BHP 310758**

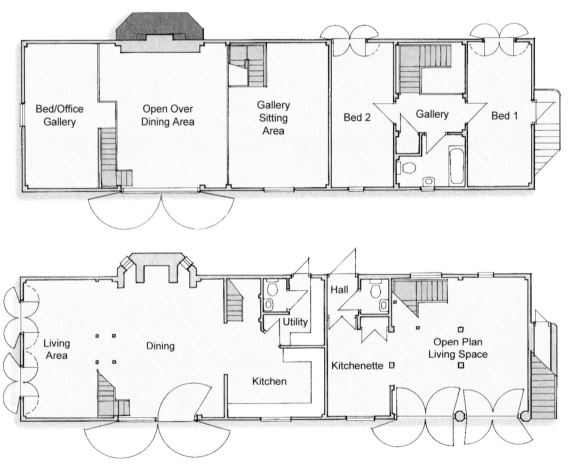

This house is all about open-plan living downstairs with excellent features like the twin galleried areas upstairs. There's also a handy annexe ideal for granny or holiday lets if you live in a tourist-friendly area.

Plan no. **BHP 310152**

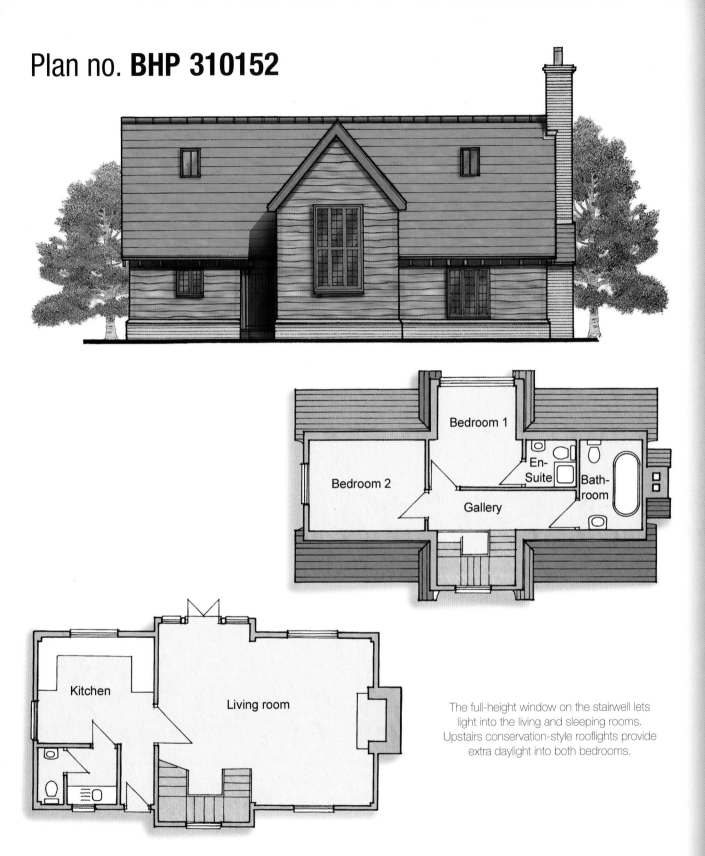

Barn style

Floor area
136m²
1464ft²

Bedrooms
2

Bathrooms
2

Floors
2

Key features
Pen plan living area,
Galleried landing
Utility room

Garaging for
0 cars

Design
Border Oak

www.borderoak.com
sales@borderoak.com
01568 708752

**Build cost
£125,000**

Design © Border Oak

The full-height window on the stairwell lets light into the living and sleeping rooms. Upstairs conservation-style rooflights provide extra daylight into both bedrooms.

Contemporary style

Floor area
146m²
1572ft²

Bedrooms
2

Bathrooms
2

Floors
2

Key features
Multi-level living
Open-plan living
Balconies
Reception hall
Both beds en-suite

Garaging for
0 cars

Design
John Braid
(at Leslie R Hutt)

lhuttarchitect@btinternet.com
01463 235566

Build cost
£134,000

Design © Leslie R Hutt

Plan no. **BHP 310836**

This John Braid design is a spectacular modernist sculpture you can live in. Features include an open-plan dining room, living room and kitchen. Two big bedrooms, a wealth of terraces and an attic store complete this package.

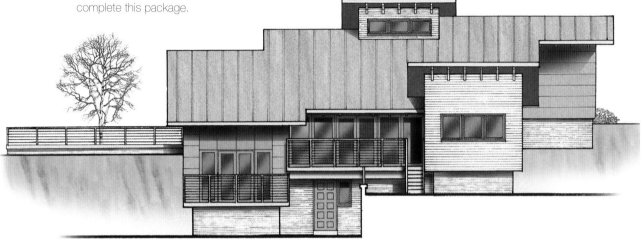

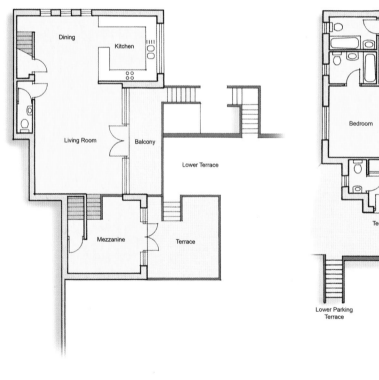

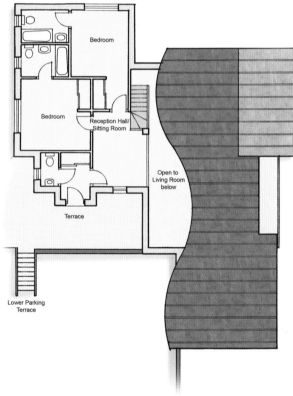

Plan no. **BHP 310833**

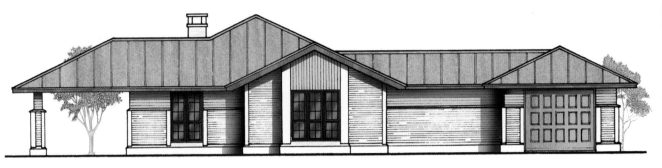

Contemporary style

Floor area
149m²
1604ft²

Bedrooms
2

Bathrooms
2

Floors
1

Key features
Living/dining room
Master en-suite
Feature fireplace
Car port

Garaging for
1 car

Design
**John Braid
(at Leslie R Hutt)**

lhuttarchitect@btinternet.com
01463 235566

Build cost
£137,000

Design © Leslie R Hutt

This bungalow has some unusual features like the multi-windowed wall on the dining and living room, a vast master bedroom suite and a galley kitchen with direct access to the outside. From the plan view you can see how well this design could frame a beautiful garden in the L-shape created by the garage and the main body of the house.

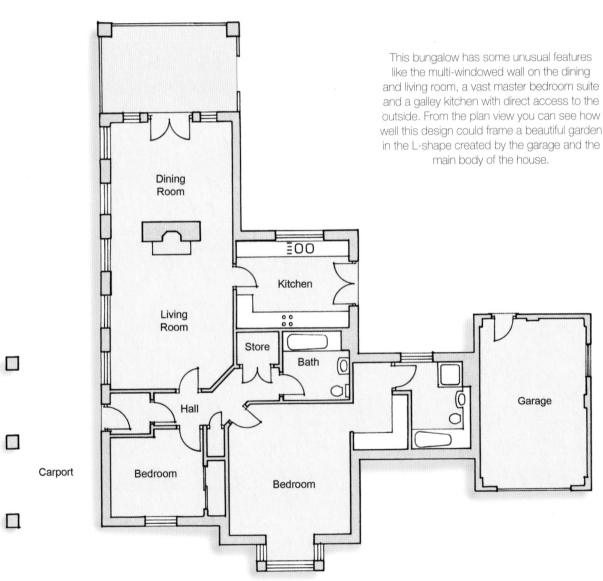

Dining Room

Kitchen

Living Room

Store

Bath

Hall

Carport

Bedroom

Bedroom

Garage

Traditional style

Floor area
160m²
1722ft²

Bedrooms
2

Bathrooms
1

Floors
1

Key features
Dining hall
Galley kitchen

Garaging for
0 cars

Design
**John Shida
(Morningtide
Developments)**

www.morningtide.fsnet.co.uk

johnshida@morningtide.
fsnet.co.uk

01621 815485

Build cost
£147,000

Design © John Shida

Plan no. **BHP 310164**

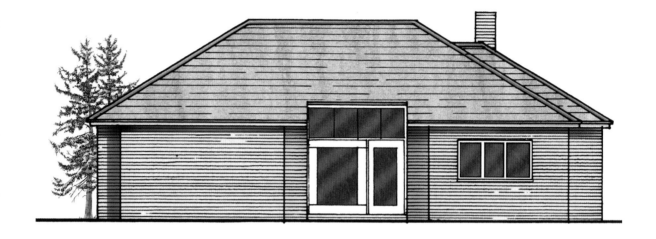

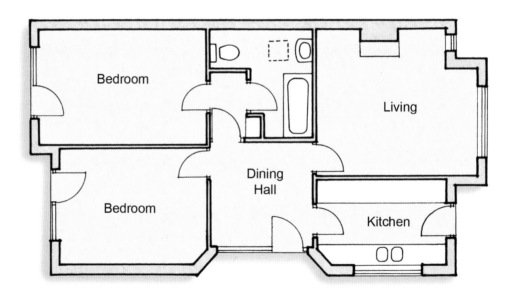

This bungalow has big rooms and space for luxuries like a dining hall off
the galley kitchen. Both bedrooms have their own access to the garden.

Plan no. **BHP 310248**

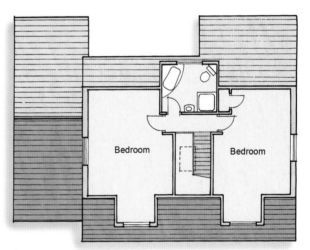

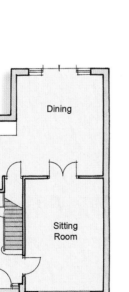

The kitchen, dining room and sitting room flow into each other while upstairs two double bedrooms share a large family bathroom. The garage can be accessed from within the house via the lobby between the kitchen and utility room.

Traditional style

Floor area
170m²
1830ft²

Bedrooms
2

Bathrooms
1

Floors
2

Key features
Kitchen/dining room
Utility room
Study

Garaging for
1 car

Design
Churchill Design

www.churchilldesign.co.uk
info@churchilldesign.co.uk
01252 325701

Build cost
£156,400

Design © Churchill Design

Traditional style

Floor area
203m²
2185ft²

Bedrooms
2

Bathrooms
2

Floors
2

Key features
Utility room
Study
Master bed en-suite
Dining hall

Garaging for
0 cars

Design
Custom Homes

www.customhomes.co.uk
admin@customhomes.co.uk
01787 377388

Build cost
£187,000

Design © Custom Homes

Plan no. **BHP 310245**

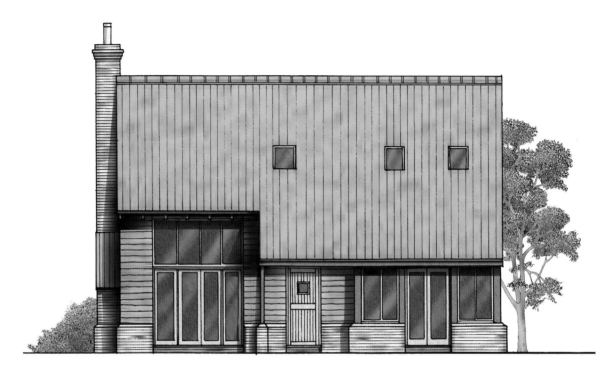

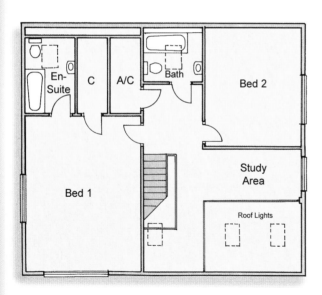

The entrance to this house opens into an open-plan dining room that leads through to a big living room and study. Putting two bedrooms upstairs leaves loads of space for an en-suite bathroom off bedroom one and a study area (which overlooks the double-height dining room) beside bedroom two.

Plan no. **BHP 310464**

Contemporary style

Floor area
203m²
2185ft²

Bedrooms
2

Bathrooms
2

Floors
2

Key features
Double-height dining
Utility room
Master en-suite

Garaging for
0 cars

Design
Custom Homes

www.customhomes.co.uk
admin@customhomes.co.uk
01787 377388

Build cost
£192,000

Design © Custom Homes

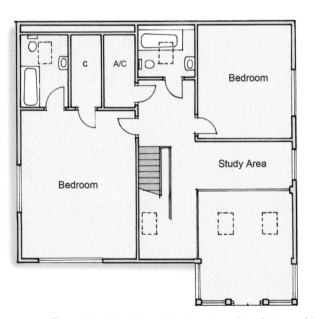

The cathedral window isn't the only striking feature of this design, but it does flood light into the dining hall. If desired the kitchen could be opened up to create a large kitchen/dining area. The addition of a pantry is also a neat touch. Upstairs the two bedrooms are both large and have a bathroom each.

Contemporary style

Floor area
214m²
2303ft²

Bedrooms
3

Bathrooms
2

Floors
2

Key features
Living/dining room
Sunken den
Guest living area
Feature landing bridge

Garaging for
0 cars

Design
Jeremy Rawlings

www.periodhome.net
01884 266444

Build cost
£197,000

Design © Jeremy Rawlings

Plan no. **BHP 310110**

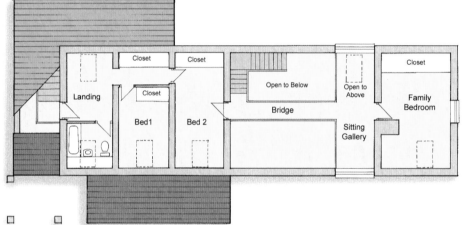

An indoor bridge, a sunken den and extensive glazing make this home an exciting proposition. There's a self-contained annexe for guests – and two staircases.

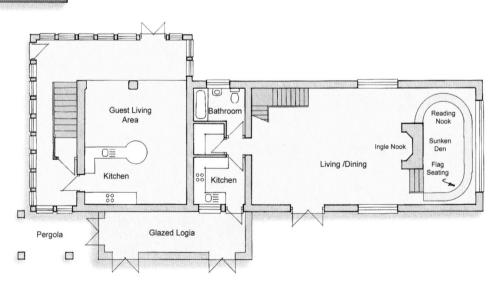

Plan no. **BHP 310818**

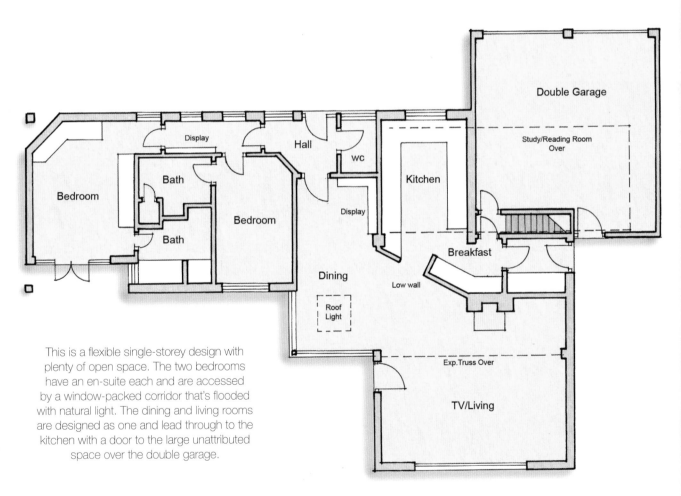

Display

Hall

WC

Bath

Bedroom

Bath

Bedroom

Display

Kitchen

Double Garage

Study/Reading Room Over

Breakfast

Dining

Low wall

Roof Light

Exp. Truss Over

TV/Living

This is a flexible single-storey design with plenty of open space. The two bedrooms have an en-suite each and are accessed by a window-packed corridor that's flooded with natural light. The dining and living rooms are designed as one and lead through to the kitchen with a door to the large unattributed space over the double garage.

Traditional style

Floor area
227m²
2443ft²

Bedrooms
2

Bathrooms
2

Floors
1

Key features
Living/dining area
Kitchen/breakfast bar
Both beds en-suite
First floor study

Garaging for
2 cars

Design
**John Shida
(Morningtide
Developments)**
www.morningtide.fsnet.co.uk
johnshida@morningtide.
fsnet.co.uk
01621 815485

Build cost
£204,000

Design © John Shida

Traditional style

Floor area
82m²
883ft²

Bedrooms
3

Bathrooms
1

Floors
2

Key features
Kitchen/dining area

Garaging for
0 cars

Design
Architecture Plus

www.architecture-plus.co.uk
01934 416416

Build cost
£88,000

Design © Architecture Plus

Plan no. **BHP 310062**

A compact design for a narrow plot which squeezes in three bedrooms and a kitchen/dining area.

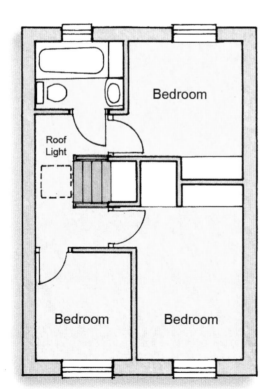

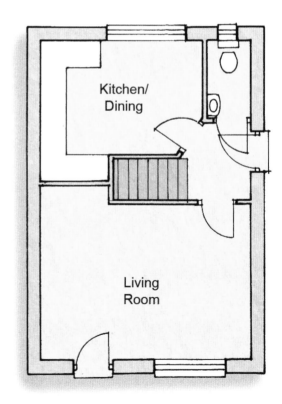

Plan no. **BHP 310968**

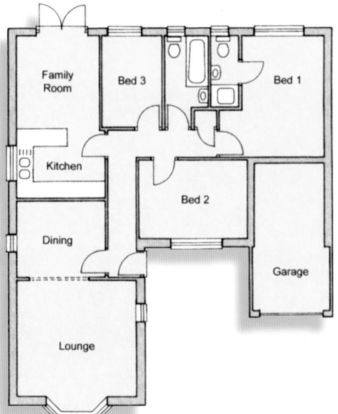

Family Room

Bed 3

Bed 1

Kitchen

Bed 2

Dining

Garage

Lounge

There's a good-sized kitchen and family room, a separate dining room and lounge. The master bed has an en-suite and there's even a single garage in this compact design.

Traditional style

Floor area
90m²
969ft²

Bedrooms
3

Bathrooms
2

Floors
1

Key features
Lounge/dining room
Kitchen/family room
Master en-suite

Garaging for
1 car

Design
Planahome

www.planahome.uk.com
plans@planahome.uk.com
01326 373600

Build cost
£97,500

House design
© Planahome

Traditional style

Floor area
90m²
969ft²

Bedrooms
3

Bathrooms
3

Floors
2

Key features
Living/dining room
Kitchen bay window
Master en-suite

Garaging for
0 cars

Design
Eclipse Design

www.eclipsedesign.cop-
perstream.co.uk
enquiries@eclipsedesignuk.net
0845 460 4758

Build cost
£94,000

Plan no. **BHP 310845**

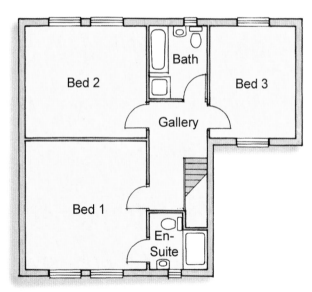

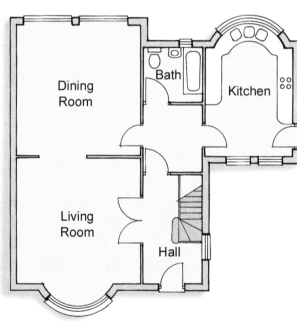

This L-shaped house makes great use of space with its three bedrooms and generous living rooms. Put in foundations at the time of building and you could easily fill in the 'L' at a later date with a family room attached to the kitchen and an en-suite accessed through the front window of Bedroom 3.

Plan no. **BHP 310857**

Kitchen/Breakfast

Dining

Bedroom

Bedroom

W

ST

Living Room

Porch

W

Bedroom

This single-storey home is split equally into living and sleeping spaces. The dining and living rooms are open-plan while the kitchen/breakfast room has direct access to the garden. Across the hall there are two double bedrooms, one single and two bathrooms.

Traditional style

Floor area
93m²
1001ft²

Bedrooms
3

Bathrooms
2

Floors
1

Key features
Linked living/dining
Master en-suite
Porch

Garaging for
0 cars

Design
Planahome

www.planahome.uk.com
plans@planahome.uk.com
01326 373600

Build cost
£96,000

Design © Planahome

Plan no. **BHP 310809**

This is a simple, stylish design that makes the best of a small site. The combined kitchen and dining room create a good-size living area across the back of the house. Upstairs the master bedroom is a good size and has its own bay window.

Plan no. **BHP 310086**

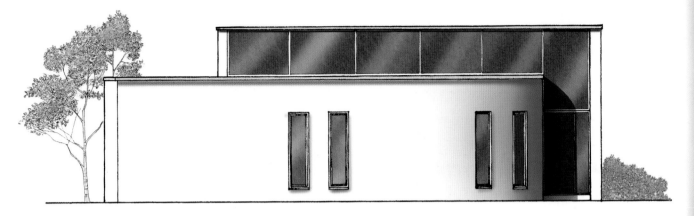

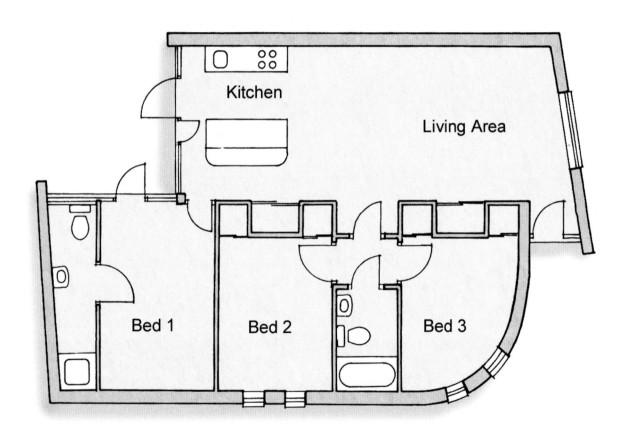

Kitchen

Living Area

Bed 1

Bed 2

Bed 3

A cool modern take on the three-bedroomed house cleverly worked into a single-storey. A good design for a site where the views are limited as the master bedroom/kitchen could open onto a courtyard.

Contemporary style

Floor area
102m²
1098ft²

Bedrooms
3

Bathrooms
2

Floors
1

Key features
Kitchen/living area
Master en-suite

Garaging for
0 cars

Design
Architecture Plus

www.architecture-plus.co.uk
01934 416416

Build cost
£106,000

Design © Architecture Plus

Traditional style

Floor area
111m²
1195ft²

Bedrooms
3

Bathrooms
1

Floors
2

Key features
Narrow design
Kitchen/dining
Bedroom balcony
Laundry room

Garaging for
0 cars

Design
Peter King

info@carden-king.co.uk
01367 253330

Build cost
£115,000

Design © Peter King

Plan no. **BHP 310044**

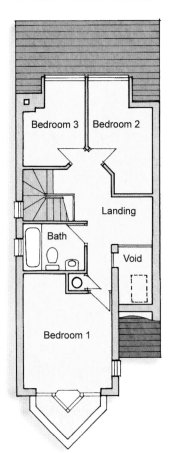

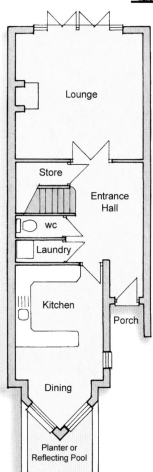

A narrow site doesn't mean you have to skimp on great living space. A Velux-type window lights the entrance hall that doubles back into a large kitchen and forward into a generous lounge. Upstairs, the biggest bedroom gets a triangular balcony.

Plan no. **BHP 310680**

This design will take advantage of a long, narrow plot. It uses the space above the carport for an extra bedroom and a big family bathroom which frees up space for two further bedrooms on the first floor and a long living/dining room downstairs.

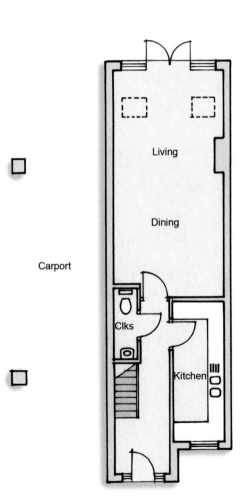

Living

Dining

Carport

Clks

Kitchen

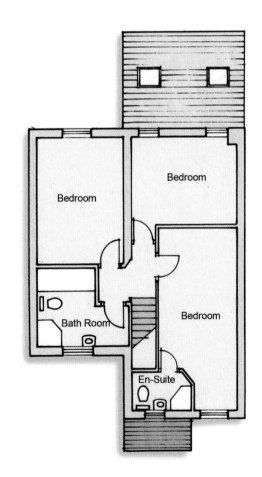

Bedroom

Bedroom

Bath Room

Bedroom

En-Suite

Traditional style

Floor area

117m²

1259ft²

Bedrooms

3

Bathrooms

1

Floors

2

Key features
Living/dining room
Hall
Internal garage access

Garaging for
1 car

Design
**John Shida
(Morningtide
Developments)**

www.morningtide.fsnet.co.uk

johnshida@morningtide.
fsnet.co.uk

01621 815485

Build cost
£121,000

Design © John Shida

Plan no. **BHP 310005**

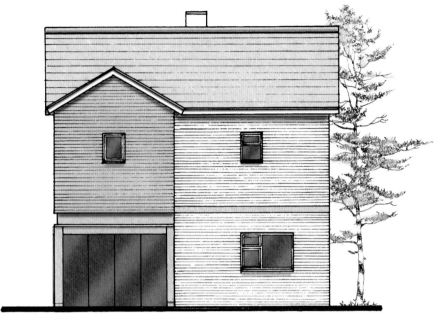

By putting the garage at
the front the width of this
house has been kept to a
minimum making it suitable
for narrower sites.

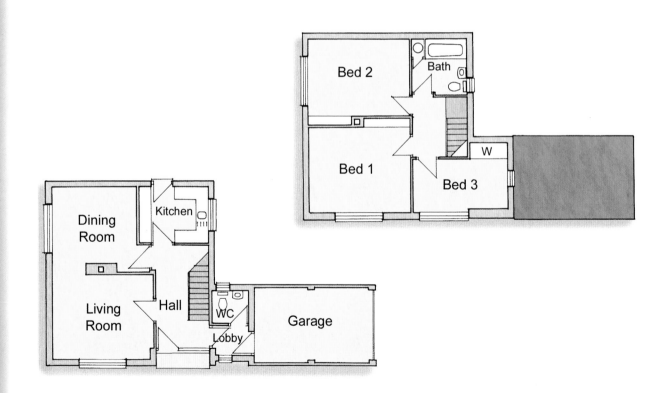

Plan no. **BHP 310914**

The full-length living room is a strong feature and if you wanted a kitchen/dining room these two rooms could be combined. Upstairs the master bedroom is also a good size.

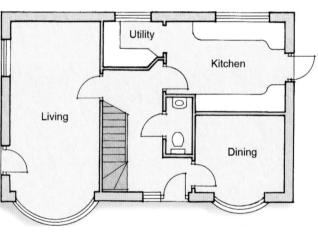

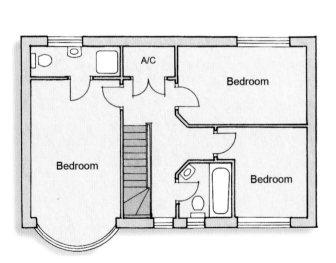

Traditional style

Floor area
127m²
1367ft²

Bedrooms
3

Bathrooms
2

Floors
2

Key features
Kitchen/dining room
Utility room
Master en-suite

Garaging for
0 cars

Design
Opus Architecture and Design

01252 861759

Build cost
£132,500

Design © Opus Architecture

Plan no. **BHP 310116**

The detailing over the windows and porch give this simple design the look of a cottage. Inside there is a sensible kitchen/dining room and a decent size en-suite bedroom.

Bedroom

Bathroom

Bedroom

Bedroom

En-Suite

Utility

wc

Kitchen

c

Dining

Lounge

Plan no. **BHP 310938**

This house offers some desirable features such as a larder off the utility room as well as a separate study and galleried landing.

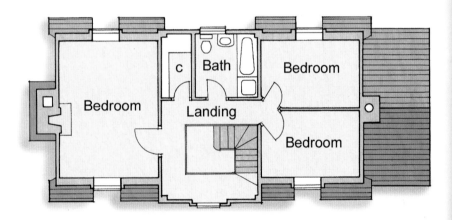

Bedroom

c · Bath · Bedroom

Landing

Bedroom

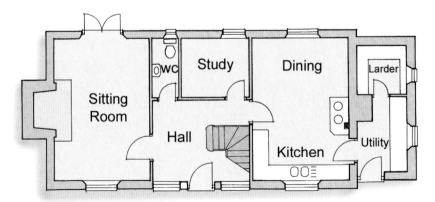

Sitting Room

WC · Study · Dining · Larder

Hall

Kitchen · Utility

Traditional style

Floor area
127m²
1367ft²

Bedrooms
3

Bathrooms
1

Floors
2

Key features
Kitchen/diner
Utility room
Larder
Study
Galleried landing

Garaging for
0 cars

Design
Border Oak

www.borderoak.com
sales@borderoak.com
01568 708752

Build cost
£132,500

Design © Border Oak

Traditional style

Floor area
128m²
1378ft²

Bedrooms
3

Bathrooms
2

Floors
2

Key features
Kitchen/breakfast room
Dining room
Master en-suite

Garaging for
0 cars

Design
Potton

www.potton.co.uk
contact@potton.co.uk
01767 676 400

Build cost
£133,500

Design © Potton

Plan no. **BHP 310398**

Inside the hall leads off into a sizeable kitchen/ breakfast room and living room. Upstairs there's a galleried landing an en-suite to the master and plenty of storage in each of the three bedrooms.

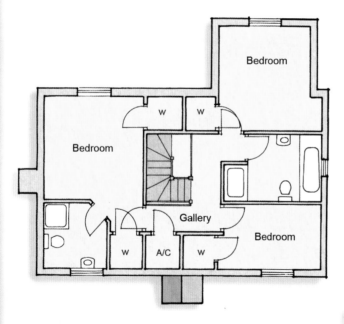

Plan no. **BHP 310383**

Overhanging eaves and jutting dormer windows give this design real character with varying roof lines and interesting details such as the exposed rafter feet.

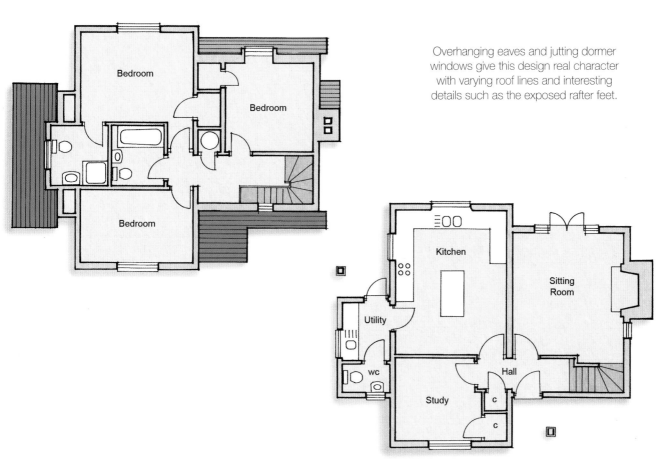

Traditional style

Floor area
134m²
1442ft²

Bedrooms
3

Bathrooms
2

Floors
2

Key features
Utility room
Study
Master en-suite

Garaging for
0 cars

Design
Border Oak

www.borderoak.com
sales@borderoak.com
01568 708752

Build cost
£123,000

Design `© Border Oak

Traditional style

Floor area
136m²
1464ft²

Bedrooms
3

Bathrooms
2

Floors
2

Key features
Utility
Separate dining room
Master en-suite
Balcony bedroom 2

Garaging for
0 cars

Design
**John Shida
(Morningtide
Developments)**

www.morningtide.fsnet.co.uk

johnshida@morningtide.
fsnet.co.uk

01621 815485

Build cost
£125,000

Design © John Shida

Plan no. **BHP 310209**

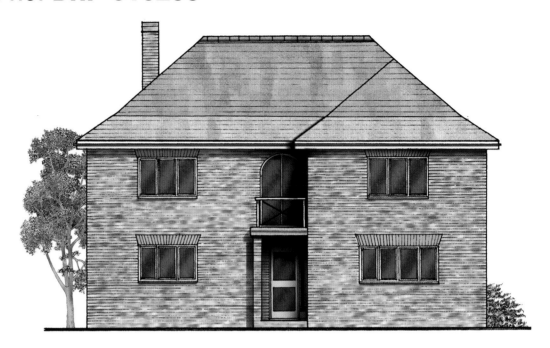

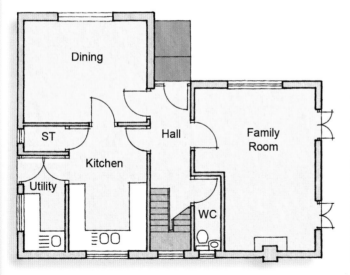

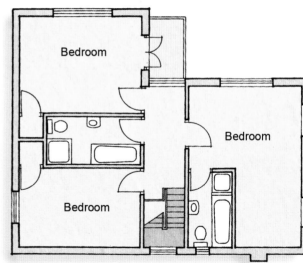

This design offers three good-sized bedrooms, one en-suite and easy access for all to the shared bathroom. The second bedroom gets its own balcony that creates a porch below.

Plan no. **BHP 310215**

This design has all the external styling cues you would expect in a thatched cottage including oak lintels and eyebrow dormers. These are combined with modern touches including a large kitchen, a full-depth lounge and a good size master bedroom suite.

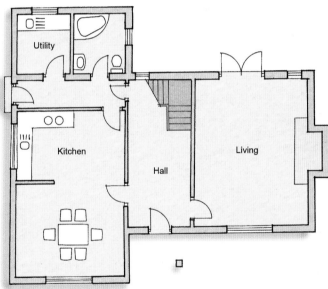

Utility

Kitchen

Hall

Living

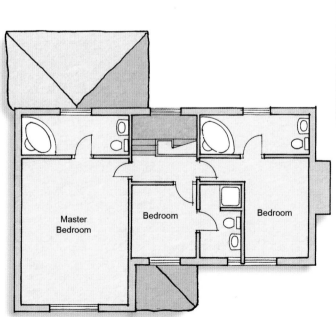

Master Bedroom

Bedroom

Bedroom

Traditional style

Floor area
137m²
1475ft²

Bedrooms
3

Bathrooms
3

Floors
2

Key features
Kitchen/dining room
Utility room
All beds en-suite

Garaging for
0 cars

Design
JS Building Consultancy

www.ukbuildingconsultancy.
co.uk
jsharples@ricsonline.org
0113 250 1303

Build cost
£126,000

Traditional style

Floor area

139m²

1496ft²

Bedrooms

3

Bathrooms

2

Floors

2

Key features
Kitchen/dining room
Utility room
Car port
Master en-suites

Garaging for

0 cars

Design

Churchill Design

www.churchilldesign.co.uk
info@churchilldesign.co.uk
01252 325701

Build cost

£128,000

Plan no. **BHP 310872**

This traditional dormer window cottage features a full-depth sitting room and master bedroom above. There's also an open-plan dining and kitchen area and a useful utility space. Smart packaging makes room for two more bedrooms, an en-suite and a family bathroom on the first floor.

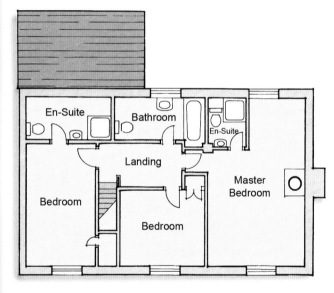

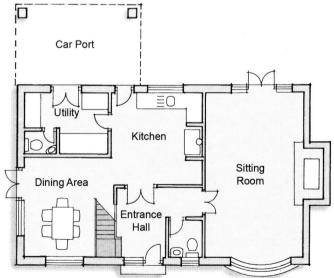

Plan no. **BHP 310506**

This country cottage has a large lounge and an
L-shaped master bedroom suite. This frees up space
in the rest of the house for a splendid kitchen/dining
space, a study and two more double bedrooms.

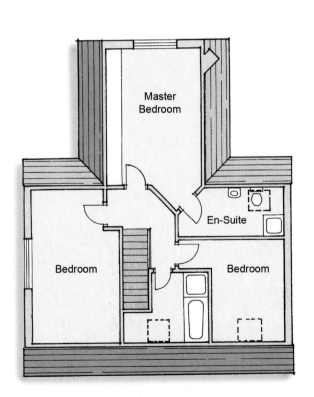

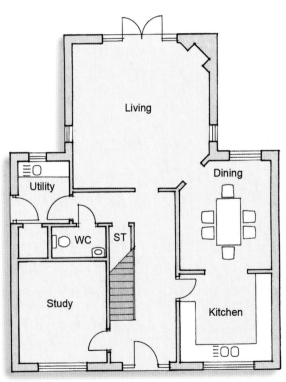

Traditional style

Floor area
140m²
1507ft²

Bedrooms
3

Bathrooms
2

Floors
2

Key features
Kitchen/dining room
Utility room
Study
Master en-suite

Garaging for
0 cars

Design
**Ormerod Design
Group**

odg@ormeroddesign.co.uk
0113 289 3763

Build cost
£129,000

Design © Ormerod Design
Group

Traditional style

Floor area

140m²

1507ft²

Bedrooms

3

Bathrooms

3

Floors

2

Key features
Kitchen/dining room
Living with inglenook
Sitting hall
All beds en-suite

Garaging for
0 cars

Design
Jeremy Rawlings

www.periodhome.net
01884 266444

Build cost
£129,000

Plan no. **BHP 310530**

The lounge, with its massive inglenook fireplace, takes centre stage in this design with all the first floor rooms flowing off it. A single flight of stairs leads up to the galleried landing that goes through to an L-shaped master suite and two en-suite bedrooms.

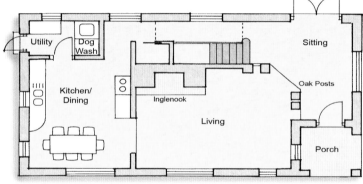

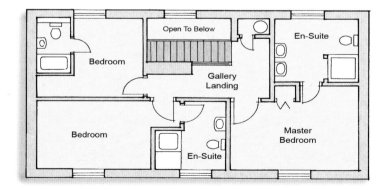

Plan no. **BHP 310272**

Good use of dormer windows give the first floor of this house extra daylight where it's most needed – over the landing and in both bathrooms. Other features include a utility room and a full-depth sitting room with twin French doors.

Contemporary style

Floor area
140m²
1507ft²

Bedrooms
3

Bathrooms
2

Floors
2

Key features
Utility room
Separate dining room
Master en-suite

Garaging for
0 cars

Design
County Contracts

countycontractsltd@fsmail.
net
01892 785153

Build cost
£129,000

Contemporary style

Floor area

142m²
1528ft²

Bedrooms

3

Bathrooms

3

Floors

2

Key features
Dining hall
Utility room
Master en-suite

Garaging for
0 cars

Design
Design 62

01484 300843

Build cost
£130,500

Design © Design 62

Plan no. **BHP 310794**

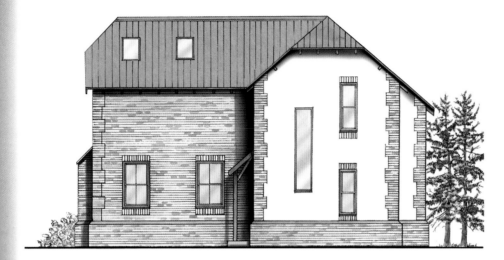

This combines double-height glazing and open-plan spaces with traditional elements including vaulted ceilings in the master and second bedroom.

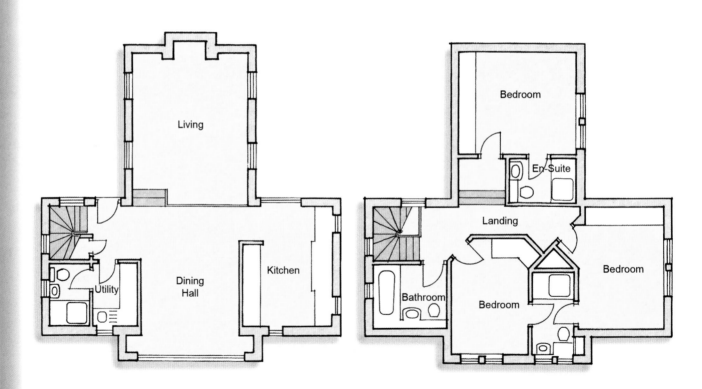

Plan no. **BHP 310935**

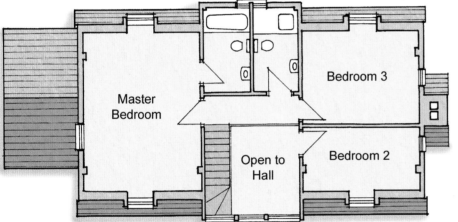

Master Bedroom

Bedroom 3

Open to Hall

Bedroom 2

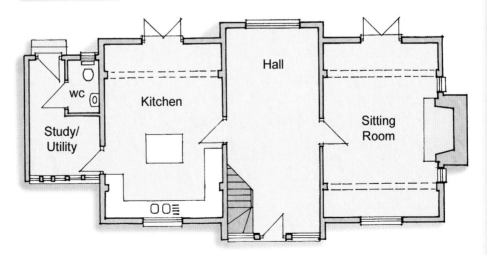

WC

Study/ Utility

Kitchen

Hall

Sitting Room

Want to live in a barn but can't find one to convert? One solution is to build your own. Great features include the double height windows that flood daylight into the expansive hall. Three good-sized bedrooms are accessed from the first floor galleried landing.

Barn style

Floor area
144m²
1550ft²

Bedrooms
3

Bathrooms
2

Floors
2

Key features
**Dining hall
Utility/study
Master bed en-suite**

Garaging for
0 cars

Design
Border Oak

www.borderoak.com
sales@borderoak.com
01568 708752

Build cost
£132,500

Design © Border Oak

Traditional style

Floor area
149m²
1615ft²

Bedrooms
3

Bathrooms
3

Floors
2

Key features
1st floor open-plan living
Feature fireplace
Study
Master en-suite

Garaging for
1 car

Design
Architecture Plus

www.architecture-plus.co.uk
01934 416416

Build cost
£137,000

Design © Architecture Plus

Plan no. **BHP 310956**

With sleeping space on the ground floor and living space up top this house is designed to take advantage of great views. The open-plan dining, kitchen and sitting room leads onto a full-width balcony. The study with its en-suite bathroom could easily become a self-contained guest suite.

Plan no. **BHP 310326**

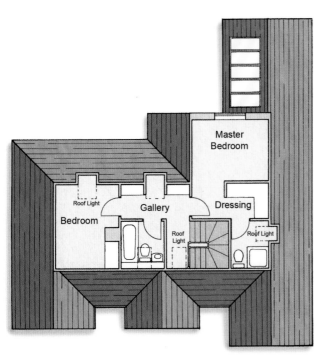

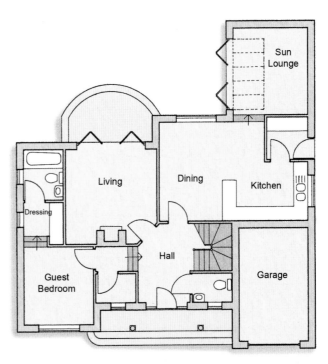

Incorporating the garage door into one of the bays on this double–fronted design makes for a neat, symmetrical façade. Up the steps and through the hall there's an L-shaped kitchen, dining and sun lounge area plus a large living room and guest suite. Upstairs there is a full-depth master suite and a good-sized second bedroom.

Traditional style

Floor area

150m²

1615ft²

Bedrooms

3

Bathrooms

3

Floors

2

Key features
Kitchen/dining room
Sun lounge
Guest suite
Master en-suite

Garaging for
1 car

Design
Design & Materials

www.designandmaterials.uk.com
enquiries@designandmateria
ls.uk.com
01909 540 123

Build cost
£138,000

Design © Design &
Materials

Traditional style

Floor area

150m²

1615ft²

Bedrooms

3

Bathrooms

2

Floors

2

Key features
Family room
Study
Utility room
Master en-suite

Garaging for
0 cars

Design
Custom Homes

www.customhomes.co.uk
admin@customhomes.co.uk
01787 377388

Build cost
£138,000

Design © Custom Homes

Plan no. **BHP 310671**

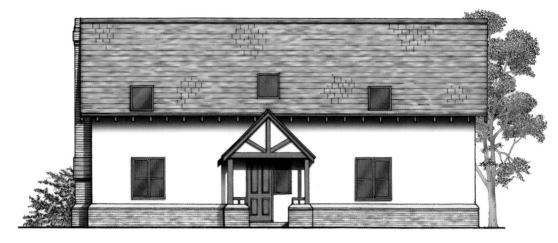

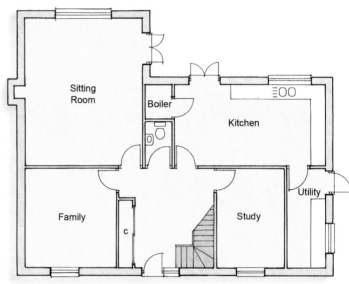

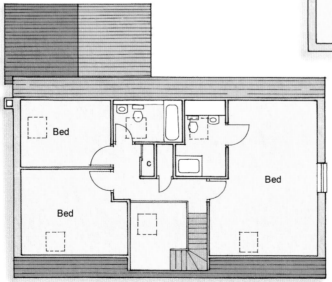

This design squeezes the maximum living and sleeping area out of a relatively small plot but all the room sizes remain large and comfortable. Virtually any building material combination could be used to suit the surrounding environment.

Plan no. **BHP 310557**

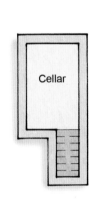

Cellar

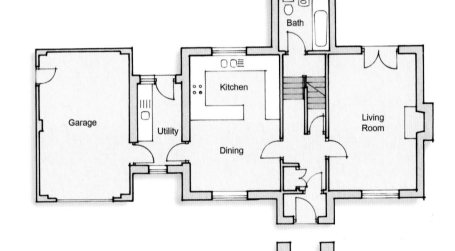

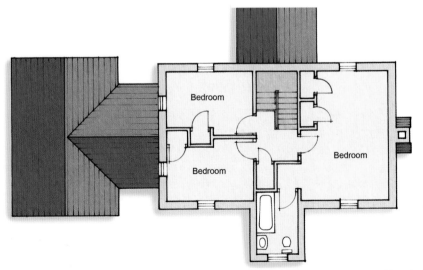

Traditional style

Floor area
152m²
1636ft²

Bedrooms
3

Bathrooms
2

Floors
3

Key features
Kitchen/dining room
Utility room
Porch
Cellar

**Garaging for
1 cars**

**Design
John Braid
(at Leslie R Hutt)**

lhuttarchitect@btinternet.com
01463 235566

There's an open-plan kitchen/dining room off the hall and a large living room and a bathroom. Upstairs the master suite takes up one side of the house and has its own bathroom built into the central gable.

**Build cost
£140,000**

Design © Leslie R Hutt

Traditional style

Floor area

154m²

1658ft²

Bedrooms

3

Bathrooms

2

Floors

2

Key features
Utility room
Study
Separate dining room
Master en-suite

Garaging for
0 cars

Design
County Contracts

countycontractsltd@fsmail.net
01892 785153

Build cost
£141,500

Design © County Contracts

Plan no. **BHP 310725**

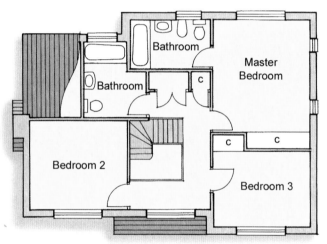

This three-bedroom house is pretty spacious but with a good roof pitch there would be the potential to build using attic trusses to allow for a future room in the roof.

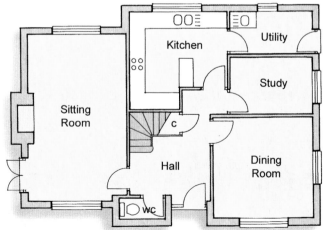

Plan no. **BHP 310401**

This modern design puts the living quarters on the first floor and the sleeping space below. Benefits include a first floor terrace with balcony and a bathroom for each bedroom.

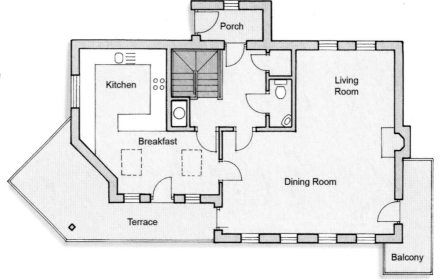

Porch

Kitchen

Living Room

Breakfast

Dining Room

Terrace

Balcony

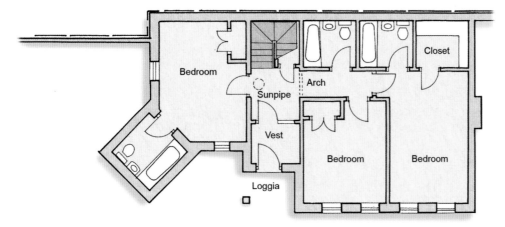

Bedroom

Sunpipe

Arch

Closet

Vest

Bedroom

Bedroom

Loggia

Contemporary style

Floor area
155m²
1668ft²

Bedrooms
3

Bathrooms
3

Floors
2

Key features
Kitchen/breakfast room
Lounge/dining room
Porch
Master en-suite
2nd en-suite

Garaging for
0 cars

Design
**John Braid
(at Leslie R Hutt)**

lhuttarchitect@btinternet.com
01463 235566

Build cost
£142,500

Traditional style

Floor area

156m²

1679ft²

Bedrooms

3

Bathrooms

2

Floors

2

Key features
Kitchen/breakfast room
Utility room
Study
Master en-suite

Garaging for
1 car

Design
Stephen Mattick

www.mattick.co.uk
mattick@mattick.co.uk
01223 891159

Build cost
£143,500

Design © Stephen Mattick

Plan no. **BHP 310683**

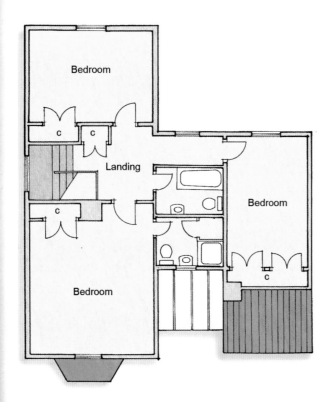

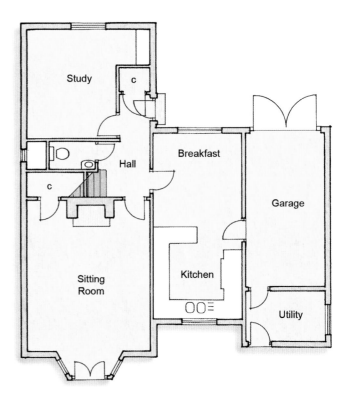

The bay-windowed sitting room and glazed-roof kitchen are great character features as is the enormous main bedroom with its built-in wardrobes and bathroom.

Plan no. **BHP 310089**

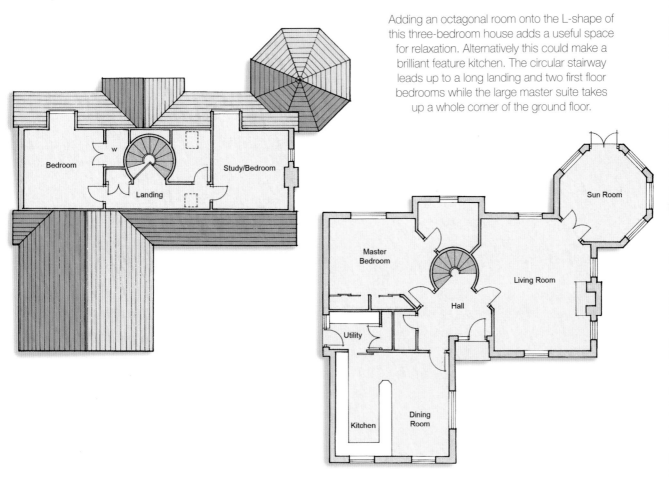

Adding an octagonal room onto the L-shape of this three-bedroom house adds a useful space for relaxation. Alternatively this could make a brilliant feature kitchen. The circular stairway leads up to a long landing and two first floor bedrooms while the large master suite takes up a whole corner of the ground floor.

Floor plan labels:
- Bedroom
- w
- Landing
- Study/Bedroom
- Master Bedroom
- Utility
- Hall
- Living Room
- Sun Room
- Kitchen
- Dining Room

Traditional style

Floor area
157m²
1690ft²

Bedrooms
3

Bathrooms
1

Floors
2

Key features
Kitchen/dining room
Circular staircase
Octagonal sunroom
Master en-suite

Garaging for
0 cars

Design
The Border Design Centre

www.borderdesign.co.uk
borderdesign@btconnect.com
01578 740218

Build cost
£144,000

Design © The Border Design Centre

Traditional style

Floor area

157m²

1690ft²

Bedrooms

3

Bathrooms

2

Floors

1

Key features
Separate dining room
Utility room
Larder
Master en-suite

Garaging for
0 cars

Design
The Border Design Centre

www.borderdesign.co.uk
borderdesign@btconnect.com
01578 740218

Build cost
£144,000

Design © The Border
Design Company

Plan no. **BHP 310566**

The shape of this bungalow forms a central courtyard that can be accessed from the hall, kitchen and the utility room.

Bedroom

Bedroom

Garden Store

Utility

Larder

Kitchen

Hall

Master Bedroom

Living Room

Dining

Plan no. **BHP 310239**

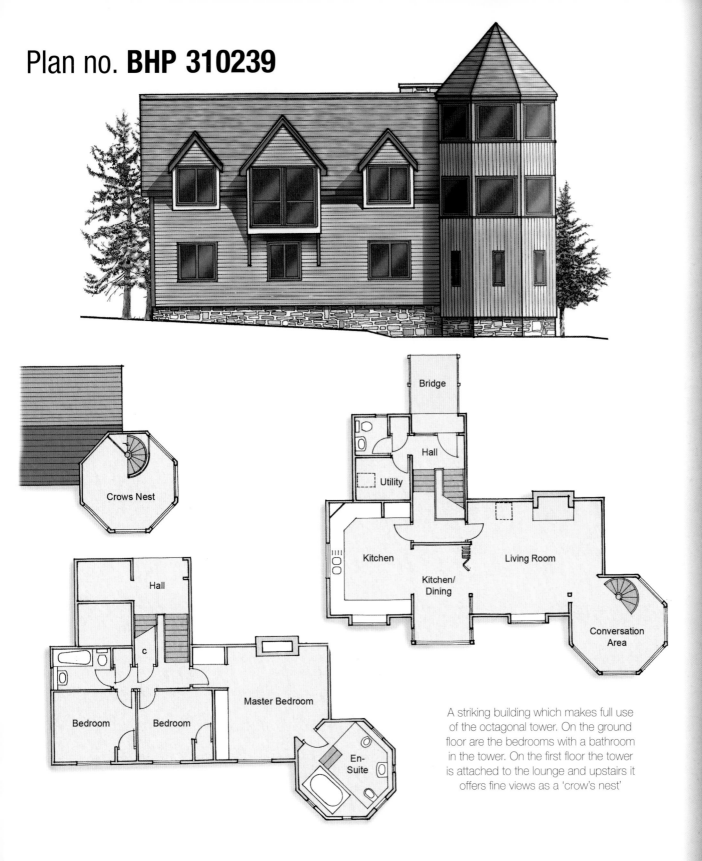

Bridge

Hall

Utility

Kitchen

Living Room

Kitchen/
Dining

Conversation
Area

Crows Nest

Hall

c

Bedroom

Bedroom

Master Bedroom

En-
Suite

A striking building which makes full use
of the octagonal tower. On the ground
floor are the bedrooms with a bathroom
in the tower. On the first floor the tower
is attached to the lounge and upstairs it
offers fine views as a 'crow's nest'

Contemporary style

Floor area
159m²
1711ft²

Bedrooms
3

Bathrooms
2

Floors
3

Key features
Kitchen/dining room
Utility room
Master en-suite
2nd floor 'crow's nest'

Garaging for
0 cars

Design
**The Border Design
Centre**

www.borderdesign.co.uk
borderdesign@btconnect.com
01578 740218

Build cost
£146,000

Design © The Border
Design Centre

Plan no. **BHP 310380**

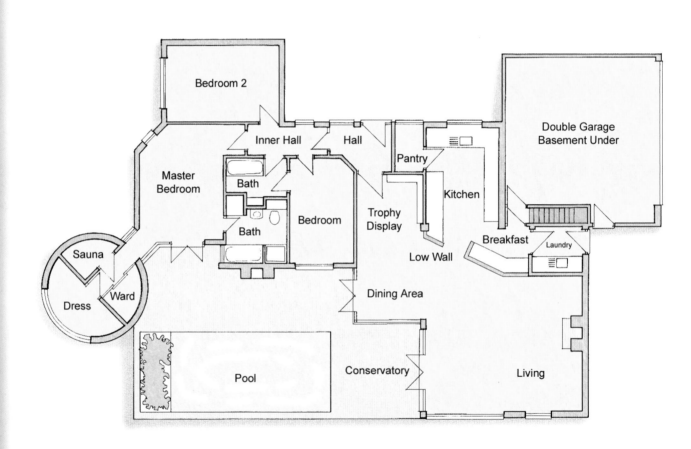

Open-plan living space and three double-sized bedrooms make this one-storey house a winning design. There's a sauna in the turreted annexe off the master bedroom and the option to create a complete health suite in a basement beneath the garage.

Plan no. **BHP 310374**

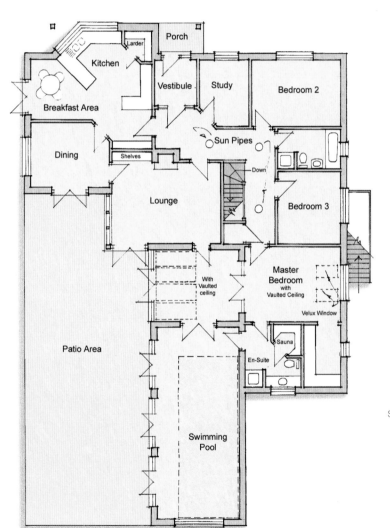

Kitchen
Larder
Porch
Breakfast Area
Vestibule
Study
Bedroom 2
Dining
Shelves
Sun Pipes
Lounge
Down
Bedroom 3
With Vaulted ceiling
Master Bedroom with Vaulted Ceiling
Velux Window
Patio Area
Sauna
En-Suite
Swimming Pool

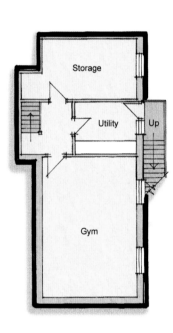

Storage
Utility
Up
Gym

Windows on all elevations and clever use of sunpipes mean that there's plenty of light. The basement gym is an added bonus

Contemporary style

Floor area
162m²
1744ft²

Bedrooms
3

Bathrooms
2

Floors
2

Key features
Basement gym & utility
Kitchen/breakfast area
Swimming pool
Separate dining room
Study

Garaging for
0 cars

Design
Design & Materials

www.designandmaterials.uk.com
enquiries@designandmaterials.uk.com
01909 540 123

Build cost
£149,000

Barn style

Floor area
162m²
1744ft²

Bedrooms
3

Bathrooms
2

Floors
2

Key features
Dining hall
Porch
Utility room
Master en-suite
Study area

Garaging for
0 cars

Design
Potton

www.potton.co.uk
contact@potton.co.uk
01767 676 400

Build cost
£149,000

Design © Potton

Plan no. **BHP 310782**

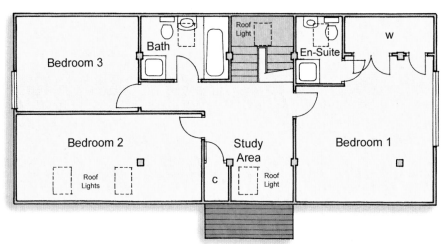

The porch opens into the dining hall with a lounge and kitchen off either side. Upstairs the three bedrooms are all large and the master offers en-suite facilities. The large landing doubles as a study area

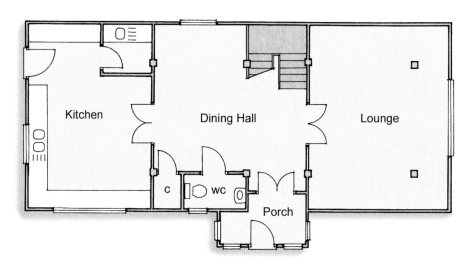

Plan no. **BHP 310512**

Breakfast/Dining

Terrace

Kitchen

Sitting Room

Utility

Entrance Hall

c

c

Music Room

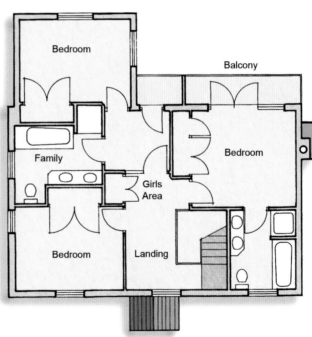

Bedroom

Balcony

Family

Bedroom

Girls Area

Bedroom

Landing

Use of double doors means the ground floor can effectively be made open-plan. Upstairs a two-way balcony and two large bathrooms add luxury while built-in storage adds practicality.

Traditional style

Floor area
162m²
1744ft²

Bedrooms
3

Bathrooms
2

Floors
2

Key features
Kitchen/breakfast room
Utility room
Music room
Master en-suite

Garaging for
0 cars

Design
Stephen Mattick

www.mattick.co.uk
mattick@mattick.co.uk
01223 891159

Build cost
£149,000

Traditional style

Floor area
165m²
1776ft²

Bedrooms
3

Bathrooms
3

Floors
1

Key features
Separate dining room
Utility room
Study
Master en-suite

Garaging for
0 cars

Design
Custom Homes

www.customhomes.co.uk
admin@customhomes.co.uk
01787 377388

Build cost
£151,000

Design © Custom Homes

Plan no. **BHP 310419**

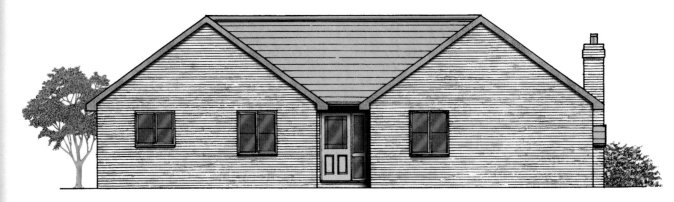

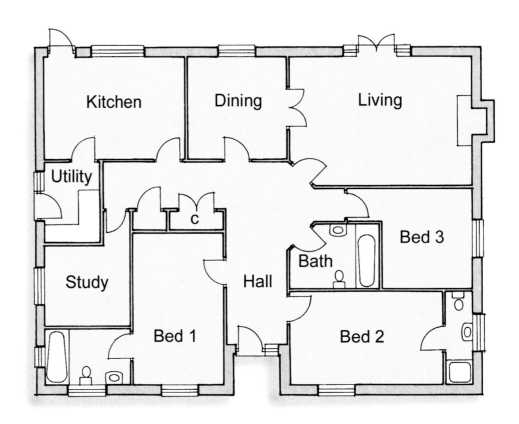

Single-storey houses don't have to be cramped as this double-fronted design proves. There is room for a separate dining room and two of the bedrooms have their own en-suites.

Plan no. **BHP 310626**

Contemporary style

Floor area
166m²
1787ft²

Bedrooms
3

Bathrooms
3

Floors
2

Key features
Dining/conservatory
Sun porch
Utility room
Pantry
Master en-suite

Garaging for
1 car

Design
**The Bespoke
Design Company**

www.planahome.uk.com
plans@planahome.uk.com
01326 373600

Build cost
£152,500

Design © The Bespoke
Design Company

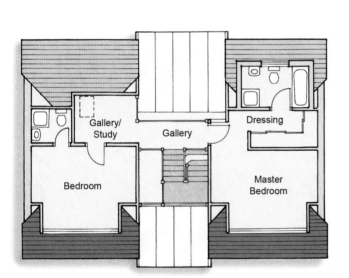

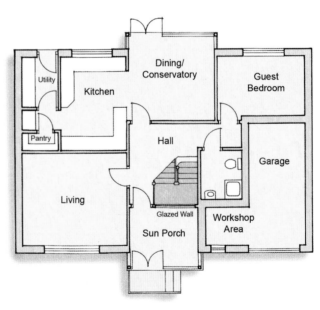

Dormers peak out of the roof of this design and blend perfectly with the
modern full-height glass frontage. There's a matching glass elevation at the rear
so the main ground floor rooms should be light. The first floor has a gallerried
landing and a pair of en-suite bedrooms.

Traditional style

Floor area
168m²
1808ft²

Bedrooms
3

Bathrooms
2

Floors
2

Key features
Kitchen/dining room
Conservatory
Utility room
Porch
Master en-suite

Garaging for
0 cars

Design
Welsh Oak Frame

www.welshoakframe.com
01686 688000

Build cost
£154,500

Design © Welsh Oak Frame

Plan no. **BHP 310548**

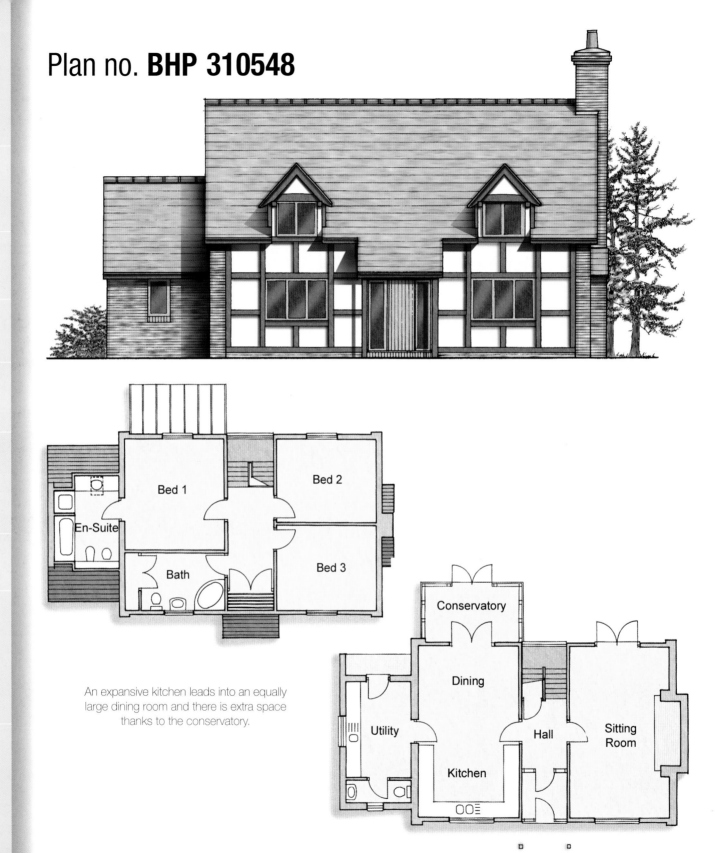

An expansive kitchen leads into an equally large dining room and there is extra space thanks to the conservatory.

En-Suite

Bed 1

Bed 2

Bath

Bed 3

Conservatory

Dining

Utility

Hall

Sitting Room

Kitchen

Plan no. **BHP 310431**

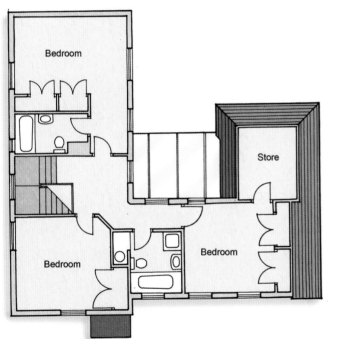

Bedroom

Bedroom

Bedroom

Store

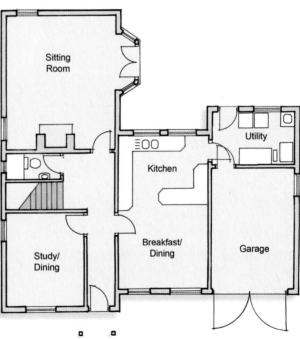

Sitting Room

Kitchen

Study/ Dining

Breakfast/ Dining

Garage

Utility

The kitchen has a glazed roof which is in contrast to the traditional frontage of the property.

Traditional style

Floor area
168m²
1808ft²

Bedrooms
3

Bathrooms
2

Floors
2

Key features
Kitchen/breakfast room
Utility room
Study/dining room
Master en-suite

Garaging for
1 car

Design
Stephen Mattick

www.mattick.co.uk
mattick@mattick.co.uk
01223 891159

Build cost
£154,500

Design © Stephen Mattick

Contemporary style

Floor area

168m²

1808ft²

Bedrooms

3

Bathrooms

2

Floors

2

Key features
Kitchen/diner
Utility room
Workshop
Dressing room

Garaging for
1 car

Design
Potton

www.potton.co.uk
contact@potton.co.uk
01767 676 400

Build cost
£154,500

Plan no. **BHP 310218**

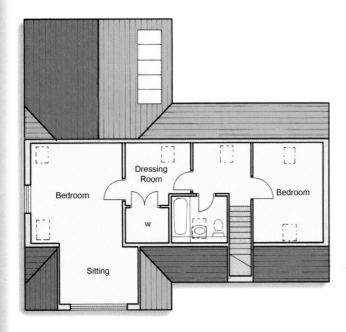

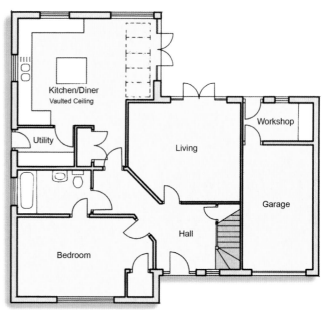

Don't let the low roofline fool you. This design features two storeys of living and sleeping space. The large kitchen is well lit by windows on three sides and from above via rooflights. Upstairs the impressive master suite gets lots of natural light thanks to the gable window and twin rooflights.

Plan no. **BHP 310908**

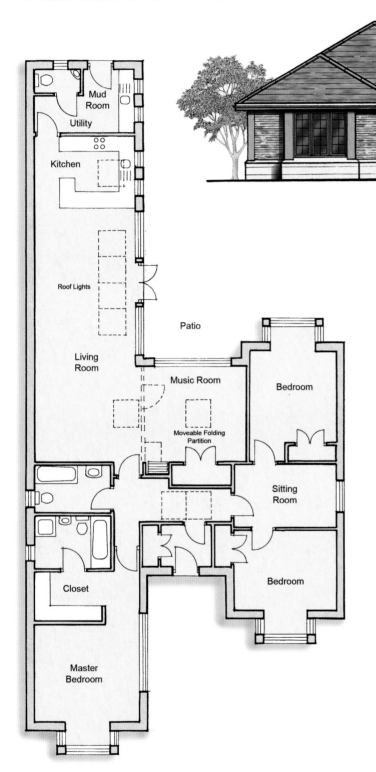

Mud Room

Utility

Kitchen

Roof Lights

Living Room

Patio

Music Room

Moveable Folding Partition

Bedroom

Sitting Room

Bedroom

Closet

Master Bedroom

This deceptive bungalow fits with a standard width plot but thanks to the deep kitchen/living room offers great living space. The two smaller bedrooms share their own sitting room while the master bedroom comes complete with its own built-in wardrobes and en-suite bathroom.

Traditional style

Floor area
173m²
1862ft²

Bedrooms
3

Bathrooms
2

Floors
1

Key features
Open-plan living space
Music room
Sitting room
Utility/mud room
Master en-suite

Garaging for
0 cars

Design
**John Braid
(at Leslie R Hutt)**

lhuttarchitect@btinternet.com
01463 235566

Build cost
£160,000

Design © Leslie R Hutt

Contemporary style

Floor area

175m²

1884ft²

Bedrooms

3

Bathrooms

2

Floors

3

Key features
Staircase in turret
Utility room
Study
Master en-suite

Garaging for
2 cars

Design
The Border Design Centre

www.borderdesign.co.uk
borderdesign@btconnect.com
01578 740218

Build cost
£161,000

Design © The Border
Design Centre

Plan no. **BHP 310974**

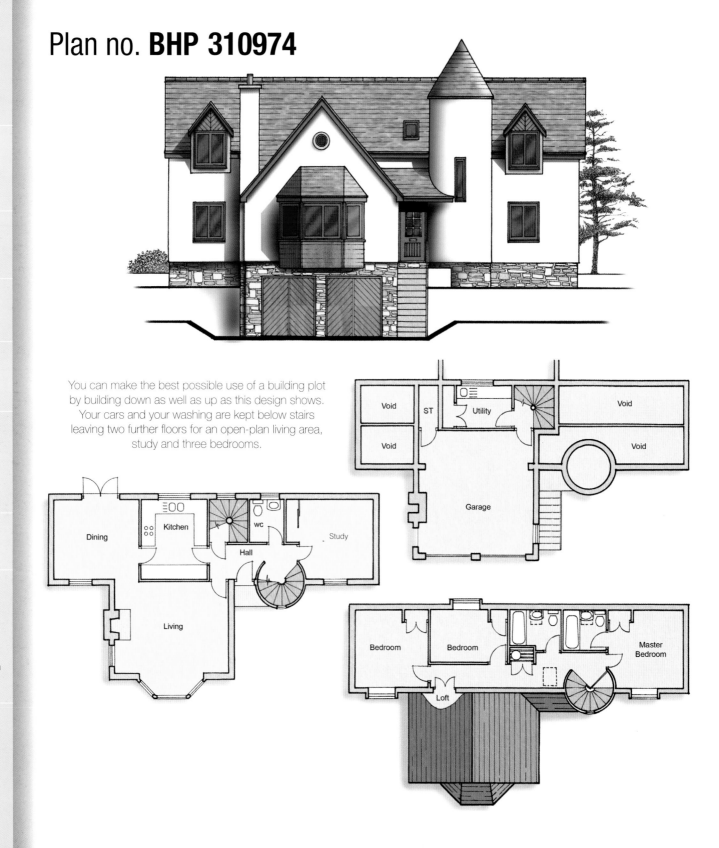

You can make the best possible use of a building plot by building down as well as up as this design shows. Your cars and your washing are kept below stairs leaving two further floors for an open-plan living area, study and three bedrooms.

Plan no. **BHP 310341**

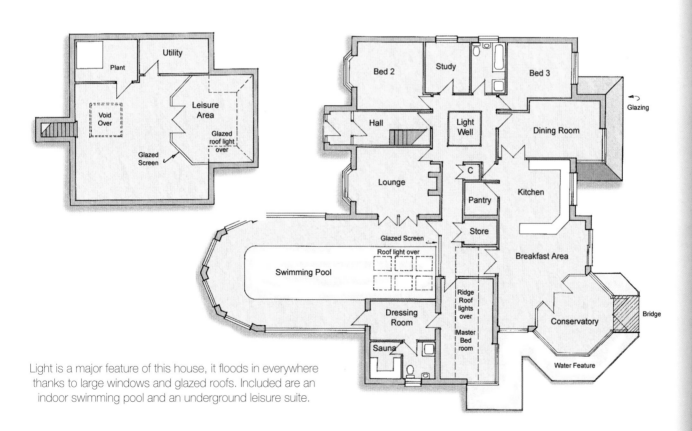

Utility

Plant

Void Over

Leisure Area

Glazed roof light over

Glazed Screen

Bed 2

Study

Bed 3

Glazing

Hall

Light Well

Dining Room

Lounge

C

Pantry

Kitchen

Store

Glazed Screen

Roof light over

Breakfast Area

Swimming Pool

Dressing Room

Ridge Roof lights over

Conservatory

Bridge

Master Bed room

Sauna

Water Feature

Light is a major feature of this house, it floods in everywhere thanks to large windows and glazed roofs. Included are an indoor swimming pool and an underground leisure suite.

Traditional style

Floor area
177m²
1905ft²

Bedrooms
3

Bathrooms
2

Floors
2

Key features
Swimming pool
Kitchen/breakfast room
Basement leisure area
Conservatory
Dining room

Garaging for
0 cars

Design
James Campbell Associates

01706 354888

Build cost
£163,000

Plan no. **BHP 310653**

The kitchen and living room are both good sized. The master suite takes a dominant, full-depth position upstairs. But the other bedrooms are generous doubles with space for an en-suite apiece.

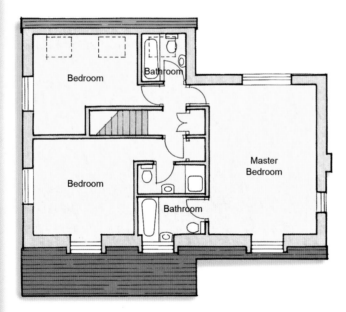

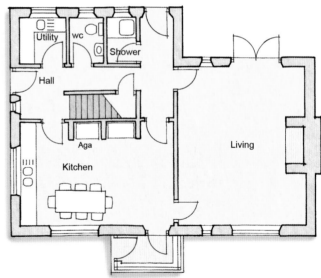

Plan no. **BHP 310281**

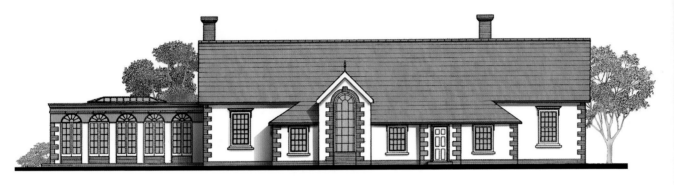

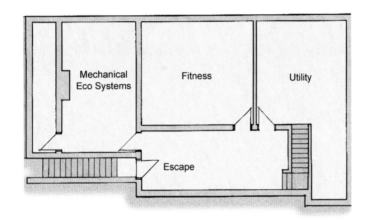

Mechanical Eco Systems · Fitness · Utility · Escape

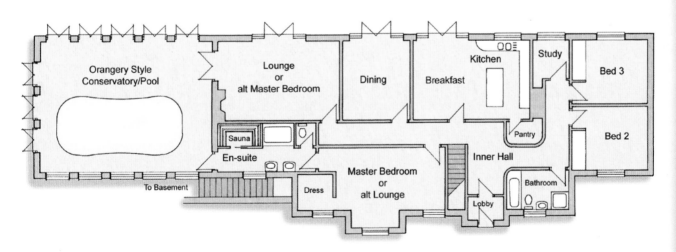

Orangery Style Conservatory/Pool · Lounge or alt Master Bedroom · Dining · Kitchen · Study · Bed 3 · Breakfast · Sauna · En-suite · Pantry · Bed 2 · To Basement · Dress · Master Bedroom or alt Lounge · Inner Hall · Lobby · Bathroom

High ceilings make this single-storey house feel extremely spacious and the well-thought-out layout adds to this impression. A large indoor pool leads on from the optional master bedroom or lounge. Downstairs in the basement there's a gym and a large utility room.

Traditional style

Floor area
183m²
1970ft²

Bedrooms
3

Bathrooms
2

Floors
2

Key features
Indoor pool

Garaging for
0 cars

Design
Jeremy Rawlings

www.periodhome.net
01884 266444

Build cost
£168,000

Design © Jeremy Rawlings

Traditional style

Floor area
191m²
2056ft²

Bedrooms
3

Bathrooms
3

Floors
2

Key features
Open-plan living area
Utility room
Study

Garaging for
0 cars

Design
**Opus Architecture
and Design**

01252 861759

Build cost
£176,000

Design © Opus Architecture

Plan no. **BHP 311001**

Open-plan living with a feature fireplace in the hall/dining area. There's a first floor lounge with a balcony to take advantage of a potential view. The first floor also includes a study and a large master suite.

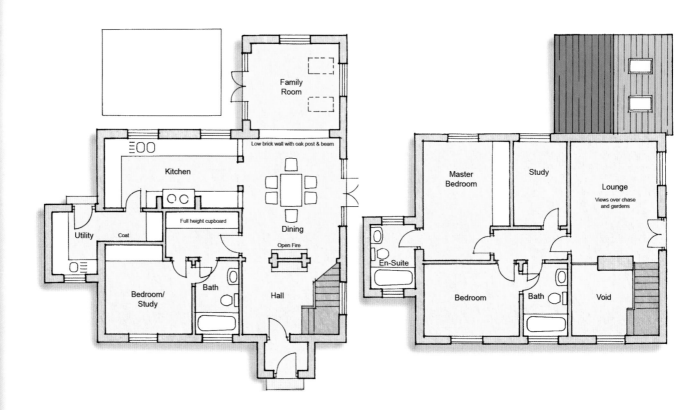

Plan no. **BHP 310473**

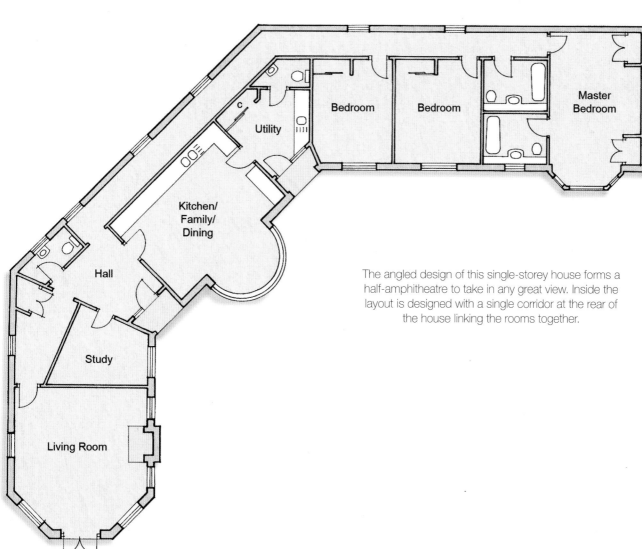

- Bedroom
- Bedroom
- Master Bedroom
- Utility
- C
- Kitchen/ Family/ Dining
- Hall
- Study
- Living Room

The angled design of this single-storey house forms a half-amphitheatre to take in any great view. Inside the layout is designed with a single corridor at the rear of the house linking the rooms together.

Contemporary style

Floor area
191m²
2056ft²

Bedrooms
3

Bathrooms
2

Floors
1

Key features
Kitchen/family room
Living room
Study
Utility
Master en-suite

Garaging for
0 cars

Design
The Border Design Centre

www.borderdesign.co.uk
borderdesign@btconnect.com
01578 740218

Build cost
£176,000

Traditional style

Floor area

193m²

2077ft²

Bedrooms

3

Bathrooms

2

Floors

2

Key features
Vaulted lounge
Kitchen/diner
Music room
Utility room
Art studio

Garaging for
0 cars

Design
Potton

www.potton.co.uk
contact@potton.co.uk
01767 676 400

Build cost
£177,500

Design © Potton

Plan no. **BHP 310575**

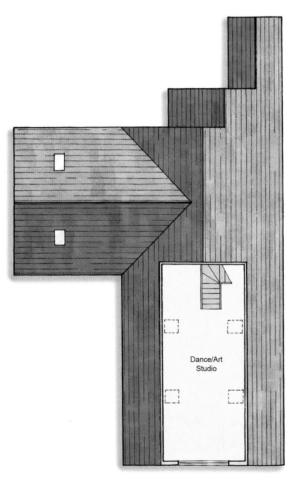

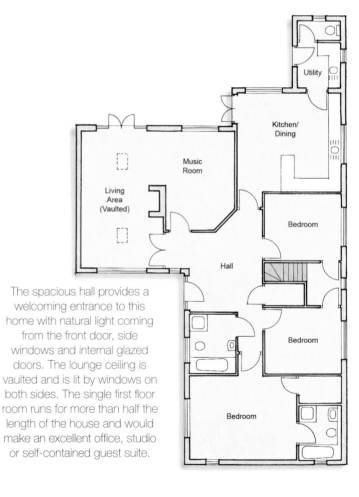

The spacious hall provides a welcoming entrance to this home with natural light coming from the front door, side windows and internal glazed doors. The lounge ceiling is vaulted and is lit by windows on both sides. The single first floor room runs for more than half the length of the house and would make an excellent office, studio or self-contained guest suite.

Plan no. **BHP 310203**

Designed for a sloping site this house has entry at first floor level where there is a kitchen, breakfast and living room as well as the master bedroom suite. Downstairs there are two further bedrooms, a bathroom and family room.

Contemporary style

Floor area
195m²
2099ft²

Bedrooms
3

Bathrooms
2

Floors
2

Key features
Upside-down living
Open-plan living area
Balconies
Family room
Master en-suite

Garaging for
0 cars

Design
Chaddock Design

www.dreamspelldesign.co.uk
info@dreamspelldesign.co.uk
01789 459148

Build cost
£179,000

Design © Chaddock Design

Contemporary style

Floor area
200m²
2153ft²

Bedrooms
3

Bathrooms
2

Floors
2

Key features
Observation tower
Separate dining room
Utility room
Galleried landing
Master en-suite

Garaging for
1 car

Design
The Border Design Centre

www.borderdesign.co.uk
borderdesign@btconnect.com
01578 740218

Build cost
£184,000

Design © The Border Design Centre

Plan no. **BHP 310980**

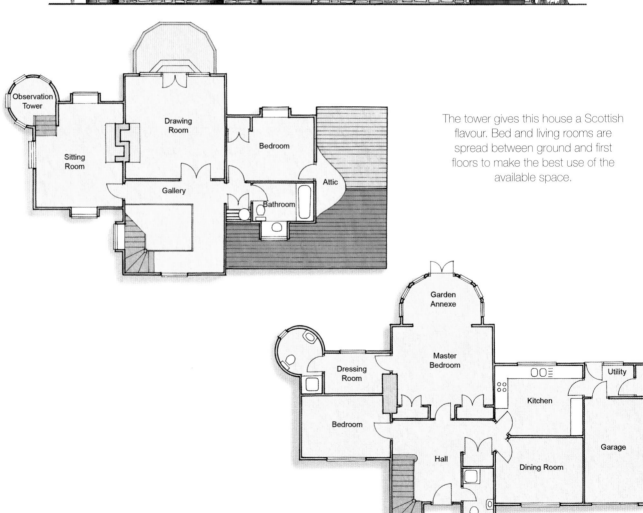

The tower gives this house a Scottish flavour. Bed and living rooms are spread between ground and first floors to make the best use of the available space.

Plan no. **BHP 310596**

The single storey garage outbuilding and single storey downstairs give this cottage the feel of the building having been extended over the years and therefore the illusion of age. The way the lounge and dining area doors open onto the terrace give added flexibility to the living space.

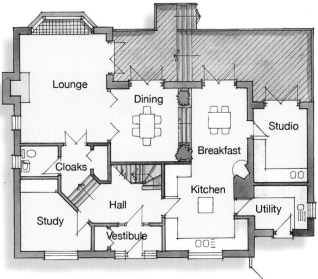

Traditional style

Floor area
200m²
2153ft²

Bedrooms
3

Bathrooms
2

Floors
2

Key features
Kitchen/breakfast room
Lounge/dining room
Utility room
Study
Master en-suite

Garaging for
1 car

Design
Design & Materials

www.designandmaterials.uk.com
enquiries@designandmaterials.
uk.com
01909 540 123

Build cost
£184,000

Design © Design &
Materials

Contemporary style

Floor area

200m²

2153ft²

Bedrooms

3

Bathrooms

2

Floors

3

Key features
Vaulted living room
Kitchen/dining room
Sun room
Garden room
Master bed en-suite

Garaging for
0 cars

Design
Design & Materials

www.designandmaterials.uk.com
enquiries@designandmaterials.
uk.com
01909 540 123

Build cost
£184,000

Design © Design and
Materials

Plan no. **BHP 310572**

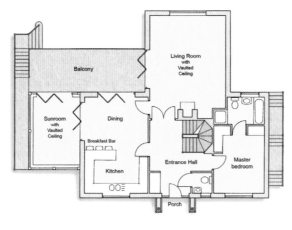

The spacious entrance hall in this house is designed to have lots of natural light thanks to strategically placed rooflights in the roof. The main living areas flow neatly into each other through fold-back doors and all have access to a large balcony. The attic space offers space for an extra bedroom, study or playroom and there's also some useful storage in the eaves.

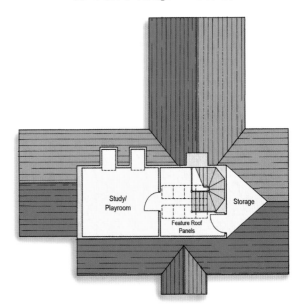

Plan no. **BHP 310563**

Traditional style

Floor area
204m²
2196ft²

Bedrooms
3

Bathrooms
3

Floors
2

Key features
Sun room
Separate dining room
Utility room
Study
Master en-suite

Garaging for
1 car

Design
The Border Design Centre

www.borderdesign.co.uk
borderdesign@btconnect.com
01578 740218

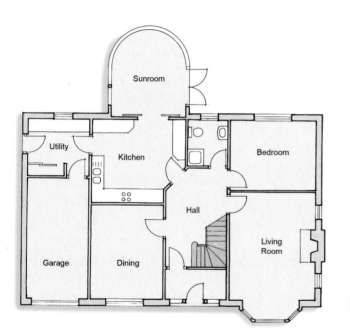

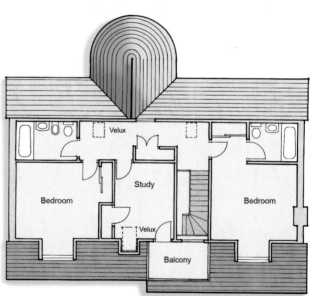

The semi-circular sun room in this house offers a great place to sit. Other
features include a first floor balcony and twin upstairs bed and bathrooms.

Build cost
£187,500

Design © The Border
Design Centre

Traditional style

Floor area
205m²
2207ft²

Bedrooms
3

Bathrooms
3

Floors
2

Key features
Kitchen/diner
Utility room
Study Master en-suite
Dressing room

Garaging for
1 car

Design
Border Oak

www.borderoak.com s
ales@borderoak.com
01568 708752

Build cost
£188,500

Design © Border Oak

Plan no. **BHP 310752**

This house combines a traditional look with interesting changes of roof line and dormers. What you get inside is an open-plan space downstairs and double-sized bedrooms upstairs plus lots of extra storage room in the eaves.

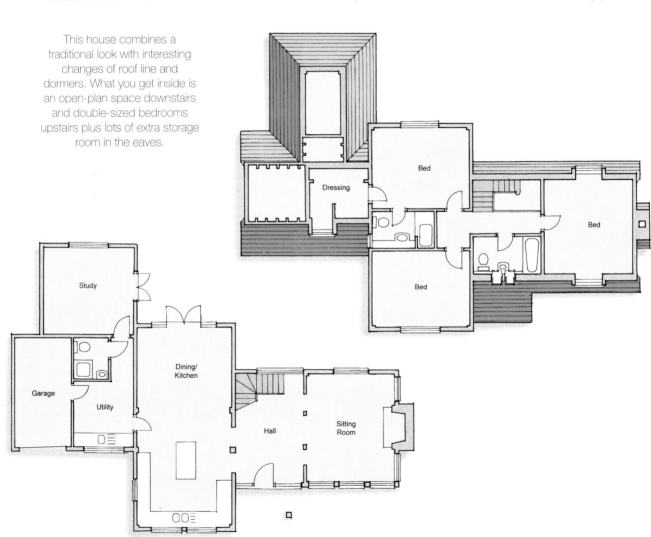

Plan no. **BHP 310497**

Traditional style

Floor area

205m²

2207ft²

Bedrooms

3

Bathrooms

2

Floors

2

Key features
Large kitchen
Dining hall
Utility room
Study
Master en-suite

Garaging for

0 cars

Design
TJ Crump
Oakwrights

www.oakwrights.co.uk
enquiries@oakwrights.co.uk
01432 353353

Build cost
£188,500

Design © TJ Crump

The first floor sitting room and balcony in this design is perfect to take advantage of a beautiful view. Across the landing the master bedroom has a generous en-suite bathroom built into the eaves. Downstairs an expansive hall leads to two more bedrooms and a large kitchen with utility and cloakroom attached.

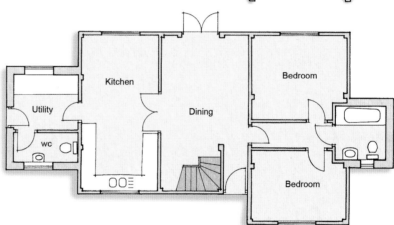

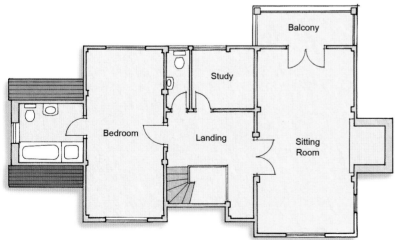

Traditional style

Floor area

205m²

2207ft²

Bedrooms

3

Bathrooms

3

Floors

2

Key features
Sun room
Utility room
Separate dining room
Master en-suite

Garaging for

0 cars

Design
Border Oak

www.borderoak.com
sales@borderoak.com
01568 708752

Build cost
£188,500

Design © Border Oak

Plan no. **BHP 310134**

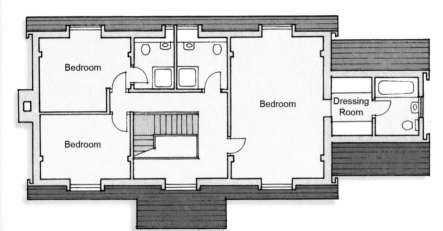

Behind the classic exterior of this house are all the accoutrements of modern living including a double-glazed sun room, big kitchen, dining and sitting rooms. The first floor features three bedrooms with a full-width master suite complete with dressing room and bathroom.

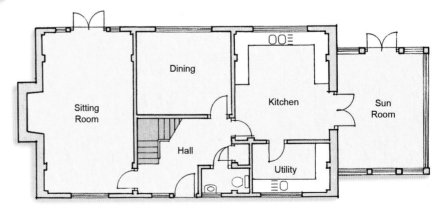

Plan no. **BHP 310476**

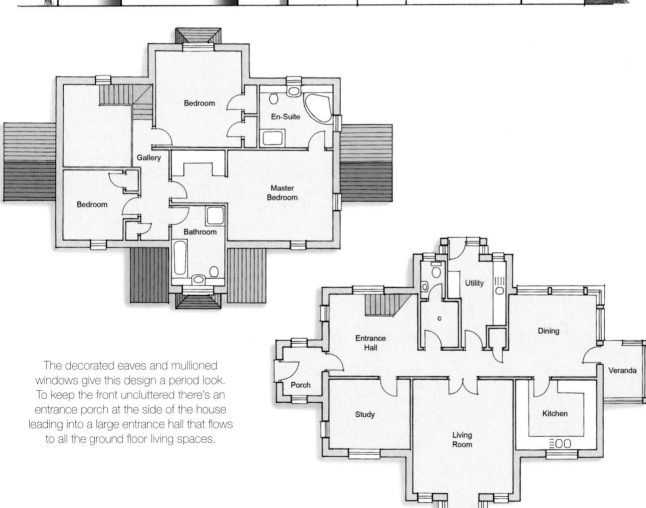

The decorated eaves and mullioned windows give this design a period look. To keep the front uncluttered there's an entrance porch at the side of the house leading into a large entrance hall that flows to all the ground floor living spaces.

Traditional style

Floor area
211m²
2271ft²

Bedrooms
3

Bathrooms
2

Floors
2

Key features
Porch
Galleried hall/landing
Utility room
Master en-suite
Veranda

Garaging for
0 cars

Design
**John Braid
(at Leslie R Hutt)**

lhuttarchitect@btinternet.com
01463 235566

Build cost
£194,000

Design © Leslie R Hutt

Traditional style

Floor area
213m²
2293ft²

Bedrooms
3

Bathrooms
3

Floors
2

Key features
Kitchen/breakfast room
Study
Utility room
Master en-suite

Garaging for
1 car

Design
Churchill Design

www.churchilldesign.co.uk
info@churchilldesign.co.uk
01252 325701

Build cost
£196,000

Design © Churchill Design

Plan no. **BHP 310212**

Despite a low roof height this house fits in three bedrooms easily by using dormer windows and rooflights. The living room has twin-aspect windows and there is a large reception hall.

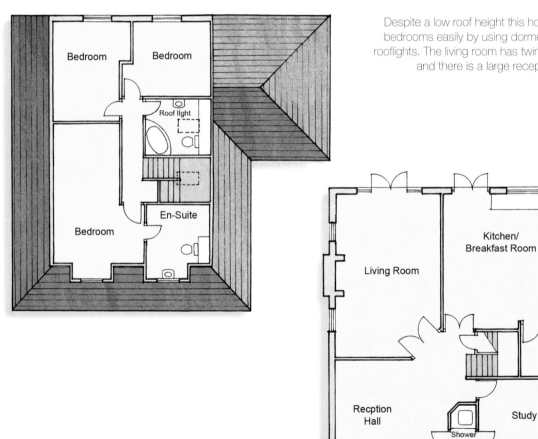

Plan no. **BHP 310014**

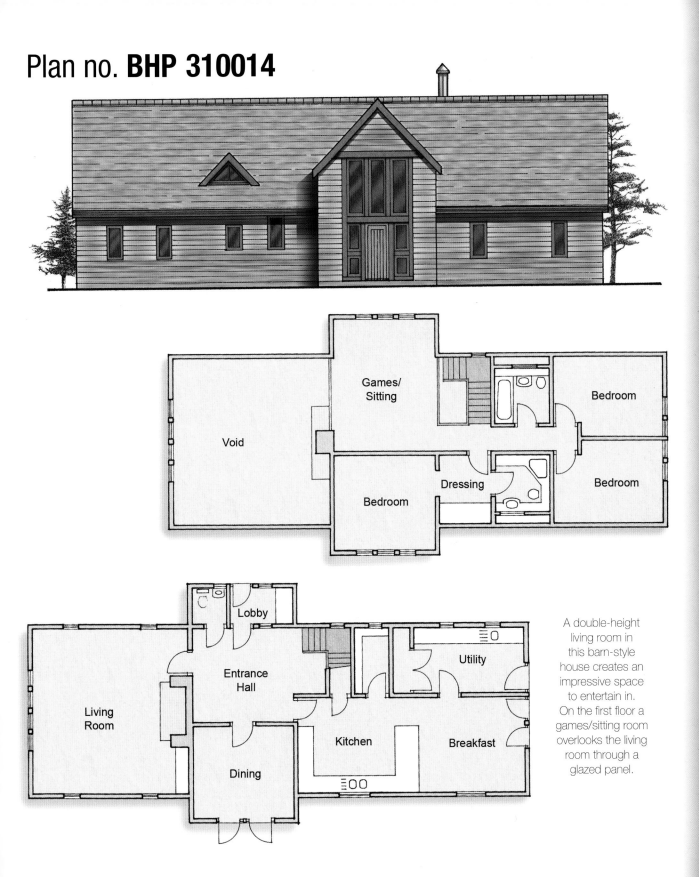

A double-height living room in this barn-style house creates an impressive space to entertain in. On the first floor a games/sitting room overlooks the living room through a glazed panel.

Barn style

Floor area
214m²
2303ft²

Bedrooms
3

Bathrooms
2

Floors
2

Key features
Kitchen/breakfast room
Separate dining room
Utility room
Double height lounge
Games room

Garaging for
0 cars

Design
Welsh Oak Frame

www.welshoakframe.com
01686 688000

Build cost
£197,000

Design © Welsh Oak Frame

Contemporary style

Floor area
220m²
2368ft²

Bedrooms
3

Bathrooms
1

Floors
2

Key features
Big entrance hall
Study
Utility room

Garaging for
1 car

Design
Churchill Design

www.churchilldesign.co.uk
info@churchilldesign.co.uk
01252 325701

Build cost
£202,500

Plan no. **BHP 310812**

The dormer windows allow bedrooms and bathrooms to be built into the eaves. Downstairs the entrance hall is large and could easily accommodate a dining table, while the kitchen and living room both have direct access to the garden through French doors.

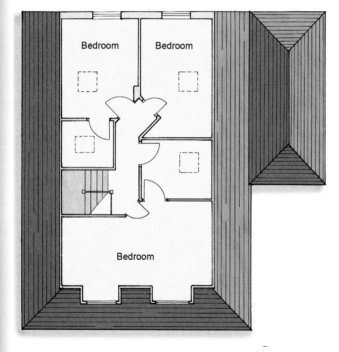

Plan no. **BHP 310269**

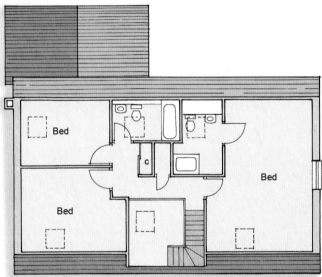

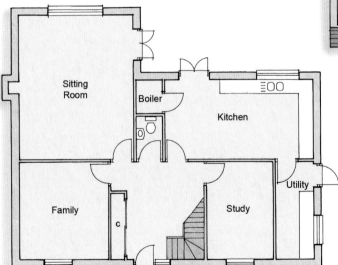

Traditional style

Floor area
223m²
2400ft²

Bedrooms
3

Bathrooms
2

Floors
2

Key features
Kitchen/breakfast room
Family room
Study
Utility room
Master en-suite

Garaging for
0 cars

Design
Custom Homes

www.customhomes.co.uk
admin@customhomes.co.uk
01787 377388

Build cost
£200,000

Design © Custom Homes

This design makes use of Velux-type windows in the roof and allows three bedrooms on the first floor. Downstairs there are two reception rooms and the potential for a vaulted ceiling detail over one end of the sitting room.

Floor area

225m²

2422ft²

Bedrooms

3

Bathrooms

2

Floors

3

Key features
Three storeys
Kitchen/dining room
Study
Playroom
Master en-suite

Garaging for

0 cars

Design

Richard Hall

07968 407129

Build cost
£202,000

Design © Richard Hall

Plan no. **BHP 310704**

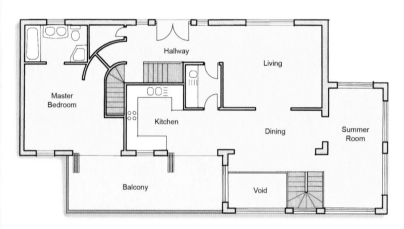

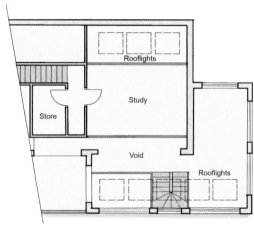

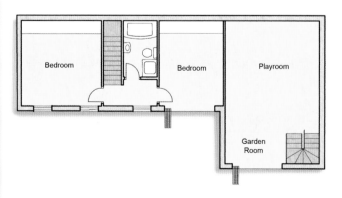

This futuristic design makes maximum use of the available space with its open-plan rooms and three-level layout. The ground floor takes in all the available sunlight with its mass of glazing and full-height folding/sliding doors.

Plan no. **BHP 310260**

From the front this house is deceptively small, but thanks to flush-fitting rooflights there's a decent-sized first floor on offer. Compact, but offering a range of rooms for those who like their living spaces separated.

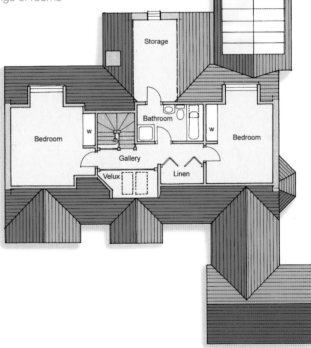

Traditional style

Floor area
230m²
2476ft²

Bedrooms
3

Bathrooms
2

Floors
2

Key features
Kitchen/breakfast room
Study
Utility room
Sun room
Separate dining room

**Garaging for
1 cars**

Design
Design & Materials

www.designandmaterials.uk.com
enquiries@designandmaterials.
uk.com
01909 540 123

**Build cost
£206,000**

Design © Design &
Materials

Contemplary style

Floor area
230m²
2476ft²

Bedrooms
3

Bathrooms
3

Floors
2

Key features
Kitchen/breakfast room
Utility room
Study
Sun lounge
Master en-suite

Garaging for
0 car

Design
John Braid
(at Leslie R Hutt)

lhuttarchitect@btinternet.com
01463 235566

Build cost
£206,000

Design © Leslie R Hutt

Plan no. **BHP 310863**

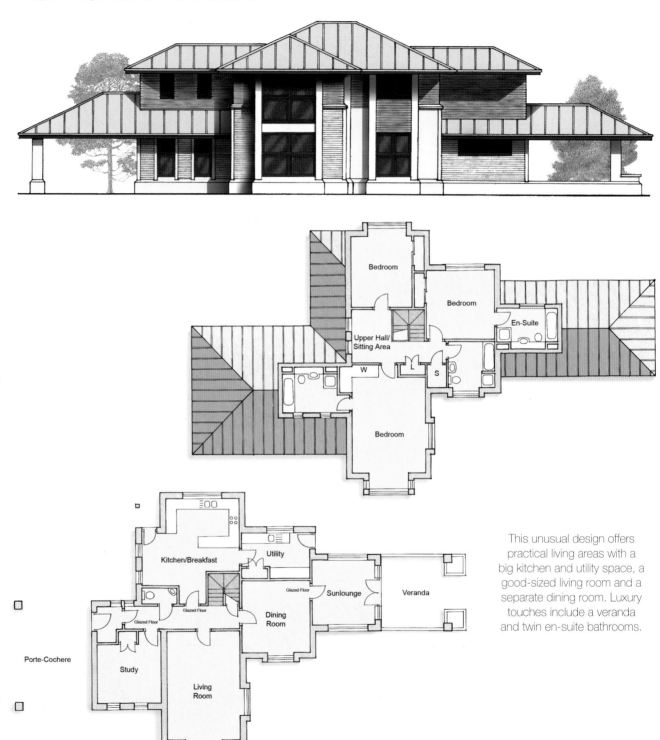

This unusual design offers practical living areas with a big kitchen and utility space, a good-sized living room and a separate dining room. Luxury touches include a veranda and twin en-suite bathrooms.

Plan no. **BHP 310941**

Here a sloping site allows for an underfloor garage, above which sits the master bedroom and a extra reception room. The bay-fronted conservatory creates a great feature at the end of a kitchen that also includes dining space and twin aspect windows. Upstairs the first floor features two large bedrooms and a family bathroom.

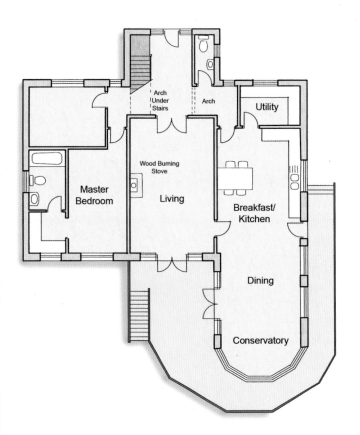

Arch Under Stairs

Arch

Utility

Wood Burning Stove

Master Bedroom

Living

Breakfast/ Kitchen

Dining

Conservatory

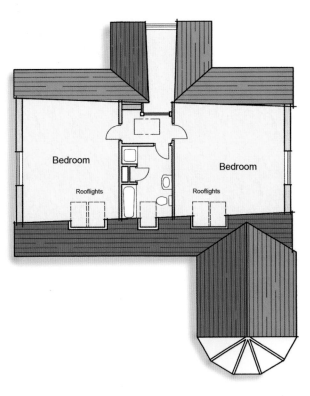

Bedroom

Rooflights

Bedroom

Rooflights

Contemporary style

Floor area
233m²
2508ft²

Bedrooms
3

Bathrooms
2

Floors
3

Key features
Kitchen/breakfast area
Conservatory
Master en-suite
Study
Utility room

Garaging for
2 cars

Design
JS Building Consultancy

www.ukbuildingconsultancy.
co.uk
jsharples@ricsonline.org
0113 250 1303

Build cost
£209,000

Design © JS Building
Consultancy

Traditional style

Floor area
235m²
2530ft²

Bedrooms
3

Bathrooms
3

Floors
2

Key features
Porch
Separate dining room
Family room
Utility room
3 en-suites

Garaging for
2 cars

Design
Border Oak

www.borderoak.com
sales@borderoak.com
01568 708752

Build cost
£211,000

Design © Border Oak

Plan no. **BHP 310071**

Thatch, timber and render give this house a really interesting exterior. The space over the garage is shown as a store but could equally make a very useful studio or office for those who want a live/work unit.

Plan no. **BHP 310584**

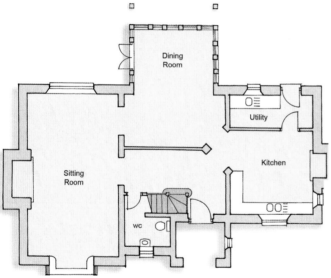

Dining Room

Utility

Sitting Room

Kitchen

wc

Behind the traditional-looking exterior lurks a modern open-plan ground floor layout. Upstairs a large landing leads on to three bedrooms.

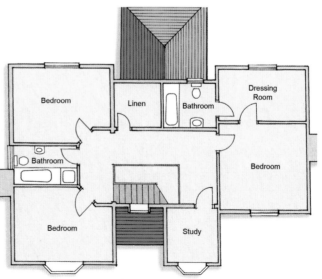

Bedroom

Linen

Bathroom

Dressing Room

Bathroom

Bedroom

Bedroom

Study

Traditional style

Floor area
240m²
2583ft²

Bedrooms
3

Bathrooms
2

Floors
2

Key features
Dining room
Galleried landing
Master en-suite
Dressing room

Garaging for
0 cars

Design
**TJ Crump
Oakwrights**

www.oakwrights.co.uk
enquiries@oakwrights.co.uk
01432 353353

Build cost
£215,000

Barn style

Floor area
260m²
2799ft²

Bedrooms
3

Bathrooms
4

Floors
2

Key features
Vaulted living space
Open-plan layout
Sauna
Utility room
En-suite master bed

Garaging for
0 cars

Design
Design & Materials

www.designandmaterials.uk.com
enquiries@designandmaterials.
uk.com
01909 540 123

Build cost
£233,000

Plan no. **BHP 310518**

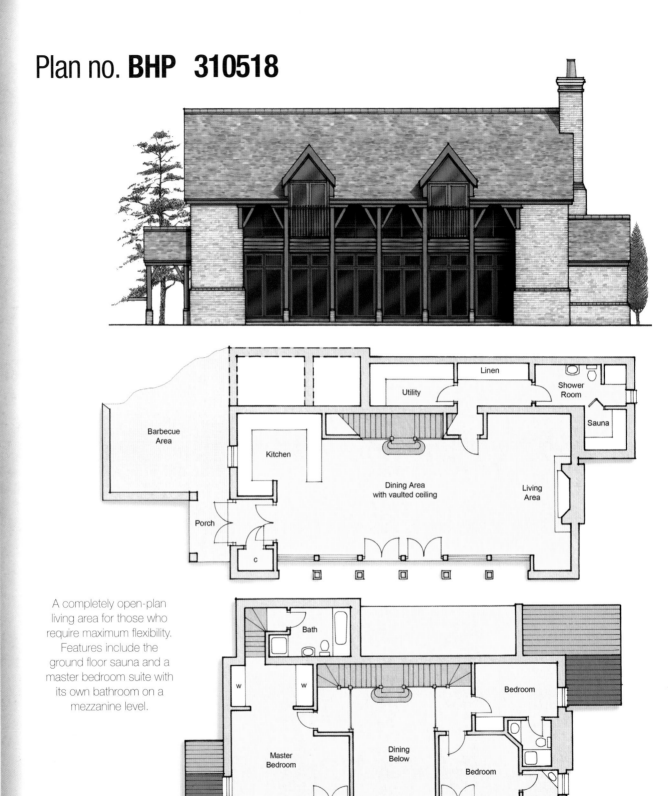

A completely open-plan living area for those who require maximum flexibility. Features include the ground floor sauna and a master bedroom suite with its own bathroom on a mezzanine level.

Plan no. **BHP 310860**

The ground floor features well laid out living space including an integral kitchen and breakfast room while the link through to the garage contains a utility room. There are three more reception rooms downstairs and three bedrooms and en-suite bathrooms upstairs.

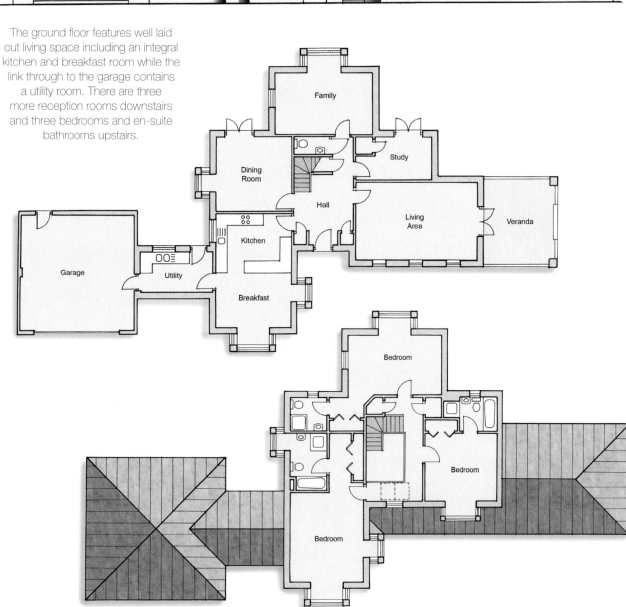

Contemporary style

Floor area
260m²
2799ft²

Bedrooms
3

Bathrooms
3

Floors
2

Key features
Kitchen/breakfast room
Family room
Study
Dining room
Utility room

Garaging for
2 cars

Design
John Braid
(at Leslie R Hutt)

lhuttarchitect@btinternet.com
01463 235566

Build cost
£233,000

Design © John Braid

Traditional style

Floor area

270m²

2906ft²

Bedrooms

3

Bathrooms

3

Floors

2

Key features
Family room
Dining room
Galleried landing
Study

Garaging for
0 cars

Design
Border Oak

www.borderoak.com
sales@borderoak.com
01568 708752

Build cost
£242,000

Design © Border Oak

Plan no. **BHP 310503**

The fully-glazed two-storey bay lights a double-height hallway that leads into an open-plan dining room and kitchen. Off the family room a second staircase leads up to a useful space above the garage – a perfect spot for a gym or home office.

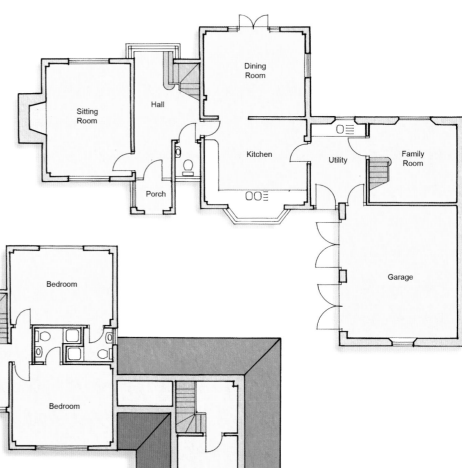

Plan no. **BHP 310167**

The veranda acts as an additional link between the main reception rooms. Upstairs are three good-sized bedrooms with a dressing room and en-suite bathroom for the master.

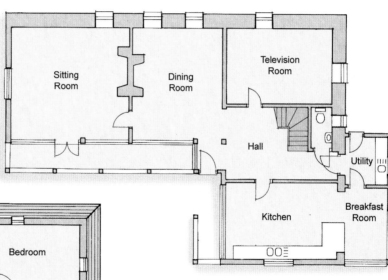

Sitting Room

Dining Room

Television Room

Hall

Utility

Kitchen

Breakfast Room

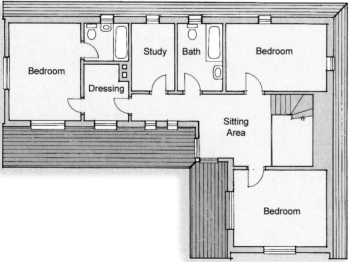

Bedroom

Dressing

Study

Bath

Bedroom

Sitting Area

Bedroom

Traditional style

Floor area

291m²

3132ft²

Bedrooms

3

Bathrooms

2

Floors

2

Key features
Kitchen/breakfast room
Television room
Study
Master bed en-suite
Dressing room

Garaging for
0 cars

Design
Border Oak

www.borderoak.com
sales@borderoak.com
01568 708752

Build cost
£261,000

Design © Border Oak

Barn style

Floor area

342m²

3681ft²

Bedrooms

3

Bathrooms

3

Floors

2

Key Features
Courtyard
Kitchen/breakfast room
Study
Dining/sitting room
Master en-suite

Garaging for
0 cars

Design
Stephen Mattick

www.mattick.co.uk
mattick@mattick.co.uk
01223 891159

Build cost
£307,000

Design © S Mattick

Plan no. **BHP 310593**

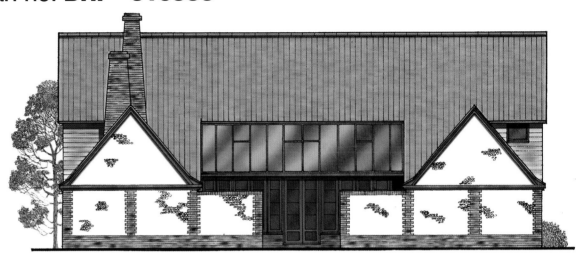

The twin single-storey sections of this house form an impressive courtyard entrance that can be seen from the kitchen, study and one of the three bedrooms. Inside, the glass-roofed hallway leads into a dining room and a double-height sitting room. The entire first floor is given over to a sleeping suite equipped with a dressing room and its own bathroom.

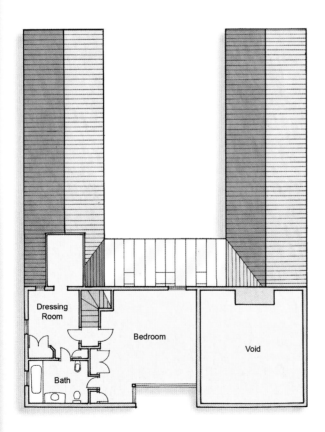

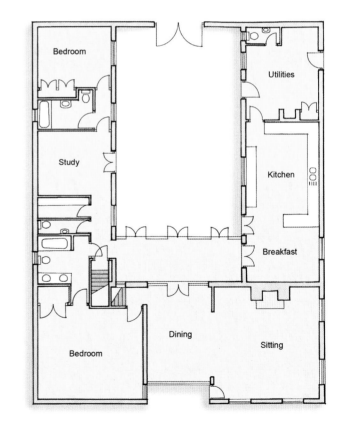

Plan no. **BHP 310959**

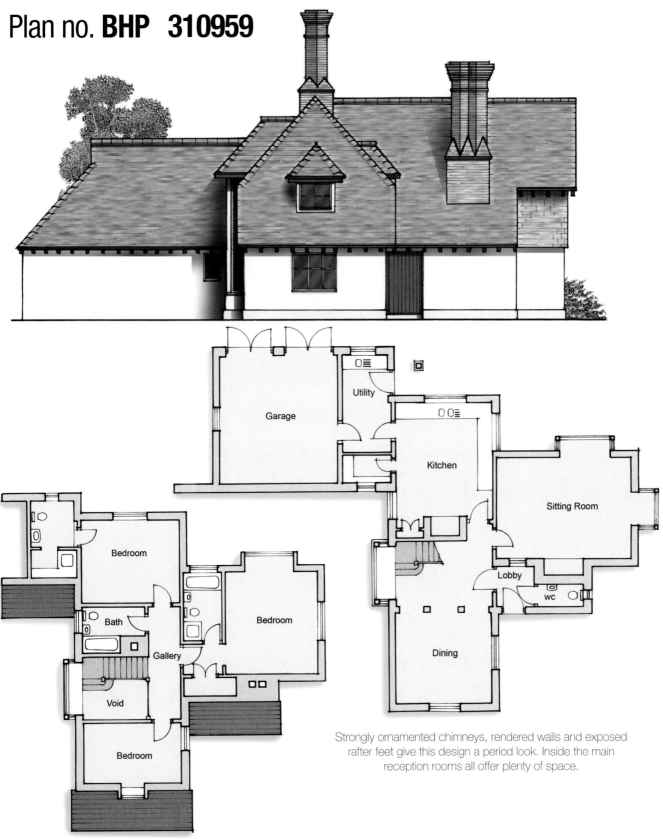

Strongly ornamented chimneys, rendered walls and exposed rafter feet give this design a period look. Inside the main reception rooms all offer plenty of space.

Garage

Utility

Kitchen

Sitting Room

Lobby

WC

Bedroom

Bath

Gallery

Bedroom

Dining

Void

Bedroom

Traditional style

Floor area
353m²
3800ft²

Bedrooms
3

Bathrooms
3

Floors
2

Exceptional Features
Integral garage
Utility room
Master en-suite

Garaging for
2 cars

Design
Border Oak

www.borderoak.com
sales@borderoak.com
01568 708752

Build cost
£316,500

Design © Border Oak

Contemporary style

Floor area

353m²
3800ft²

Bedrooms

3

Bathrooms

3

Floors

3

Key features
Open-plan living
TV room
Bedroom balconies
Gym
Swimming pool

Garaging for
2 cars

Design
Design & Materials

www.designandmaterials.uk.com
enquiries@designandmaterials.
uk.com
01909 540 123

Build cost
£316,500

Design © Design and
Materials

Plan no. **BHP 310608**

This house featres a downstairs gym and a poolside terrace that leads into an open-plan living area. A vast double-height window lights the stairwell up to the first floor sleeping quarters where all the bedrooms have their own balconies.

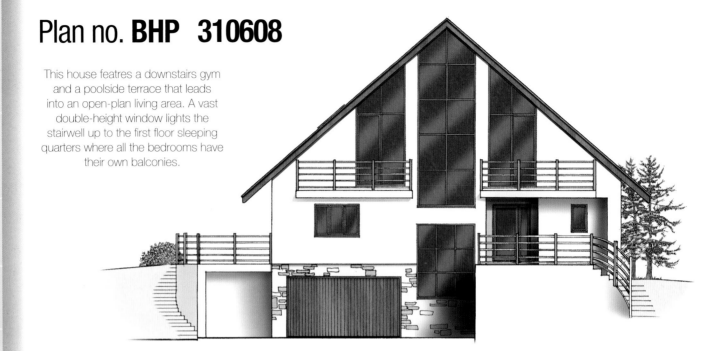

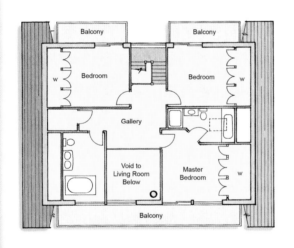

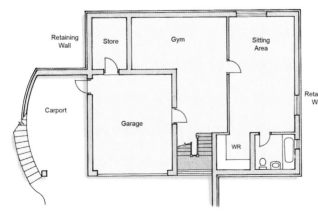

Plan no. **BHP 310707**

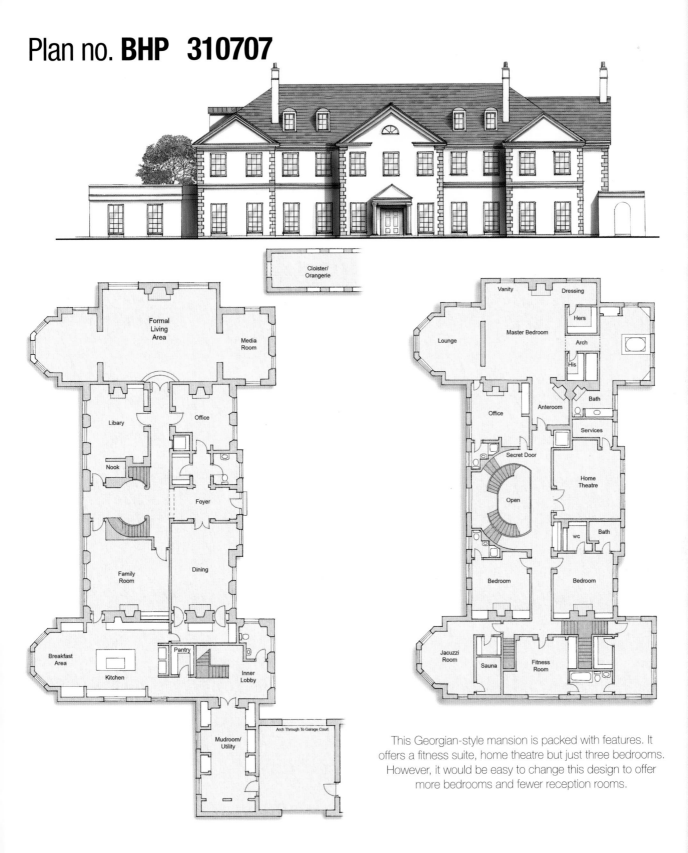

Cloister/Orangerie

Formal Living Area

Media Room

Libary

Office

Nook

Foyer

Family Room

Dining

Breakfast Area

Kitchen

Pantry

Inner Lobby

Mudroom/Utility

Arch Through To Garage Court

Vanity

Dressing

Hers

Master Bedroom

Lounge

Arch

His

Office

Anteroom

Bath

Services

Secret Door

Home Theatre

Open

wc

Bath

Bedroom

Bedroom

Jacuzzi Room

Sauna

Fitness Room

This Georgian-style mansion is packed with features. It offers a fitness suite, home theatre but just three bedrooms. However, it would be easy to change this design to offer more bedrooms and fewer reception rooms.

Traditional style

Floor area
371m²
3993ft²

Bedrooms
3

Bathrooms
5

Floors
2

Key features
Home theatre
Sauna
Jacuzzi room
Library
Orangery

Garaging for
0 cars

Design
Angel Design and Development

01788 573676

Build cost
£333,000

Design © Angel Design and Development

Barn style

Floor area
585m²
6297ft²

Bedrooms
3

Bathrooms
3

Floors
2

Key features
Office
Separate dining room
Mud room
Bedrooms en-suite
Two staircases

Garaging for
2 cars

Design
**TJ Crump
Oakwrights**

www.oakwrights.co.uk
enquiries@oakwrights.co.uk
01432 353353

Build cost
£525,000

Design © Oakwrights

Plan no. **BHP 310803**

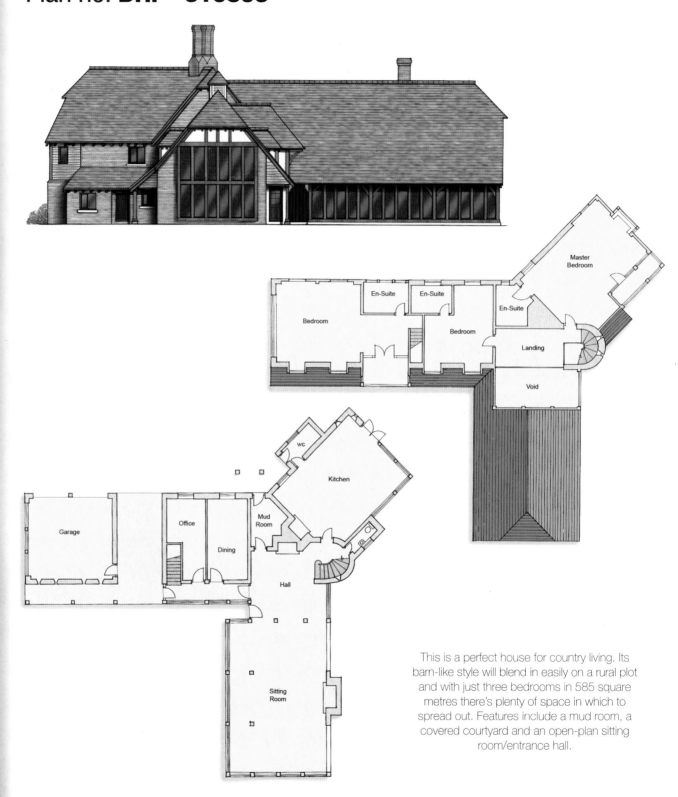

This is a perfect house for country living. Its barn-like style will blend in easily on a rural plot and with just three bedrooms in 585 square metres there's plenty of space in which to spread out. Features include a mud room, a covered courtyard and an open-plan sitting room/entrance hall.

Plan no. **BHP 3106**

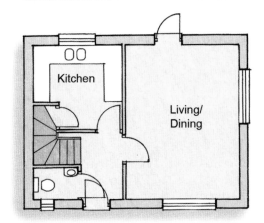

Kitchen

Living/Dining

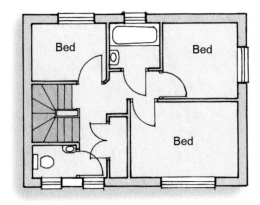

Bed

Bed

Bed

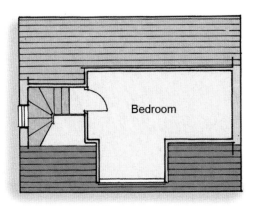

Bedroom

This design's dormer window creates space and light for an extra bedroom in a house with a very small footprint. The ground floor provides a living/dining area.

Traditional style

Floor area
106m²
1141ft²

Bedrooms
4

Bathrooms
1

Floors
3

Key features
Living/dining room
Attic bedroom

Garaging for
0 cars

Design
Architecture Plus

www.architecture-plus.co.uk
01934 416416

Build cost
£110,000

Design © Architecture Plus

Traditional style

Floor area
114m²
1227ft²

Bedrooms
4

Bathrooms
2

Floors
3

Key features
Kitchen/dining room
Top floor suite

Garaging for
1 car

Design
Planahome

www.planahome.uk.com
plans@planahome.uk.com
01326 373600

Build cost
£119,000

Design © Planahome

Plan no. **BHP 310764**

Living

Garage

Hall

Dining/Kitchen

Study/
Bedroom

Bedroom

Bedroom

Bedroom

This house sees a a bedroom and bathroom located in the second floor roofspace while two of the first floor bedrooms have twin-aspect windows to bring in additional daylight.

Plan no. **BHP 310965**

Four bedrooms are fitted into the first floor of this compact home. The living room features a conservatory which adds to the flexibility and helps create a sheltered terrace.

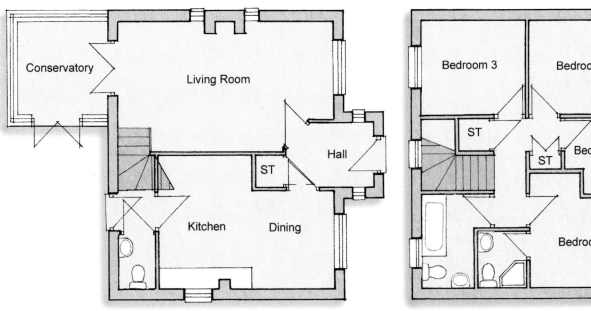

Floor area
121m²
1302ft²

Bedrooms
4

Bathrooms
2

Floors
2

Key features
Conservatory
Kitchen/dining room
Hall
Master en-suite

Garaging for
0 cars

Design
Architecture Plus

www.architecture-plus.co.uk
01934 416416

Build cost
£126,000

Design © Architecture Plus

Traditional style

Floor area
122m²
1313ft²

Bedrooms
4

Bathrooms
2

Floors
2

Key features
Kitchen/beakfast room
Utility room
Separate dining room
Master bed en-suite

Garaging for
1 car

Design
Planahome

www.planahome.uk.com
plans@planahome.uk.com
01326 373600

Build cost
£128,000

Design © Planahome

Plan no. **BHP 310275**

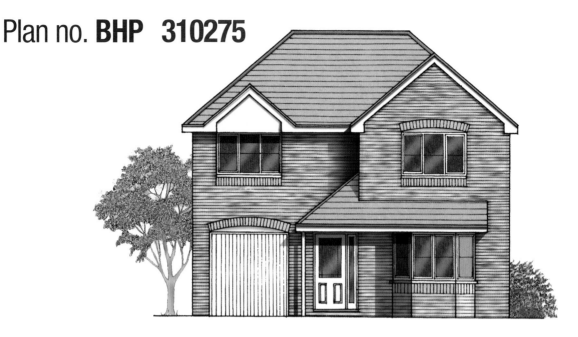

A four-bed family home with a kitchen/breakfast room and a lounge/dining room which can be separated by closing the interconnecting double doors.

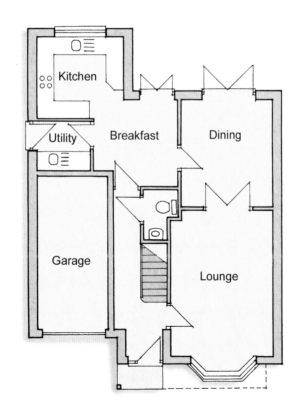

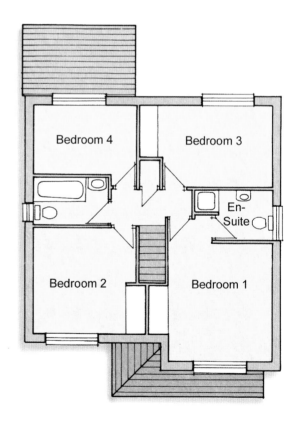

Plan no. **BHP 310899**

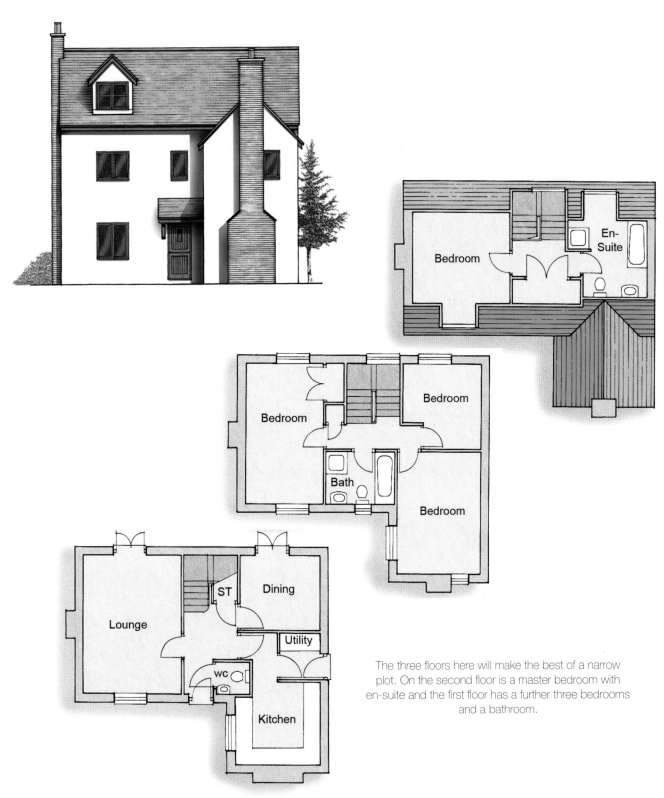

The three floors here will make the best of a narrow plot. On the second floor is a master bedroom with en-suite and the first floor has a further three bedrooms and a bathroom.

Traditional style

Floor area
124m²
1335ft²

Bedrooms
4

Bathrooms
2

Floors
2

Key features
Utility room
Separate dining room
Master bed en-suite

Garaging for
1 car

Design
Planahome

www.planahome.uk.com
plans@planahome.uk.com
01326 373600

Build cost
£129,000

Design © Planahome

Plan no. **BHP 310356**

The conventional design of the reception rooms could be opened up to give a kitchen/ diner or a completey open-plan living area if you wanted to be more radical.

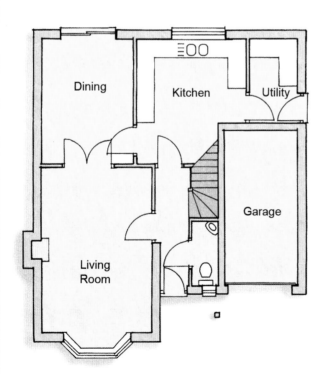

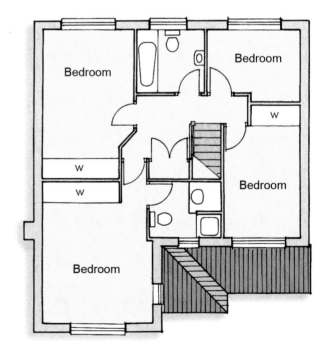

Plan no. **BHP 310197**

Another period style house, this one with a half tile-hung exterior, which would look good in many a village setting.

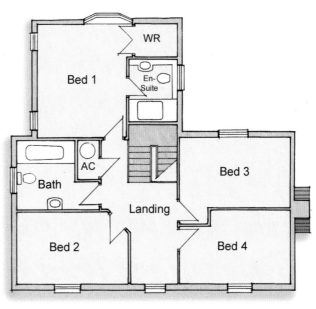

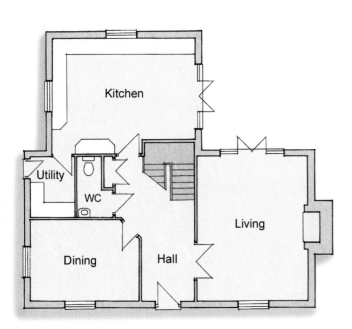

Traditional style

Floor area
125m²
1345ft²

Bedrooms
4

Bathrooms
2

Floors
2

Key features
Separate dining room
Utility room
Master en-suite

Garaging for
0 cars

Design
Potton

www.potton.co.uk
contact@potton.co.uk
01767 676 400

Build cost
£130,500

Design © Potton

Traditional style

Floor area

133m²

1432ft²

Bedrooms

4

Bathrooms

1

Floors

2

Key features
Open-plan living
Utility room

Garaging for
0 cars

Design
Architecture Plus

www.architecture-plus.co.uk
01934 416416

Build cost
£122,000

Design © Architecture Plus

Plan no. **BHP 310173**

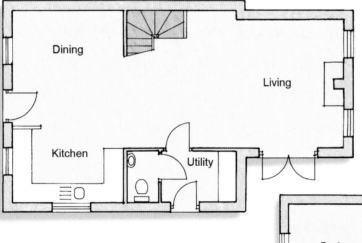

The shape of this cottage would make it ideal for a narrow or infill plot – especially where the visual impact from the kerb needs to be minimised.

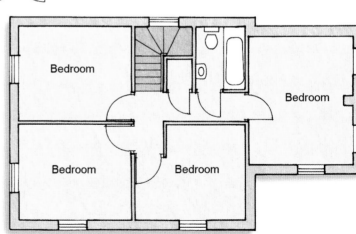

Plan no. **BHP 310989**

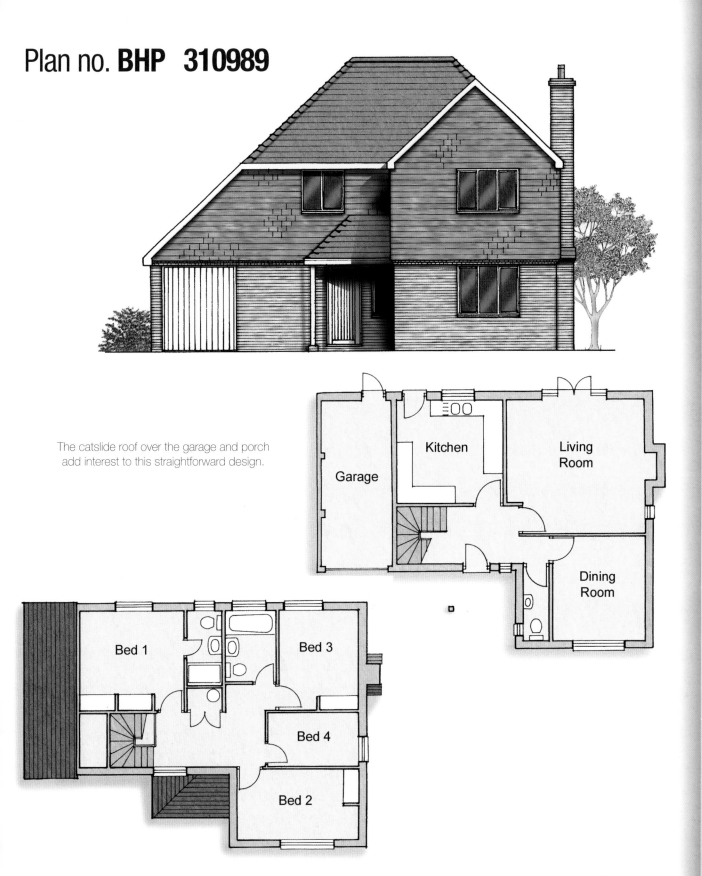

The catslide roof over the garage and porch add interest to this straightforward design.

Garage

Kitchen

Living Room

Dining Room

Bed 1

Bed 3

Bed 4

Bed 2

Traditional style

Floor area
135m²
1453ft²

Bedrooms
4

Bathrooms
2

Floors
2

Key features
Master bed en-suite
Separate dining room

Garaging for
1 car

Design
County Contracts

countycontractsltd@fsmail.net
01892 785153

Build cost
£124,000

Design © County Contracts

Traditional style

Floor area

138m²

1485ft²

Bedrooms

4

Bathrooms

2

Floors

2

Key features
Kitchen/breakfast room
Separate dining room
Study
Utility room
Master bed en-suite

**Garaging for
2 cars**

**Design
Planahome**

www.planahome.uk.com
plans@planahome.uk.com
01326 373600

**Build cost
£127,000**

Design © Planahome

Plan no. **BHP 310200**

This developer-style design ticks all of the boxes for standard spec - including the double garage, kitchen/breakfast room and master en-suite.

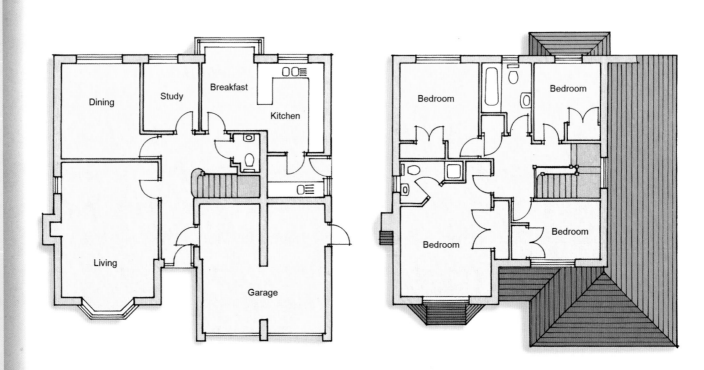

Plan no. **BHP 310395**

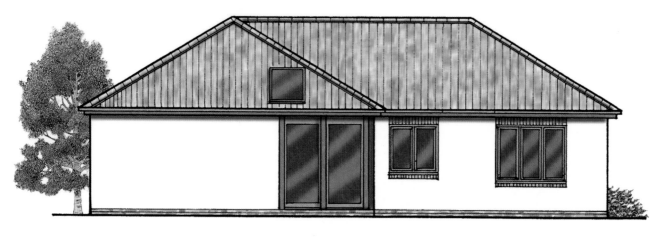

- Living Room
- Bedroom
- Bedroom
- Bedroom
- Bathroom
- Bedroom/ Study
- Kitchen/ Dining
- Entrance
- Conservat

Traditional style

Floor area
140m²
1507ft²

Bedrooms
4

Bathrooms
2

Floors
1

Key features
Kitchen/diner
Master bed en-suite

Garaging for
0 cars

Design
Architecture Plus

www.architecture-plus.co.uk
01934 416416

Build cost
£129,000

Four bedrooms, a large living room with 'bring the outside in' folding doors and a family-sized kitchen make up house-sized accommodation in a single storey.

Design © Architecture Plus

Traditional style

Floor area

143m²

1539ft²

Bedrooms

4

Bathrooms

2

Floors

2

Key features
Master en-suite

Garaging for
1 car

Design
Architecture Plus

www.architecture-plus.co.uk
01934 416416

Build cost
£131,500

Design © Architecture Plus

Plan no. **BHP 310737**

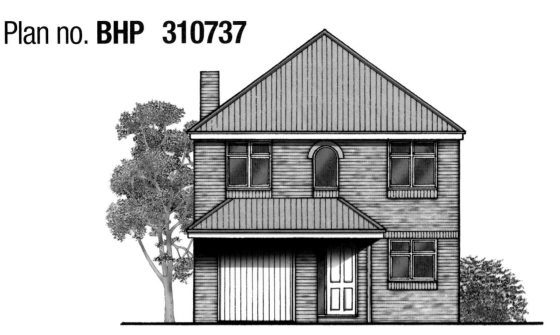

This house offers a compact package with inbuilt garage and would work well on a smaller plot. It also packs in four bedrooms, a bathroom and en-suite.

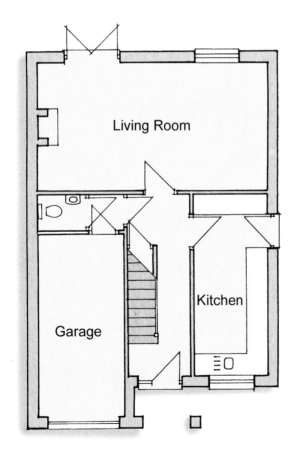

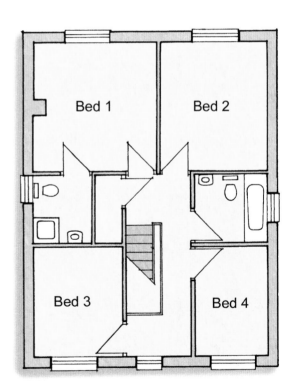

Plan no. **BHP 310797**

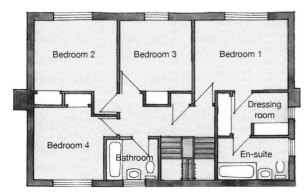

Bedroom 2   Bedroom 3   Bedroom 1

Dressing room

Bedroom 4   Bathroom   En-suite

Featuring a compact kitchen, hall and dining room with four bedrooms upstairs. The decorative detail such as timberwork and small half-hip on the garage roof add visual interest.

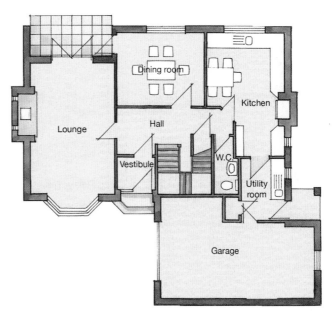

Dining room

Kitchen

Lounge   Hall

Vestibule   W.C.

Utility room

Garage

Traditional style

Floor area
143m²
1539ft²

Bedrooms
4

Bathrooms
2

Floors
2

Key features
Kitchen/breakfast room
Utility room
Separate dining room
Master bedroom suite

Garaging for
1 car

Design
**David Bateman/
Oregon Homes**

**Build cost
£131,500**

Design © Oregon Homes

Traditional style

Floor area
144m²
1550ft²

Bedrooms
4

Bathrooms
2

Floors
2

Key features
Kitchen/breakfast room
Study
Linked lounge/diner
Master en-suite

Garaging for
0 cars

Design
Planahome

www.planahome.uk.com
plans@planahome.uk.com
01326 373600

Build cost
£132,500

Design © Planahome

Plan no. **BHP 310038**

A long porch, supported by an impressive brick pillar, adds a twist to the front of this design. Inside the hall leads on to twin reception rooms a kitchen and study. Upstairs there are three double and one single bedrooms.

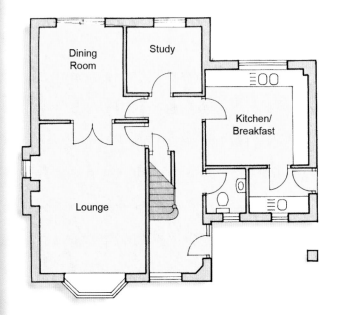

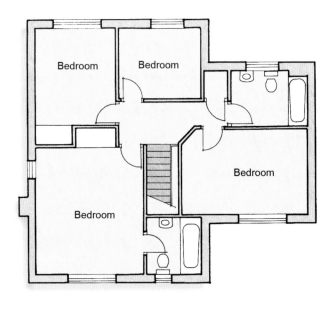

Plan no. **BHP 310668**

Through the covered porch the hall leads through to an open-plan living area. Upstairs bedrooms two and three are amply proportioned and share a good-sized family bathroom.

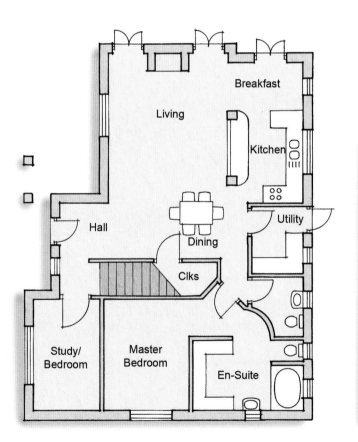

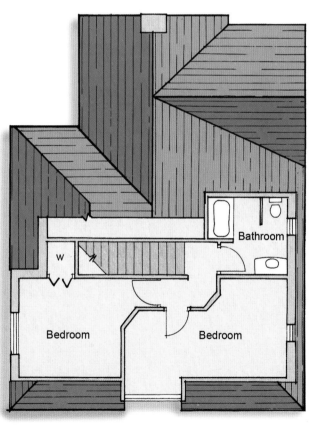

Traditional style

Floor area
147m²
1582ft²

Bedrooms
4

Bathrooms
2

Floors
2

Key features
Open-plan living
Utility room
Master en-suite

Garaging for
0 cars

Design
Jeremy Rawlings

www.periodhome.net 01884
266444

Build cost
£135,000

Design © Jeremy Rawlings

Traditional style

Floor area
147m²

1582ft²

Bedrooms
4

Bathrooms
2

Floors
2

Key features
Utility room
Linked lounge/diner
Study
Master en-suite

Garaging for
0 cars

Design
**JS Building
Consultancy**

www.ukbuildingconsultancy.
co.uk
jsharples@ricsonline.org
0113 250 1303

Build cost
£135,000

Design © JS Building
Consultancy

Plan no. **BHP 310233**

Eyebrow dormer windows lend a cottage look to this design. Inside, the layout of reception rooms is as traditional as the look with a separate dining room. Upstairs are four double bedrooms.

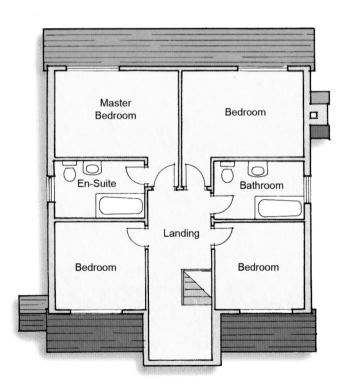

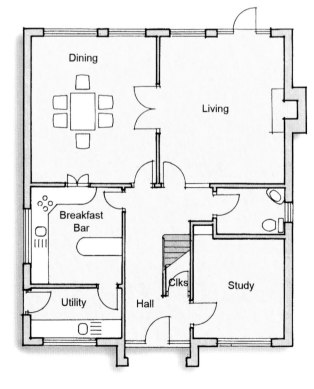

Plan no. **BHP 310083**

The protruding garage gives the opportunity to create a balcony for the en-suite bedroom and a sheltered approach to the front door. Accomodation includes kitchen/dining room, a large living room and four double bedrooms.

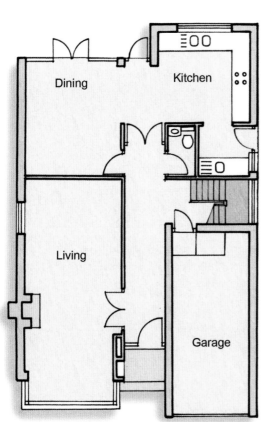

Dining

Kitchen

Living

Garage

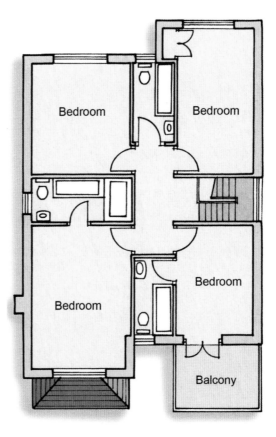

Bedroom

Bedroom

Bedroom

Bedroom

Balcony

Traditional style

Floor area

149m²

1604ft²

Bedrooms

4

Bathrooms

3

Floors

2

Key features
Kitchen/dining room
Balcony
Two en-suites

Garaging for
1 car

Design
**John Shida
(Morningtide
Developments)**

www.morningtide.fsnet.co.uk

johnshida@morningtide.
fsnet.co.uk

01621 815485

Build cost
£137,000

Design © John Shida

Traditional style

Floor area
152m²
1636ft²

Bedrooms
4

Bathrooms
4

Floors
2

Key features
Kitchen/breakfast room
Dining conservatory
Family room
Utility room
Two en-suites

Garaging for
0 cars

Design
Planahome

www.planahome.uk.com
plans@planahome.uk.com
01326 373600

Build cost
£140,000

Design © Planahome

Plan no. **BHP 310731**

This home would make the best of a sunny spot with its extensively glazed dining room and lounge areas. Upstairs a galleried landing leads on to three bedrooms, two en-suites and a decent-sized family bathroom.

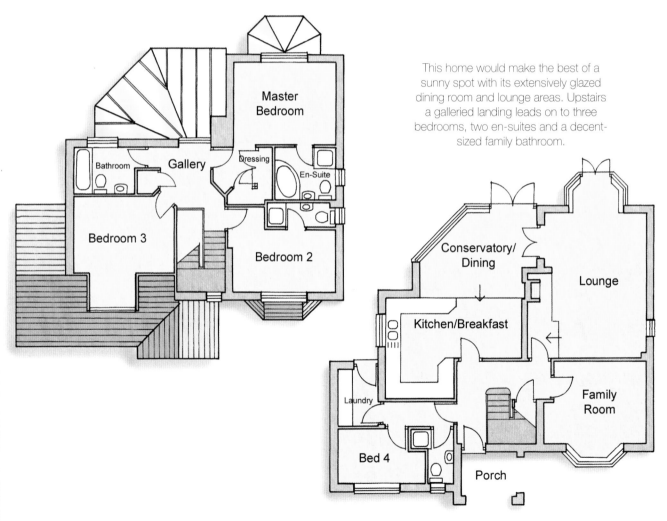

Plan no. **BHP 310443**

In spite of being a basic box the detailing on this design lifts it out of the ordinary. Inside there is a kitchen/dining room and separate lounge and study.

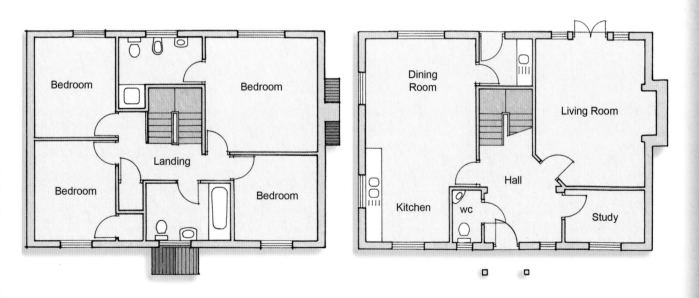

Bedroom

Bedroom

Landing

Bedroom

Bedroom

Dining Room

Living Room

Kitchen

Hall

wc

Study

Traditional style

Floor area
152m²
1636ft²

Bedrooms
4

Bathrooms
2

Floors
2

Key features
Kitchen/dining room
Study
Master en-suite

Garaging for
0 cars

Design
Potton

www.potton.co.uk
contact@potton.co.uk
01767 676 400

Build cost
£140,000

Design © Potton

Traditional style

Floor area

153m²
1647ft²

Bedrooms

4

Bathrooms

2

Floors

2

Key features
Open-plan living
Master en-suite

Garaging for
0 cars

Design
Potton

www.potton.co.uk
contact@potton.co.uk
01767 676 400

Build cost
£141,000

Design © Potton

Plan no. **BHP 310617**

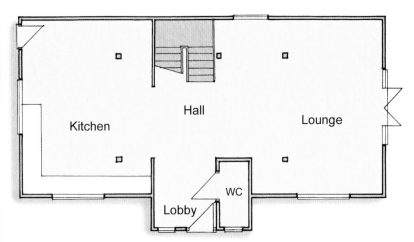

Open-plan downstairs and four
bedrooms upstairs - three of which
are lit by Velux-style windows.
The master bedroom comes with
en-suite while the other three beds
share a family bathroom.

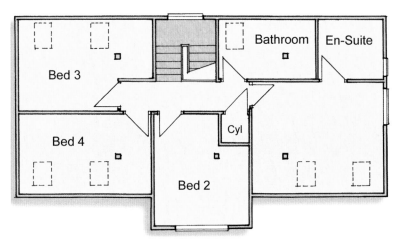

Plan no. **BHP 310359**

The living room has triple-aspect windows and in the kitchen/breakfast room there are French doors to the garden. There is a Georgian feel to this design with the classically-influenced porch.

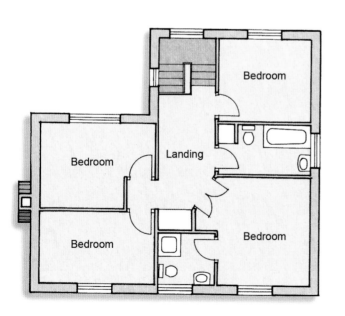

Bedroom

Landing

Bedroom

Bedroom

Bedroom

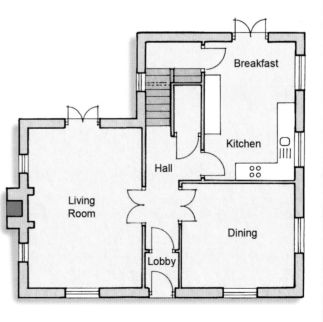

Breakfast

Kitchen

Hall

Living Room

Dining

Lobby

Traditional style

Floor area
154m²
1658ft²

Bedrooms
4

Bathrooms
2

Floors
2

Key features
Kitchen/breakfast room
Separate dining room
Porch
Master en-suite

Garaging for
0 cars

Design
Custom Homes

www.customhomes.co.uk
admin@customhomes.co.uk
01787 377388

Build cost
£141,500

Design © Custom Homes

Traditional style

Floor area
159m²
1711ft²

Bedrooms
4

Bathrooms
3

Floors
2

Key features
Sun lounge
Kitchen/dining room
Utility room
Two en-suites
Vaulted bedroom

Garaging for
1 car

Design
John Braid
(at Leslie R Hutt)

lhuttarchitect@btinternet.com
01463 235566

Build cost
£146,000

Design © John Braid

Plan no. **BHP 310329**

Inside this house benefits from generous areas of glazing and full-height ceilings to give a light, contemporary feel. The living areas are designed to flow through from each other. The first floor features three well-proportioned bedrooms set neatly into the eaves.

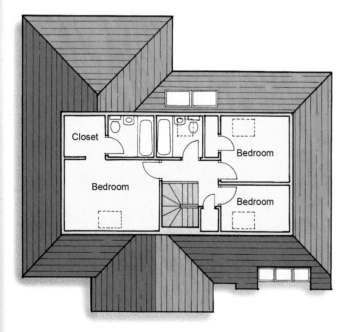

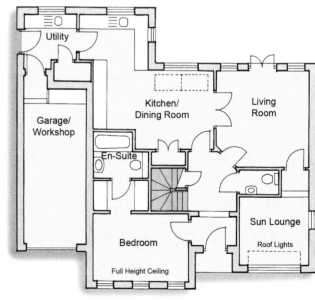

Plan no. **BHP 310368**

This design incorporates a dining hall, a combined kitchen and breakfast room and two bedrooms on the ground floor. Upstairs there are two further bedrooms, a balcony and a bathroom.

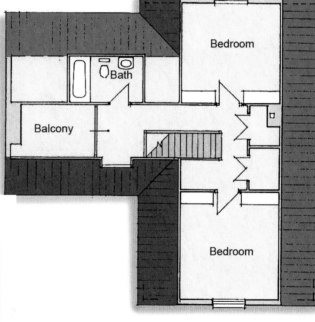

Bath

Balcony

Bedroom

Bedroom

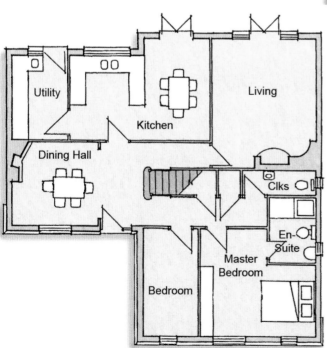

Utility

Kitchen

Living

Dining Hall

Clks

En-Suite

Master Bedroom

Bedroom

Traditional style

Floor area
160m²
1722ft²

Bedrooms
4

Bathrooms
2

Floors
2

Key features
Kitchen/dining room
Dining hall
Utility room
Balcony
Master en-suite

Garaging for
0 cars

Design
Design & Materials

www.designandmaterials.uk.com
enquiries@designandmaterials.
uk.com
01909 540 123

Build cost
£147,000

Design © Design &
Materials

Traditional style

Floor area

160m²

1722ft²

Bedrooms

4

Bathrooms

2

Floors

2

Key features
Kitchen/breafast room
Lounge/dining room
Utility room
Master bed en-suite

Garaging for
0 cars

Design
Design & Materials

www.designandmaterials.uk.com
enquiries@designandmaterials.
uk.com
01909 540 123

Build cost
£147,000

Design © Design &
Materials

Plan no. **BHP 310905**

The ground floor of this house is open-plan and the living room and dining room are separated only by a feature fireplace. The kitchen is accessed through a wide opening marked by twin feature posts. The first floor has a galleried landing and four bedrooms with one en-suite.

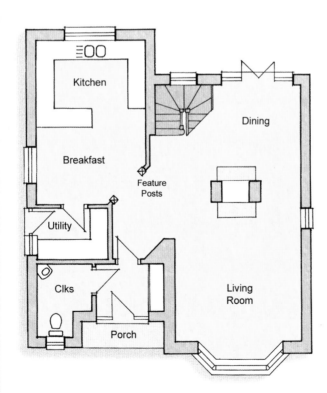

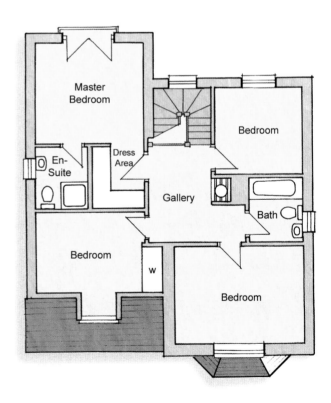

Plan no. **BHP 310710**

This family home has a vaulted ceiling in the master bedroom while a double-height hallway with gallery add to the impression of space. Downstairs there is an inglenook fireplace and separate dining room.

Traditional style

Floor area
160m²
1722ft²

Bedrooms
4

Bathrooms
2

Floors
2

Key features
Kitchen/breakfast room
Utility room
Study
Separate dining room
Vaulted master bed

Garaging for
1 car

Design
Potton

www.potton.co.uk
contact@potton.co.uk
01767 676 400

Build cost
£147,000

Design © Potton

Barn style

Floor area

161m²

1733ft²

Bedrooms

4

Bathrooms

2

Floors

2

Key features
Double-height lounge
Kitchen/diner
Utility room
Master en-suite

Garaging for
0 cars

Design
Welsh Oak Frame

www.welshoakframe.com
01686 688000

Build cost
£148,000

Design © Welsh Oak Frame

Plan no. **BHP 310494**

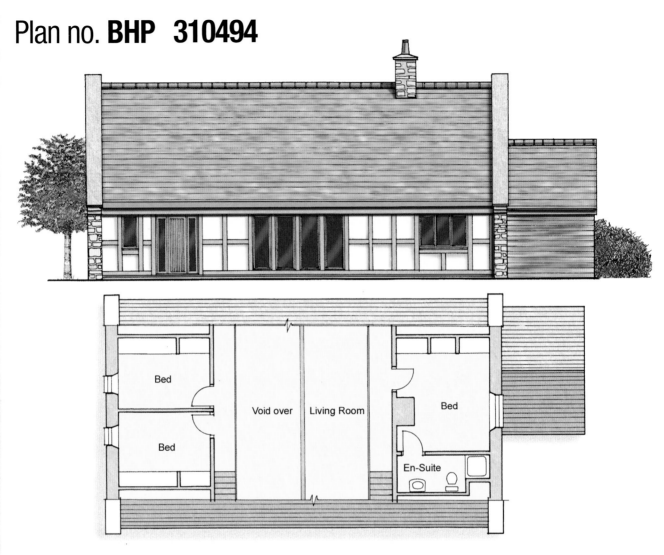

The first floor of this house works as two separate mezzanine levels each with their own staircase. This design allows for a stunning double-height ceiling above the living room.

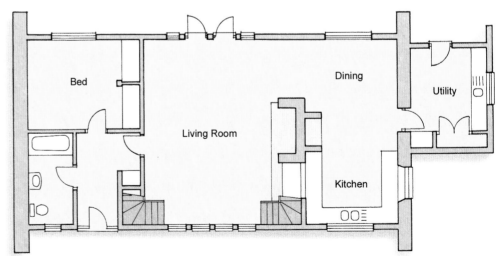

Plan no. **BHP 310425**

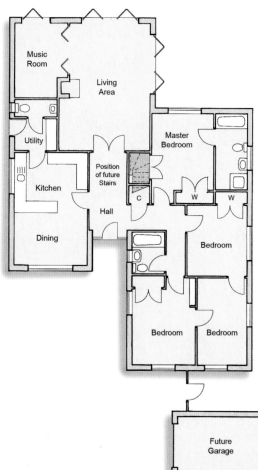

Folding doors brings the outside in to the key living areas in this design. The single-storey building has room for four bedrooms but there's space for a staircase if you want to use the generous loft area for more sleeping accommodation later on and a velux is already in place to provide light.

Traditional style

Floor area

162m²

1744ft²

Bedrooms

4

Bathrooms

2

Floors

1

Key features
Kitchen/dining room
Utility room
Music room
Master en-suite

Garaging for
1 car

Design
Design & Materials

www.designandmaterials.uk.com
enquiries@designandmaterials.
uk.com
01909 540 123

**Build cost
£140,000**

Traditional style

Floor area

162m²

1744ft²

Bedrooms

4

Bathrooms

2

Floors

2

Key features
Kitchen/breakfast room
Separate dining room
Utility room
Study
Master en-suite

Garaging for
0 cars

Design
Design & Materials

www.designandmaterials.uk.com
enquiries@designandmaterials.
uk.com
01909 540 123

Build cost
£149,000

Plan no. **BHP 310560**

This design manages to fit a breakfast area into the kitchen as well as a separate dining room, study and utility room. Upstairs three of the bedrooms feature built-in wardrobes - and for the master there's an en-suite.

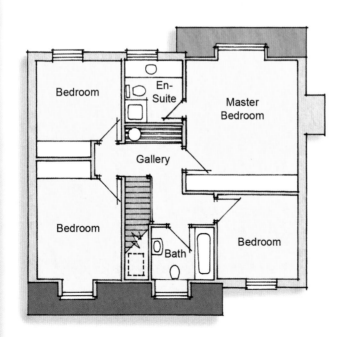

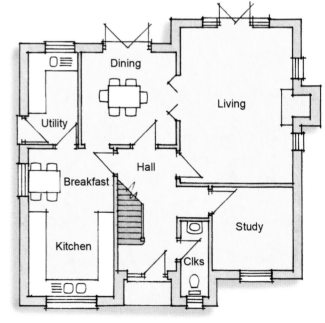

Plan no. **BHP 310800**

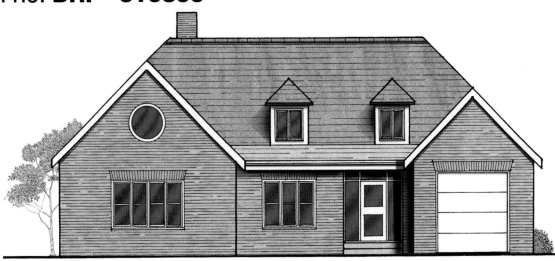

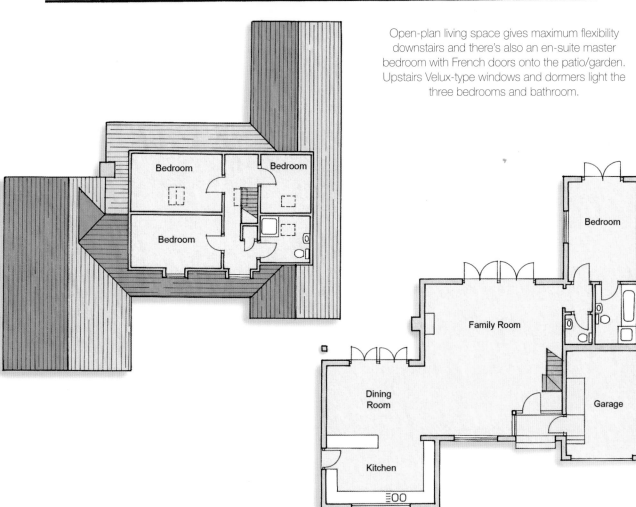

Open-plan living space gives maximum flexibility downstairs and there's also an en-suite master bedroom with French doors onto the patio/garden. Upstairs Velux-type windows and dormers light the three bedrooms and bathroom.

Bedroom

Bedroom

Bedroom

Bedroom

Family Room

Dining Room

Kitchen

Garage

Traditional style

Floor area
162m²
1744ft²

Bedrooms
4

Bathrooms
2

Floors
2

Key features
Open-plan living
Master bed en-suite

Garaging for
1 car

Design
**John Shida
(Morningtide
Developments)**
www.morningtide.fsnet.co.uk
johnshida@morningtide.
fsnet.co.uk
01621 815485

Build cost
£149,000

Design © John Shida

Contemporary style

Floor area

168m²

1808ft²

Bedrooms

4

Bathrooms

2

Floors

2

Key features
Conservatory
Sauna
Courtyard
Lap pool
Basement

Garaging for
0 cars

Design
Architecture Plus

www.architecture-plus.co.uk
01934 416416

Build cost
£154,500

Design © Architecture Plus

Plan no. **BHP 310677**

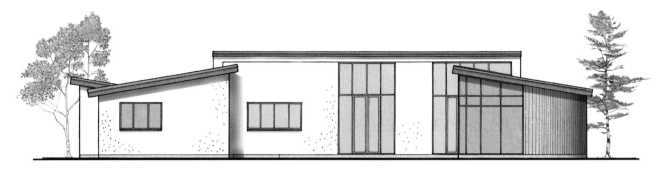

This design uses separate wings to create defined living, relaxing and sleeping spaces. The conservatory with its built-in sauna is accessed from a bridge from the main sleeping area which leads onto the kitchen and dining area via the entrance hall and its pretty courtyard.

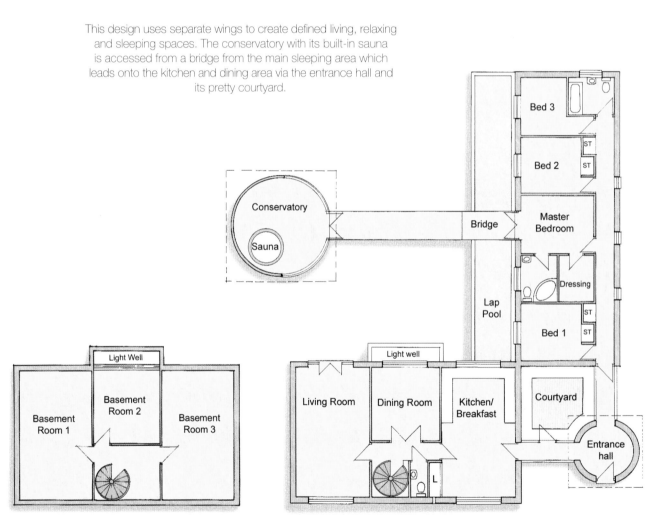

Plan no. **BHP 310104**

Traditional style

Floor area
170m^2
1830ft^2

Bedrooms
4

Bathrooms
3

Floors
2

Key features
Kitchen/family room
Study
Separate dining room
Galleried landing
2 beds en-suite

Garaging for
2 cars

Design
Planahome

www.planahome.uk.com
plans@planahome.uk.com
01326 373600

Build cost
£156,400

Design © Planahome

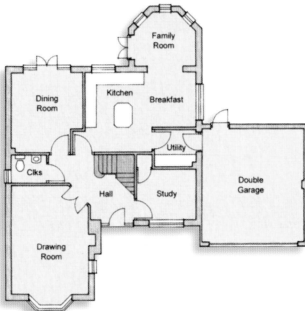

Lots of interesting external detail and roof lines
add to the appeal of this design. There's plenty
of space in the kitchen/family area thanks to the
conservatory and upstairs there are four bedrooms
and two en-suite shower rooms.

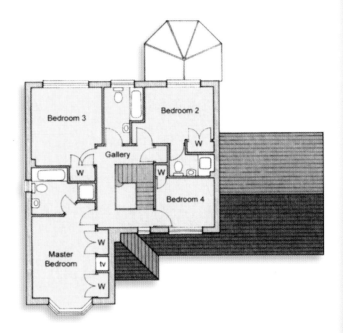

Traditional style

Floor area
170m²
1830ft²

Bedrooms
4

Bathrooms
3

Floors
2

Key features
Kitchen/breakfast room
Separate dining room
Study
Master en-suite
2nd en-suite

Garaging for
0 cars

Design
Design & Materials

www.designandmaterials.uk.com
enquiries@designandmaterials.
uk.com
01909 540 123

Build cost
£156,400

Design © Design &
Materials

Plan no. **BHP 310662**

This design has the look of a cottage but the accommodation of a family-sized house with two en-suite bedrooms, two single bedrooms and lots of living space on the ground floor.

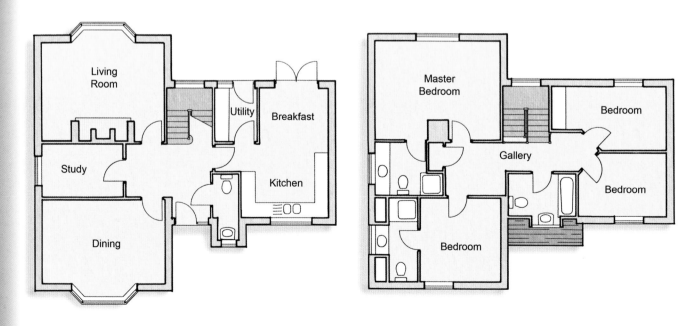

Plan no. **BHP 310539**

This house features a big hall and internal access to the garage. The kitchen and dining room could be combined to create more open-plan accomodation. Upstairs the master bedroom has its own en-suite.

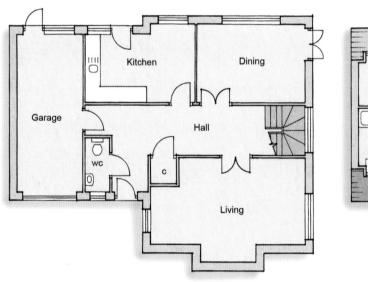

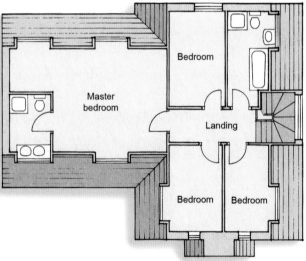

Traditional style

Floor area
171m²
1841ft²

Bedrooms
4

Bathrooms
2

Floors
2

Key features
Separate dining room
Master en-suite

Garaging for
1 car

Design
Custom Homes

www.customhomes.co.uk
admin@customhomes.co.uk
01787 377388

Build cost
£157,000

Design © Custom Homes

Traditional style

Floor area
172m²
1851ft²

Bedrooms
4

Bathrooms
2

Floors
2

Key features
Kitchen/dining room
Boot room
Study

Garaging for
2 cars

Design
Border Oak

www.borderoak.com s
ales@borderoak.com
01568 708752

Build cost
£158,000

Plan no. **BHP 310041**

Lots of external period features including a half-hipped roof on the garage, brick arches over the windows and open timber work on the porch front. Inside there is a large kitchen/family area and sparate sitting room.

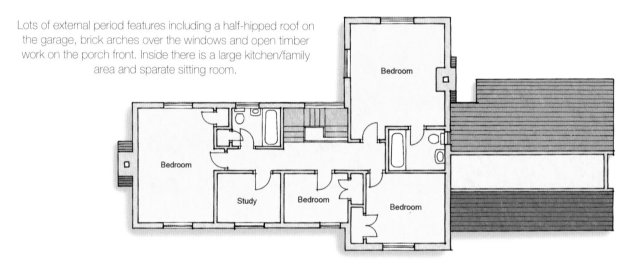

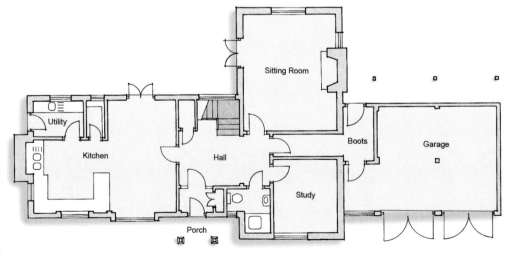

Plan no. **BHP 310221**

Traditional style

Floor area
172m²
1851ft²

Bedrooms
4

Bathrooms
2

Floors
2

Key features
Utility room
Separate dining room
Master en-suite

Garaging for
1 car

Design
Potton

www.potton.co.uk
contact@potton.co.uk
01767 676 400

Build cost
£158,000

Design © Potton

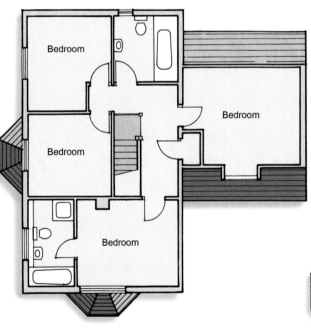

Dormer and bay windows punctuate this design's lines and add extra light into the rooms. The kitchen, dining area and living room are all linked by double doors. Upstairs the roof space above the garage has been used to create room for a fourth bedroom.

Traditional style

Floor area
173m²
1862ft²

Bedrooms
4

Bathrooms
3

Floors
2

Key features
Kitchen/breakfast room
Utility room
Separate dining room
Study
2 en-suite bedrooms

Garaging for
0 cars

Design
Planahome

www.planahome.uk.com
plans@planahome.uk.com
01326 373600

Build cost
£160,000

Design © Planahome

Plan no. **BHP 310146**

Two en-suite bedrooms, a dressing area for the master suite and a lounge and
separate dining room are amongst the features in this design.

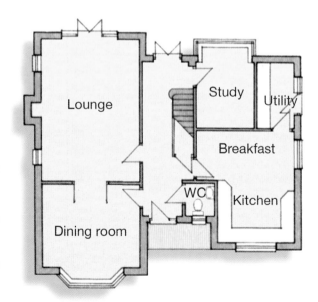

Plan no. **BHP 310887**

This Tudor-look house has plenty of living space and four double bedrooms. Smart touches include a balcony, a large double garage and a covered outside store.

Children's Room

Children's Room

Main Bedroom

Guest Room

Balcony

Dining

Kitchen

Boat Store

Utility

Living Area

c

Hall

Garage

Traditional style

Floor area
173m²
1862ft²

Bedrooms
4

Bathrooms
3

Floors
2

Key features
Kitchen/dining room
Utility room
Two en-suites
Balcony

Garaging for
2 cars

Design
**John Shida
(Morningtide
Developments)**

www.morningtide.fsnet.co.uk
johnshida@morningtide.fsnet.co.uk
01621 815485

Build cost
£160,000

Design © John Shida

Traditional style

Floor area
176m²
1894ft²

Bedrooms
4

Bathrooms
2

Floors
2

Key features
Study
Separate dining room
Master en-suite

Garaging for
1 car

Design
Custom Homes

www.customhomes.co.uk
admin@customhomes.co.uk
01787 377388

Build cost
£162,000

Design © Custom Homes

Plan no. **BHP 310791**

The hall is kept small to allow the available space to be used in the reception rooms.
Upstairs the master bedroom has an en-suite shower room.

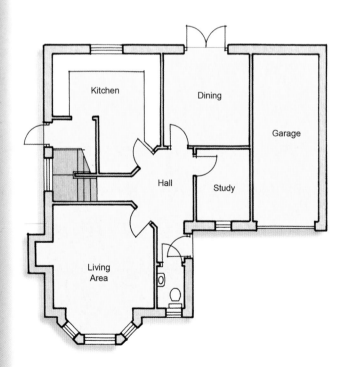

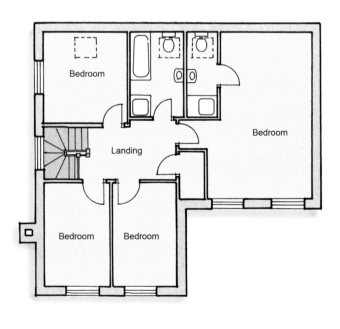

Plan no. **BHP 310569**

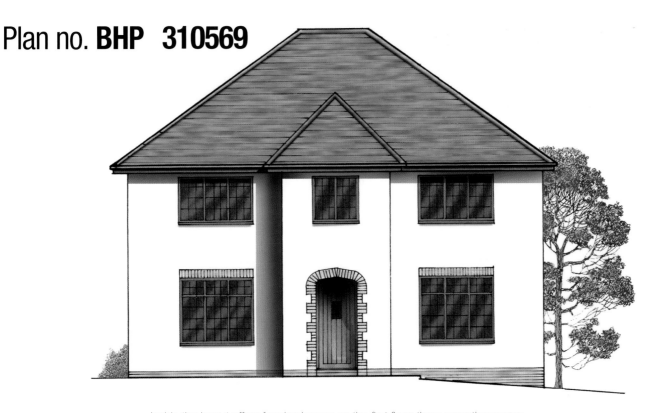

Inside the layout offers four bedrooms on the first floor, three reception rooms downstairs and a kitchen/utility area.

Traditional style

Floor area
177m²
1905ft²

Bedrooms
4

Bathrooms
2

Floors
2

Key features
Living/sitting room
Separate dining room
Utility room
Porch
Master en-suite

Garaging for
0 cars

Design
Architecture Plus

www.architecture-plus.co.uk
01934 416416

Build cost
£163,000

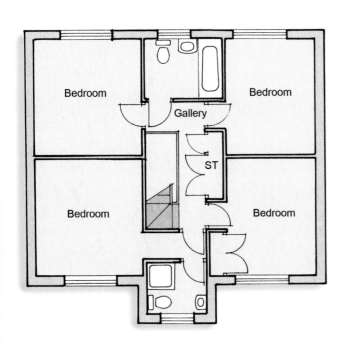

Bedroom

Bedroom

Gallery

ST

Bedroom

Bedroom

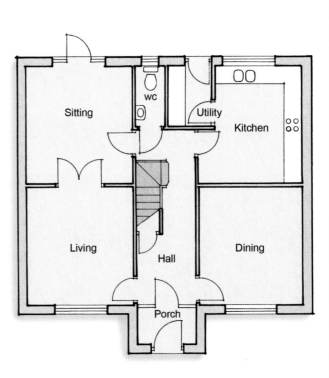

Sitting

WC

Utility

Kitchen

Living

Hall

Dining

Porch

Design © Architecture Plus

Traditional style

Floor area
178m²
1916ft²

Bedrooms
4

Bathrooms
2

Floors
2

Key features
Lounge/dining room
Utility room
Master bed en-suite

Garaging for
1 car

Design
Churchill Design

www.churchilldesign.co.uk
info@churchilldesign.co.uk
01252 325701

Build cost
£164,000

Design © Churchill Design

Plan no. **BHP 310770**

The basic layout of this house still manages to fit in an en-suite for the master bedroom
and a utility next to the kitchen.

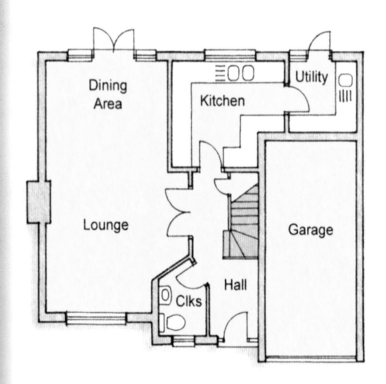

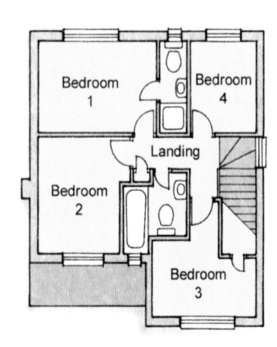

Plan no. **BHP 311004**

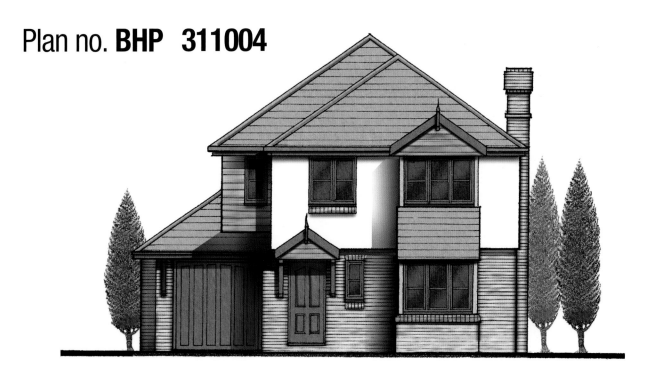

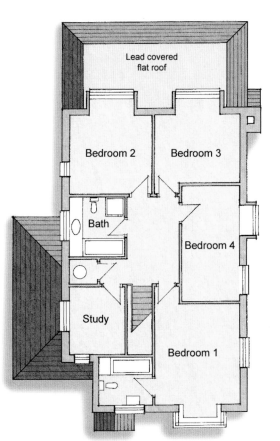

Lead covered flat roof

Bedroom 2

Bedroom 3

Bath

Bedroom 4

Study

Bedroom 1

Interesting features in this design include access to the integral garage through the utility room and a dining area adjacent to the lounge. There is also space for a play room and study as well as the four bedrooms – one of which is en-suite.

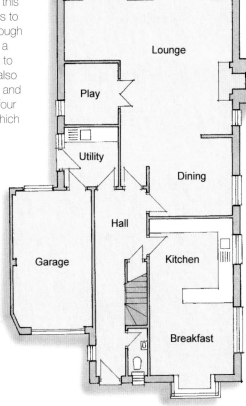

Lounge

Play

Utility

Dining

Hall

Garage

Kitchen

Breakfast

Traditional style

Floor area
180m²
1938ft²

Bedrooms
4

Bathrooms
2

Floors
2

Key features
Lounge/diner
Kitchen/breakfast
Study
Playroom
Master en-suite

Garaging for
1 car

Design
Building Design

01323 410095

Build cost
£165,500

Design © Building Design

Traditional style

Floor area

180m²

1938ft²

Bedrooms

4

Bathrooms

2

Floors

2

Key features
Kitchen/dining room
Utility room
Study
Master en-suite
Dressing room

Garaging for
0 cars

Design
Border Oak

www.borderoak.com
sales@borderoak.com
01568 708752

Build cost
£165,500

Design © Border Oak

Plan no. **BHP 310449**

The timber exterior detailing on this house gives it a vaguely 'Arts & Crafts' feel, as does the porch. The large hall is also in keeping with this style – as is the galleried landing.

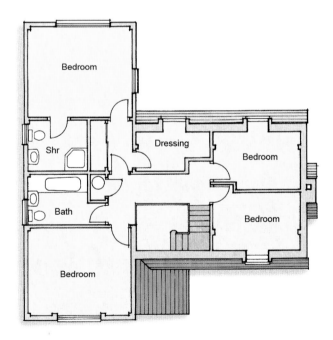

Plan no. **BHP 310590**

The twin dormers and central entrance bay create symmetry in this design. The family room sits conveniently between the kitchen and lounge. The single-storey garage wing adds interest to the design as well as extra space for a utility room, downstairs cloakroom and a store. The first floor features a master suite, three double bedrooms and a large family bathroom.

Traditional style

Floor area

181m²

1948ft²

Bedrooms

4

Bathrooms

2

Floors

2

Key features
Kitchen/dining
Family room
Utility room
Master en-suite

Garaging for
2 cars

Design
Reed Architects

01544 260523

Build cost
£166,500

Barn style

Floor area
181m²
1948ft²

Bedrooms
4

Bathrooms
2

Floors
2

Key features
Separate dining room
Study
Utility room
Double-height hall
Master bed en-suite

Garaging for
2 cars

Design
Custom Homes

www.customhomes.co.uk
admin@customhomes.co.uk
01787 377388

Build cost
£166,500

Design © Custom Homes

Plan no. **BHP 310263**

The double-height entrance hall with a staircase which divides at half-landing level adds to the barnlike feel of this design. If you can't find a barn to convert, why not build one?

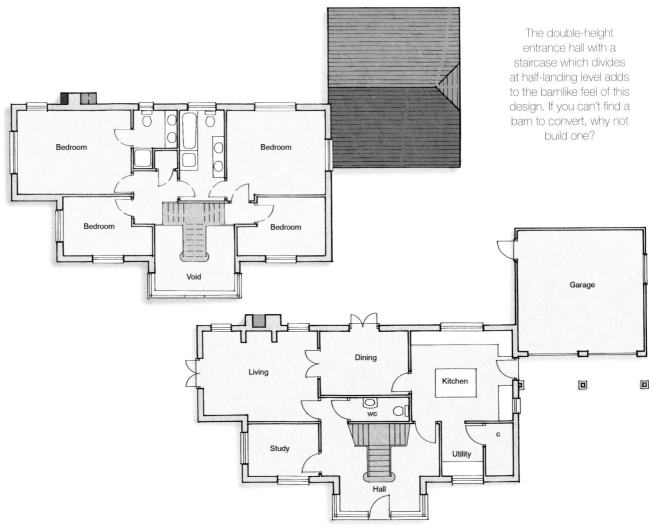

Plan no. **BHP 310101**

Kitchen

Dining Hall

Master Bedroom

C

Utility

Garage

Garden Shed

An exciting mix of turrets, levels and materials makes this an intersting design. The turrett creates a Scottish feel and there is a dining hall and a large first floor living room with triple aspect windows and a balcony.

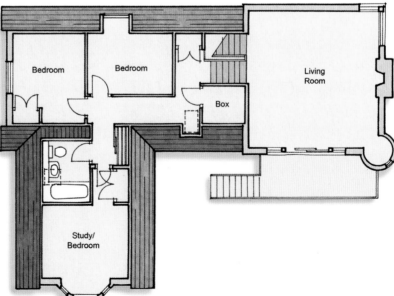

Bedroom

Bedroom

Box

Living Room

Study/ Bedroom

Traditional style

Floor area
183m²
1970ft²

Bedrooms
4

Bathrooms
2

Floors
2

Key features
Dining hall
Utility room
Garden store
Master en-suite

Garaging for
1 car

Design
The Border Design Centre

www.borderdesign.co.uk
borderdesign@btconnect.com
01578 740218

Build cost
£165,500

Design © The Border Design Centre

Traditional style

Floor area

185m²

1991ft²

Bedrooms

4

Bathrooms

2

Floors

3

Key features
Open-plan living
space
Separate lounge
Utility room

Garaging for
0 cars

Design
Churchill Design

www.churchilldesign.co.uk
info@churchilldesign.co.uk
01252 325701

Build cost
£170,000

Design © Churchill Design

Plan no. **BHP   310284**

How do you pack four bedrooms into
a narrow plot? Simple, add a second
floor with a top-floor en-suit bedroom.
Downstairs the living area is open-plan
with a sitting room that can be shut off
by closing a pair of double doors.

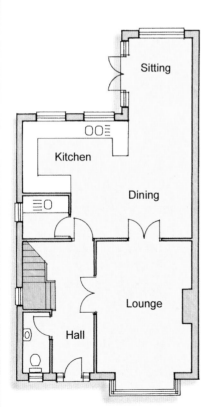

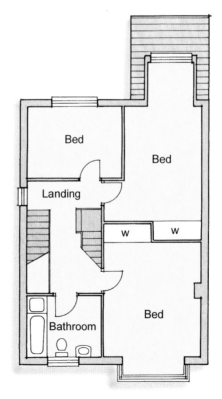

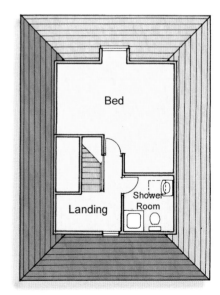

Plan no. **BHP 310461**

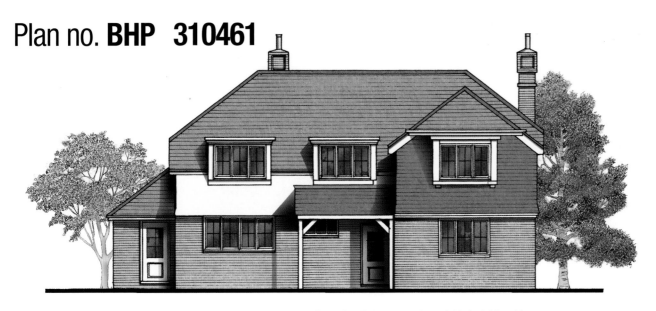

The brick, render and tile façade set off this family home and would help it blend in many locations. The key living areas are arranged in an open, flowing style and there's a well-lit galleried landing leading to four double bedrooms upstairs.

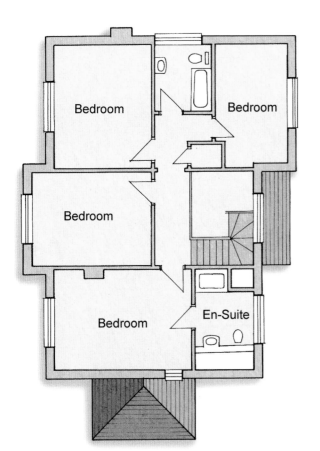

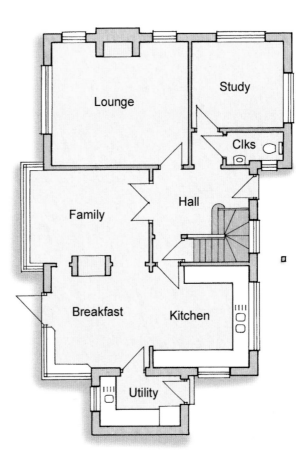

Traditional style

Floor area
186m²
2002ft²

Bedrooms
4

Bathrooms
2

Floors
2

Key features
Kitchen/breakfast room
Family room
Study
Utility room
Master en-suite

Garaging for
0 cars

Design
**Opus Architecture
and Design**

01252 861759

Build cost
£171,000

Traditional style

Floor area
187m²
2013ft²

Bedrooms
4

Bathrooms
3

Floors
2

Key features
Kitchen/dining room
Study
Utility room
Car port
2 beds en-suite

Garaging for
1 car

Design
Potton

www.potton.co.uk
contact@potton.co.uk
01767 676 400

Build cost
£172,000

Design © Potton

Plan no. **BHP 310854**

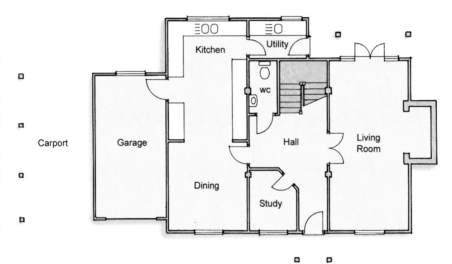

This design has a living room
which runs the full depth of
the house and features an
inglenook fireplace. Upstairs
the master bedroom features
an en-suite shower room and
walk-in wardrobe and the second
bedroom an en-suite bathroom.

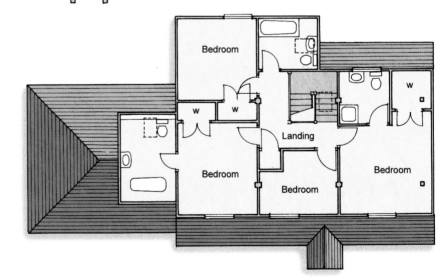

Plan no. **BHP** **310377**

Once through the porch you enter a full-width open-plan lounge and dining hall. The kitchen and family room also provide plenty of space. The first floor has three bedrooms and a master suite while the attic room could house an office or play area.

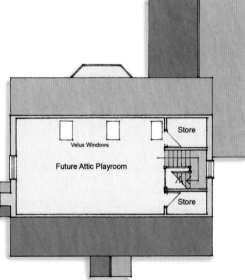

Traditional style

Floor area
190m²
2045ft²

Bedrooms
4

Bathrooms
2

Floors
3

Key features
Vaulted family room
Living room/dining hall
Study
Master en-suite
Attic playroom

Garaging for
0 cars

Design
Design & Materials

www.designandmaterials.uk.com
enquiries@designandmaterials.
uk.com
01909 540 123

Build cost
£175,000

Design © Design &
Materials

Traditional style

Floor area
190m²
2045ft²

Bedrooms
4

Bathrooms
3

Floors
2

Key features
Kitchen/family room
Utility room
study
Separate dining room
2 beds en-suite

Garaging for
2 cars

Design
Design & Materials

www.designandmaterials.uk.com
enquiries@designandmaterials.
uk.com
01909 540 123

Build cost
£175,000

Design © Design &
Materials

Plan no. **BHP 310713**

This double-fronted home features an L-shaped kitchen/family room and large living room. Upstairs the master and second bedrooms share a balcony but each gets its own en-suite bathroom.

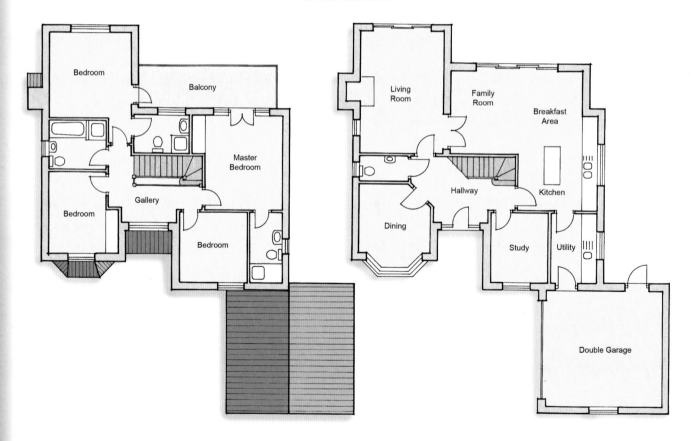

Plan no. **BHP 310479**

The deep bay window on this house design creates lots of extra space in the living room and bedroom above. The house also offers a separate study, a first floor sitting area and a combined kitchen and breakfast room.

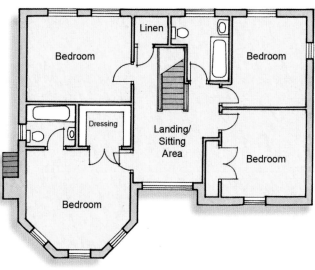

Bedroom

Linen

Bedroom

Dressing

Landing/
Sitting
Area

Bedroom

Bedroom

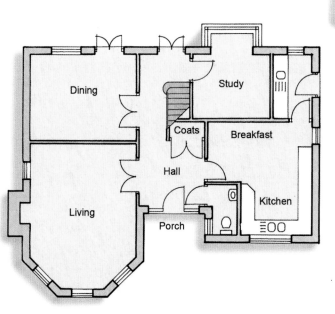

Dining

Study

Coats

Breakfast

Hall

Living

Porch

Kitchen

Traditional style

Floor area
192m²
2067ft²

Bedrooms
4

Bathrooms
2

Floors
2

Key features
Kitchen/breakfast room
Separate dining room
Study
Utility room
Master en-suite

Garaging for
0 cars

Design
**The Bespoke
Design Company**

www.planahome.uk.com
plans@planahome.uk.com
01326 373600

Build cost
£177,000

Design © The Bespoke
Design Company

Traditional style

Floor area
202m²
2174ft²

Bedrooms
4

Bathrooms
2

Floors
2

Key features
Kitchen/breakfast room
Separate dining room
Family room
Galleried landing
Master bed en-suite

Garaging for
0 cars

Design
Gordon Melrose Building Design

www.gmbuildingdesign.
co.uk enquiries@gmbuildingd
esign.co.uk
01750 725333

Build cost
£186,000

Design © Gordon Melrose
Building Design

Plan no. **BHP 310515**

Either side of the hall, with its cloakroom and storage, is a twin-aspect living room and family room. An open-plan dining and kitchen area takes up the back of the house. The first floor features a 360 degree gallery around the staircase, three double bedrooms and a master suite with its own balcony.

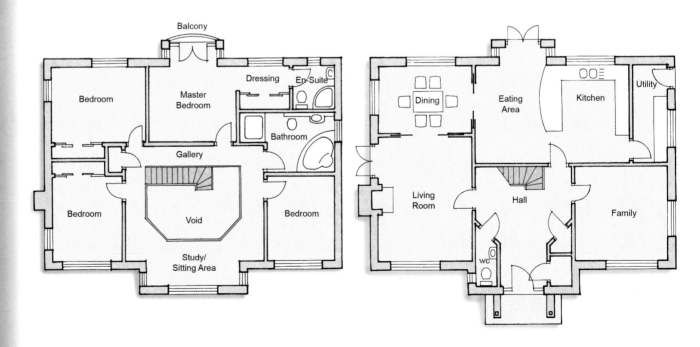

Plan no. **BHP 310656**

The ground floor offers open-plan living but with the ability to close sliding or hinged doors to create a more conventional layout. The first floor layout is more formal and features a galleried landing, a full-depth master suite and three further bedrooms.

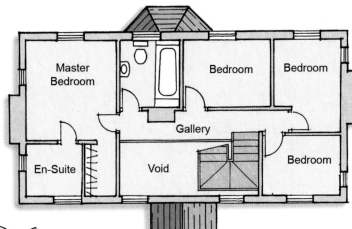

Master Bedroom

Bedroom

Bedroom

Gallery

En-Suite

Void

Bedroom

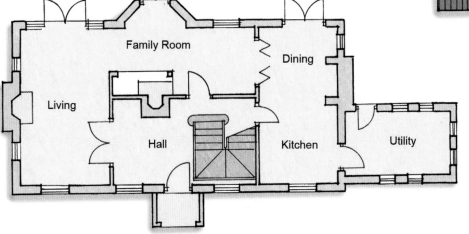

Family Room

Dining

Living

Hall

Kitchen

Utility

Traditional style

Floor area
203m²
2185ft²

Bedrooms
4

Bathrooms
2

Floors
2

Key features
Galleried landing
Double-height hall
Family room
Kitchen/diner
Large utility room

Garaging for
0 cars

Design
Jeremy Rawlings

www.periodhome.net
01884 266444

Build cost
£187,000

Traditional style

Floor area
203m²
2185ft²

Bedrooms
4

Bathrooms
3

Floors
2

Key features
Kitchen/family room
Conservatory
Study
Utility room
2 beds en-suite

Garaging for
2 cars

Design
**The Bespoke
Design Company**

www.planahome.uk.com
plans@planahome.uk.com
01326 373600

Build cost
£187,000

Design © The Bespoke
Design Company

Plan no. **BHP 310650**

The main entrance is at the side leaving the impressive double-frontage free for separate twin French door access to the family room and kitchen. At the rear of the house part of the conservatory goes double height creating a great view from the galleried landing on the first floor. Four bedrooms and three bathrooms complete the picture upstairs.

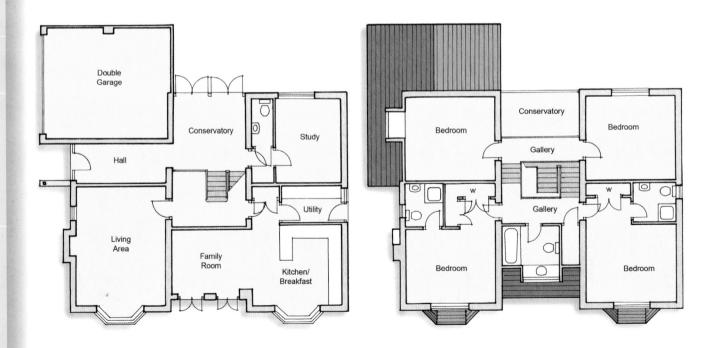

Plan no. **BHP 310266**

Go through the porch and vestibule and you're in a dining/living room divided by a feature fireplace. The kitchen and breakfast area are similarly open-plan and lead onto a family room. Upstairs all but one of the bedrooms has its own en-suite and the master bedroom gets its own balcony and dressing room.

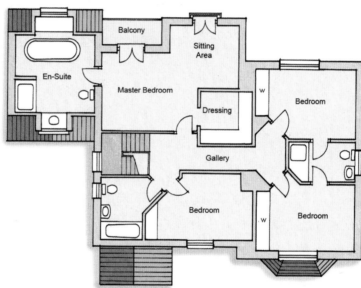

Balcony

Sitting Area

En-Suite

Master Bedroom

Dressing

Bedroom

w

Gallery

Bedroom

Bedroom

w

Bedroom

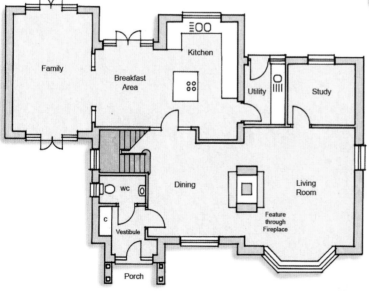

Family

Breakfast Area

Kitchen

Utility

Study

WC

c

Dining

Living Room

Vestibule

Feature through Fireplace

Porch

Traditional style

Floor area

204m²

2196ft²

Bedrooms

4

Bathrooms

3

Floors

2

Key features
Living/dining room
Kitchen/breakfast room
Family room
Study
Master bedroom suite

**Garaging for
0 cars**

Design
Design & Materials

www.designandmaterials.uk.com
enquiries@designandmaterials.uk.com
01909 540 123

**Build cost
£187,500**

Design © Design & Materials

Floor area

208m²

2239ft²

Bedrooms

4

Bathrooms

2

Floors

2

Key features
Kitchen/breakfast room
Separate dining room
Feature staircase
Study
Master en-suite

Garaging for
0 cars

Design
Custom Homes

www.customhomes.co.uk
admin@customhomes.co.uk
01787 377388

Build cost
£191,000

Design © Custom Homes

Plan no. **BHP** **310251**

There's an entrance hall with a feature central staircase, a large lounge and a kitchen/breakfast room that take up a whole side of the house each. Upstairs the master bedroom dominates one corner of the house with an en-suite bathroom and dressing room attached.

Plan no. **BHP 310614**

The master bedroom suite is twin-aspect with its own terrace. On the ground floor the layout offers an interesting arrangment of rooms with the option for the fourth bedroom to be used as a study.

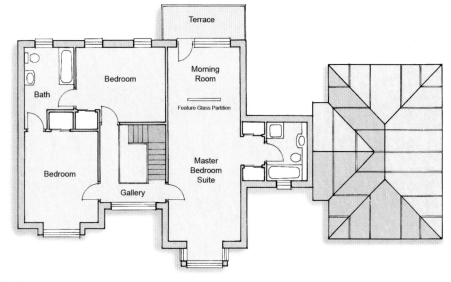

Terrace

Bedroom

Morning Room

Bath

Feature Glass Partition

Bedroom

Master Bedroom Suite

Gallery

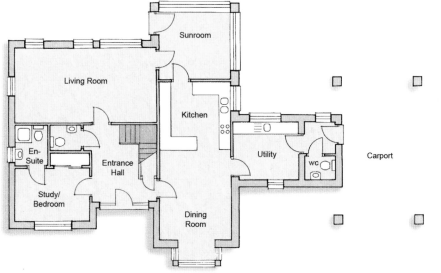

Sunroom

Living Room

Kitchen

En-Suite

Entrance Hall

Utility

WC

Carport

Study/ Bedroom

Dining Room

Contemporary style

Floor area
211m²
2271ft²

Bedrooms
4

Bathrooms
3

Floors
2

Key features
Kitchen/diner
Sun room
Master bed suite
Galleried landing
Car port

Garaging for
0 cars

Design
**John Braid
(at Leslie R Hutt)**

lhuttarchitect@btinternet.com
01463 235566

Build cost
£194,000

Traditional style

Floor area

214m²

2302ft²

Bedrooms

4

Bathrooms

3

Floors

2

Key features
Kitchen/dining room
Large utility room
Galleried landing
2 beds en-suite

Garaging for
1 car

Design
Border Oak

www.borderoak.com
sales@borderoak.com
01568 708752

Build cost
£197,000

Design © Border Oak

Plan no. **BHP 310065**

The en-suite for the master bedroom is cleverly located in the roofspace over the utility room. On the ground floor the large hall could be used for dining and the utility offers direct access to the garage and the garden.

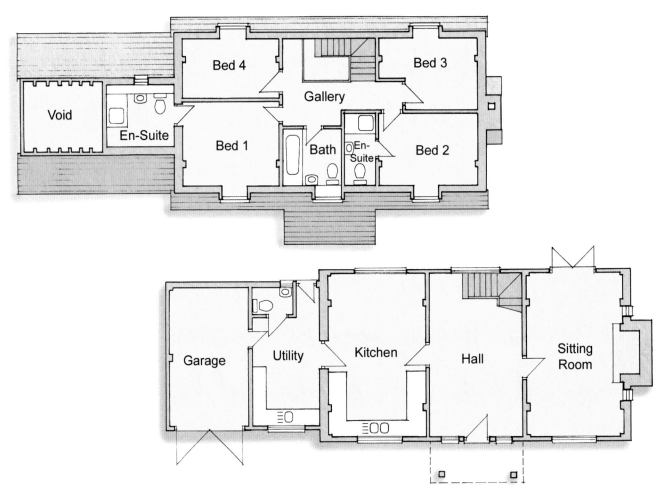

Plan no. **BHP 310029**

A house packed full of useful spaces including a study, garage, separate dining room and a master bedroom with a separate dressing room and dormer-windowed en-suite bathroom.

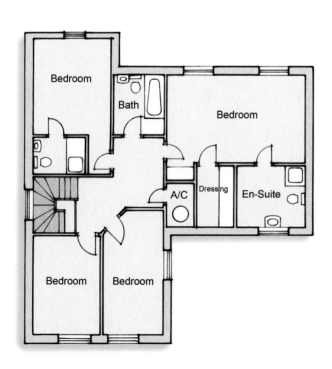

Bedroom

Bath

Bedroom

A/C   Dressing   En-Suite

Bedroom   Bedroom

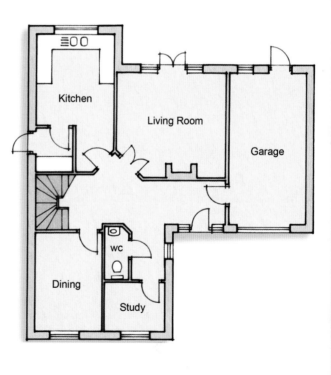

Kitchen

Living Room

Garage

wc

Dining

Study

Traditional style

Floor area
214m²
2303ft²

Bedrooms
4

Bathrooms
3

Floors
2

Key features
Separate dining room
Study
Master bed suite

Garaging for
1 car

Design
Custom Homes

www.customhomes.co.uk
admin@customhomes.co.uk
01787 377388

Build cost
£197,000

Design © Custom Homes

Traditional style

Floor area

216m²

2325ft²

Bedrooms

4

Bathrooms

3

Floors

2

Key features
Dining/family room
Study
Utility room
Galleried landing
2 beds en-suite

Garaging for
2 cars

Design

John Braid
(at Leslie R Hutt)

lhuttarchitect@btinternet.com
01463 235566

Build cost
£199,000

Design © John Braid

Plan no. **BHP 310191**

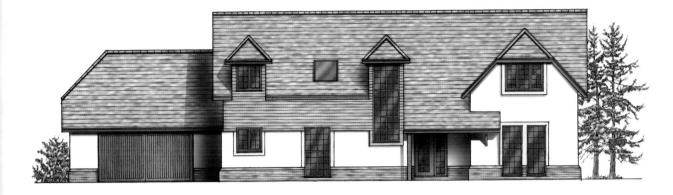

This house packs in
a living room, family
room, study, utility
room and en-suite bedroom
downstairs. Upstairs the
galleried landing gives
way to three further
bedrooms.

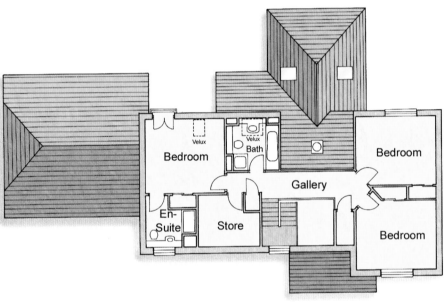

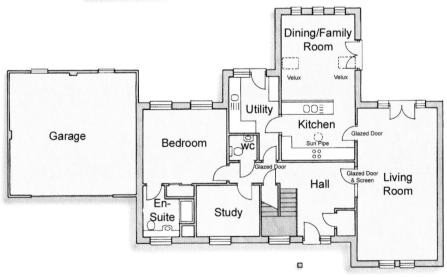

Plan no. **BHP 310743**

This house has plenty of natural light in the kitchen and hall. The garage extends right back and becomes an open-sided boat shed. All the rooms are large but you could add even more space by pushing up into the attic later on.

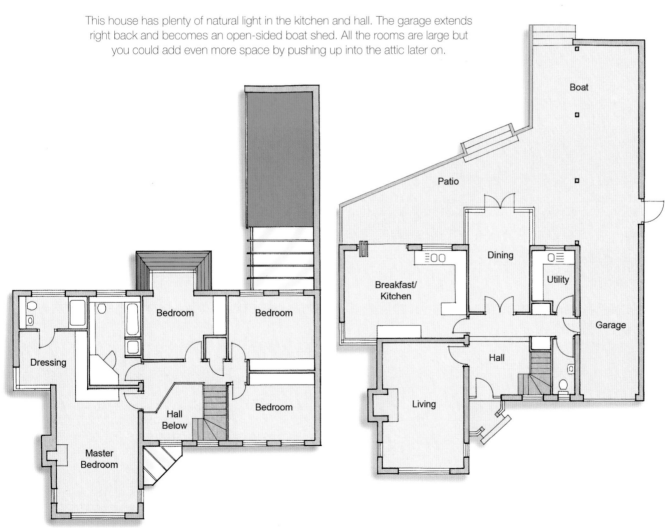

Traditional style

Floor area
220m²
2368ft²

Bedrooms
4

Bathrooms
2

Floors
2

Key features
Kitchen/breakfast room
Separate dining room
Boat/car port
Master dressing area
Galleried landing

Garaging for
1 car

Design
**Fine Modern
Homes (R.Robins)**

www.finemodernhomes.co.uk
01225 777727

Build cost
£202,500

Design © Fine Modern
Homes

Traditional style

Floor area
222m²
2390ft²

Bedrooms
4

Bathrooms
2

Floors
2

Key features
Separate dining room
Utility room
Study
Office
Master en-suite

Garaging for
0 cars

Design
Border Oak

www.borderoak.com
sales@borderoak.com
01568 708752

Build cost
£199,000

Design © Border Oak

Plan no. **BHP 310755**

The house will appeal to many who enjoy a lifestyle based around the kitchen.
There is also a separate dining room for entertaining, a study, utility room and larder.
Upstairs there is a galleried landing and master bedroom with en-suite shower room.

Plan no. **BHP 310362**

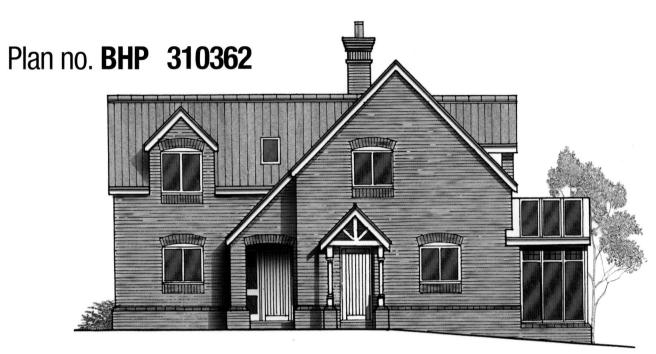

Unusually the front door and utility room door are on the same aspect of this design. One benfit can be that shopping being unloaded from the car can be taken straight into the utility room/kitchen. The master bedroom offers an en-suite and dressing room.

Traditional style

Floor area
222m²
2390ft²

Bedrooms
4

Bathrooms
3

Floors
2

Key features
Kitchen/breakfast room
Study
Separate dining room
Master bedroom suite
Galleried landing

Garaging for
0 cars

Design
Design & Materials

www.designandmaterials.uk.com
enquiries@designandmaterials.uk.com
01909 540 123

Build cost
£199,000

Design © Design & Materials

Traditional style

Floor area
223m²
2400ft²

Bedrooms
4

Bathrooms
4

Floors
2

Key features
Lobby
Kitchen/family room
Dining hall
Sudy
2 beds en-suite

Garaging for
0 cars

Design
**The Bespoke
Design Company**

www.planahome.uk.com
plans@planahome.uk.com
01326 373600

Build cost
£200,000

Plan no. **BHP 310866**

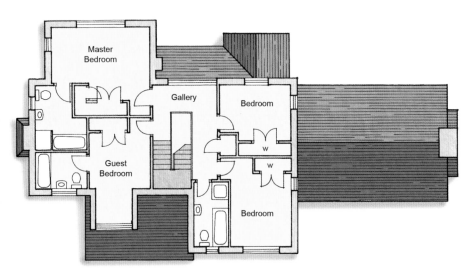

Master
Bedroom

Gallery

Bedroom

Guest
Bedroom

w

w

Bedroom

The splayed walls of
the porch give a feeling
of solidity as well as a
period look which is re-
enforced by the number
of chimneys. There are
open fires in the familly
room and living room.
Upstairs there is a guest
bedroom with en-suite
as well as a master
bedroom with en-suite.

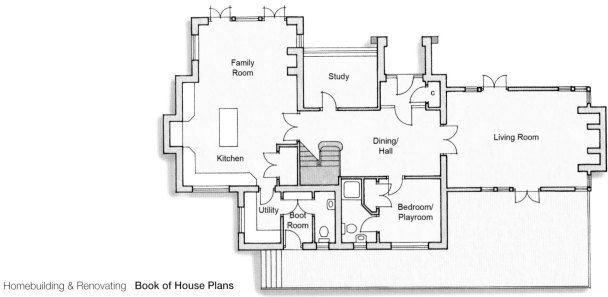

Family
Room

Study

c

Kitchen

Dining/
Hall

Living Room

Utility

Boot
Room

Bedroom/
Playroom

Plan no. **BHP 310587**

The upstairs of this design offers a reading area as well as a dressing room and shower room for the master bedroom.

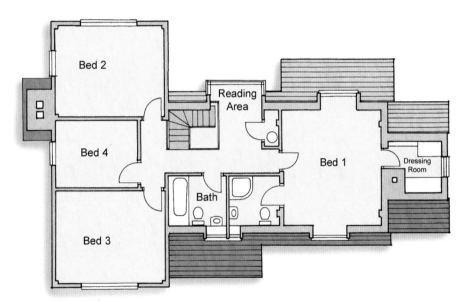

Bed 2

Reading Area

Bed 4

Bed 1

Dressing Room

Bath

Bed 3

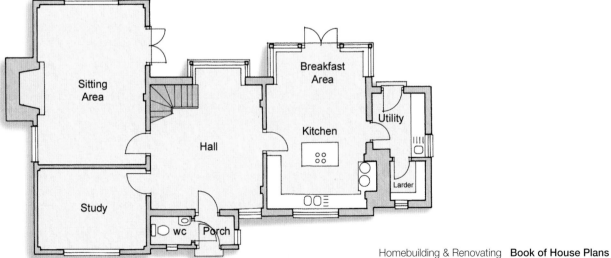

Sitting Area

Breakfast Area

Utility

Hall

Kitchen

Larder

Study

wc

Porch

Traditional style

Floor area
225m²
2422ft²

Bedrooms
4

Bathrooms
2

Floors
2

Key features
Kitchen/breakfast room
Dining Hall
Study
Utility room
Master bedroom suite

Garaging for
0 cars

Design
Border Oak

www.borderoak.com
sales@borderoak.com
01568 708752

Build cost
£202,000

Traditional style

Floor area
225m²
2422ft²

Bedrooms
4

Bathrooms
3

Floors
2

Key features
Dining hall
Kitchen/day room
Study
Self-contained flat
Workshop

Garaging for
2 cars

Design
Welsh Oak Frame

www.welshoakframe.com
01686 688000

Build cost
£202,000

Design © Welsh Oak Frame

Plan no. **BHP   310992**

From the double-height dining hall with twin staircases to the linked reception rooms this house sets out to offer a range of facilities. Designed to offer a 'granny annexe' over the double garage this hosue gets over the problem of locating it on the first floor by having space for a lift.

Plan no. **BHP   310551**

The part-timbered gable of this design overhangs the entrance. Behind the staircase the double-height dining hall leads onto the kitchen and living room. These rooms all have doors opening onto the garden. Upstairs there are four double bedrooms, twin en-suites and a big family bathroom.

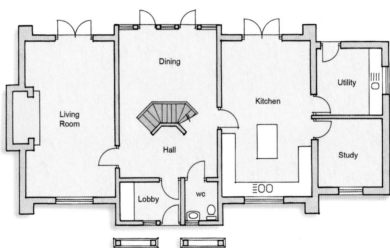

Dining

Utility

Kitchen

Living Room

Study

Hall

Lobby

wc

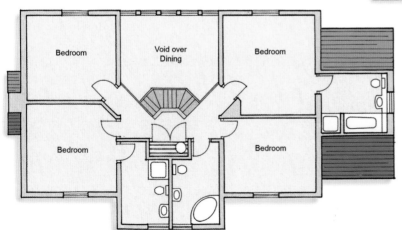

Bedroom

Void over Dining

Bedroom

Bedroom

Bedroom

Traditional style

Floor area
225m²
2422ft²

Bedrooms
4

Bathrooms
3

Floors
2

Key features
Lobby
Dining hall
Utility
Study
Two en-suites

Garaging for
0 cars

Design
Welsh Oak Frame

www.welshoakframe.com
01686 688000

Build cost
£202,000

Contemporary style

Floor area

226m²

2433ft²

Bedrooms

4

Bathrooms

3

Floors

2

Key features
Double-height living
Open-plan receptions
Library
Office
Master bed suite

Garaging for
0 cars

Design
Opus Architecture
and Design

01252 861759

Build cost
£203,000

Design © Opus Architecture
and Design

Plan no. **BHP 310950**

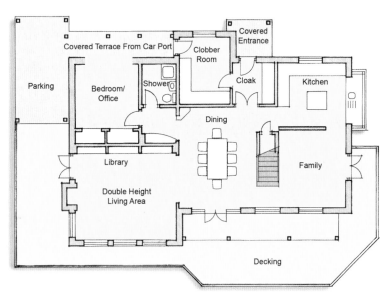

There is lots of decking outside
this house and inside there's a
double-height lounge, an open-
plan dining room, a family room
and a bay-windowed kitchen.
Upstairs a gallery overlooks the
lounge and leads off to three
double bedrooms and a master
suite.

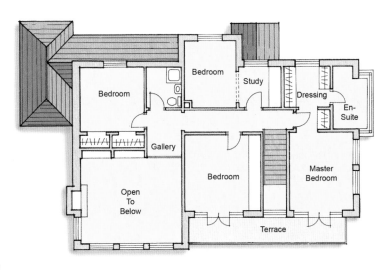

Plan no. **BHP 310107**

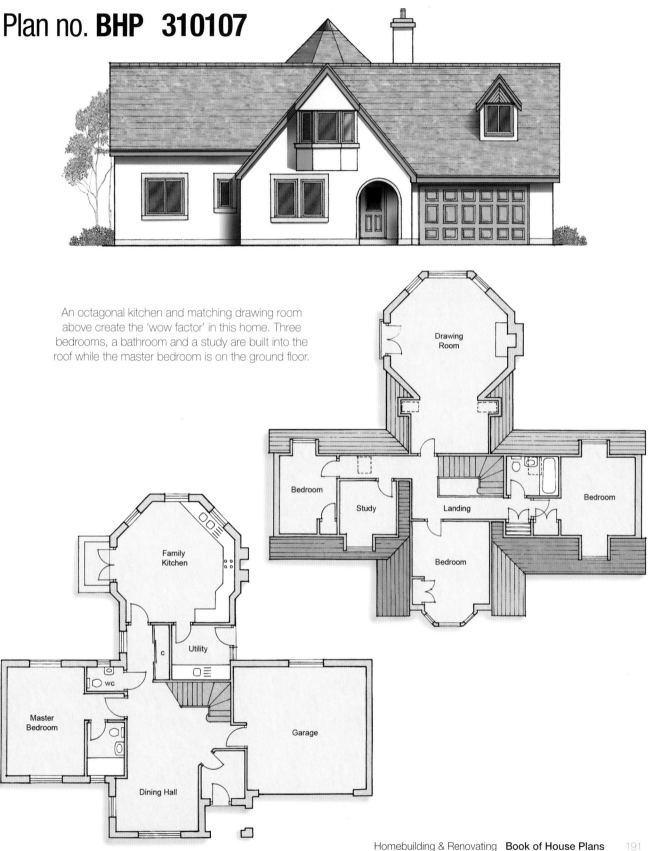

An octagonal kitchen and matching drawing room above create the 'wow factor' in this home. Three bedrooms, a bathroom and a study are built into the roof while the master bedroom is on the ground floor.

Traditional style

Floor area
226m²
2433ft²

Bedrooms
4

Bathrooms
2

Floors
2

Key features
Family kitchen
Dining hall
Utility room
Galleried landing
study

Garaging for
2 cars

Design
The Border Design Centre

www.borderdesign.co.uk
borderdesign@btconnect.com
01578 740218

Build cost
£203,000

Contemporary style

Floor area

227m²

2443ft²

Bedrooms

4

Bathrooms

2

Floors

2

Key features
Kitchen/dining room
Gallery/study
Reflecting pool
Master en-suite
Loggia

Garaging for
2 cars

Design
Peter King

info@carden-king.co.uk
01367 253330

Build cost
£204,000

Design © Peter King

Plan no. **BHP 310230**

Double-height glazing floods light into the reflecting pool and living room. Upstairs a study is located on the gallery which overlooks the living area. There are also four bedrroms and a family bathroom on the first floor.

Plan no. **BHP 310806**

This home offers open-plan living and different areas of character and appeal. The front of the main living room, which features a large timber conservatory, leads on to a cosier living area through the galley kitchen. Upstairs there's a balconied living space, three bedrooms and a study area.

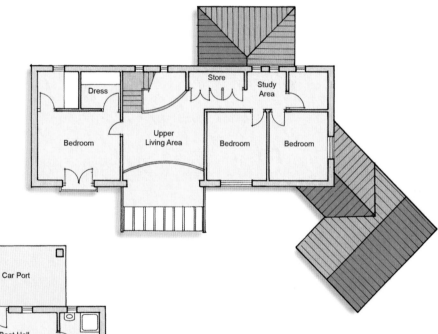

Dress

Store

Study Area

Bedroom

Upper Living Area

Bedroom

Bedroom

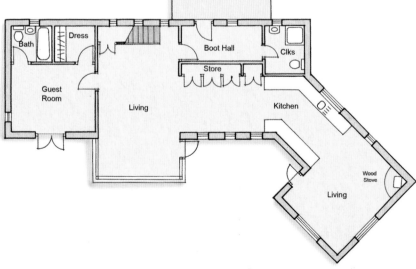

Car Port

Bath

Dress

Boot Hall

Clks

Store

Guest Room

Living

Kitchen

Wood Stove

Living

Contemporary style

Floor area
227m²
2443ft²

Bedrooms
4

Bathrooms
3

Floors
2

Key features
Open-plan living area
Car port
Upper living room
Master en-suite

Garaging for
2 cars

Design
Architecture Plus

www.architecture-plus.co.uk
01934 416416

Build cost
£202,000

Design © Architecture Plus

Plan no. **BHP 310605**

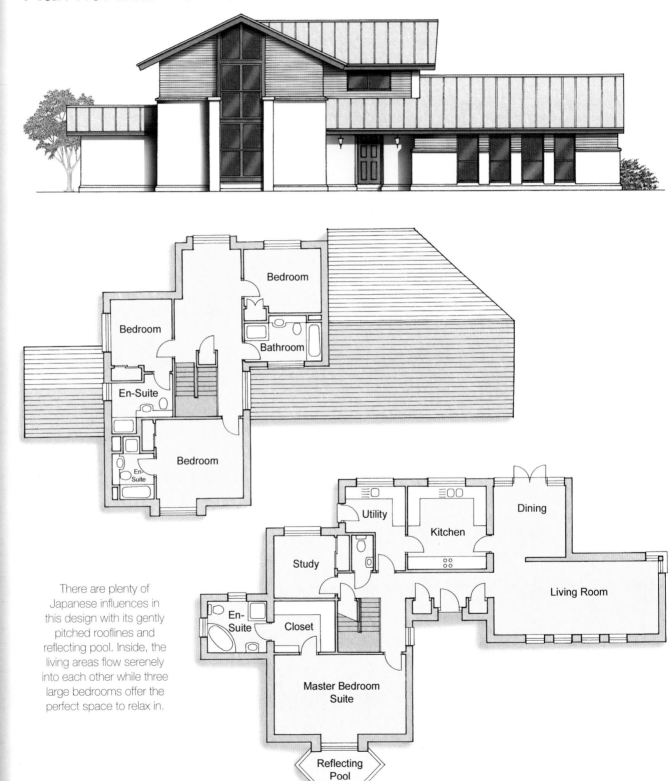

There are plenty of Japanese influences in this design with its gently pitched rooflines and reflecting pool. Inside, the living areas flow serenely into each other while three large bedrooms offer the perfect space to relax in.

Plan no. **BHP 310482**

The double-height glazed porch provides a grand entrance into this house. Other touches include folding doors between the kitchen and conservatory, a galleried sitting area and a first-floor study area.

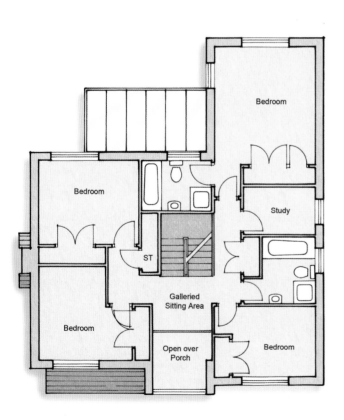

Bedroom

Bedroom

Study

ST

Galleried Sitting Area

Bedroom

Open over Porch

Bedroom

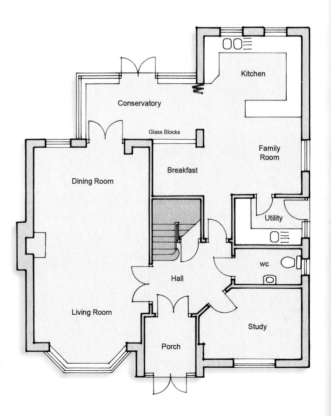

Kitchen

Conservatory

Glass Blocks

Family Room

Breakfast

Dining Room

Utility

Hall

wc

Living Room

Study

Porch

Traditional style

Floor area

230m²

2476ft²

Bedrooms

4

Bathrooms

2

Floors

2

Key features
Living/dining room
Kitchen/family room
Conservatory
Study
Galleried sitting area

Garaging for
0 cars

Design
Design & Materials

www.designandmaterials.uk.com
enquiries@designandmaterials.uk.com
01909 540 123

Build cost
£206,000

Design © Design & Materials

Floor area

230m²
2476ft²

Bedrooms

4

Bathrooms

2

Floors

3

Key features
Kitchen/breakfast room
Separate dining room
Workshop
2nd floor playroom
Master dressing room

Garaging for
2 cars

Design
Design & Materials

www.designandmaterials.uk.com
enquiries@designandmaterials.
uk.com
01909 540 123

Build cost
£206,000

Design © Design &
Materials

Plan no. **BHP   310521**

The large porch creates a grand entrance
to this three-storey home Within the double
garage is masses of space for a workshop
which can be accessed from the utility room.

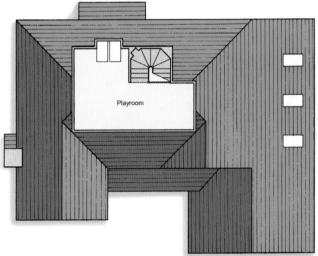

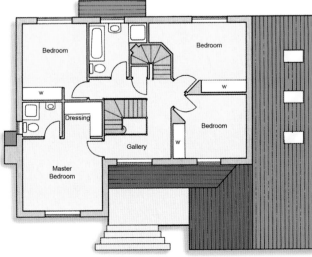

Plan no. **BHP 310716**

This design offers lots of external interest and a great open-plan living space, based around the kitchen. The master bedroom suite boasts a balcony as well as en-suite bathroom and dressing room.

Balcony

Bedroom

Bedroom

Bath

Balcony

Master Bedroom

Bedroom

Gallery

Libary

Dressing

En-Suite

Future Games Room

Family Room

Breakfast

wc

Kitchen

Study

Hall

Living

Porch

Utility

Carport

Traditional style

Floor area

232m²

2497ft²

Bedrooms

4

Bathrooms

3

Floors

2

Key features
Family room
Kitchen/breakfast room
Games room
Library
Car port

Garaging for
0 cars

Design
Design & Materials

www.designandmaterials.uk.com
enquiries@designandmaterials.uk.com
01909 540 123

Build cost
£208,000

Design © Design & Materials

Traditional style

Floor area
235m²
2530ft²

Bedrooms
4

Bathrooms
5

Floors
2

Key features
Separate dining room
Study
Shower room
3 en-suites

Garaging for
0 cars

Design
Custom Homes

www.customhomes.co.uk
admin@customhomes.co.uk
01787 377388

Build cost
£211,000

Design © Custom Homes

Plan no. **BHP 310224**

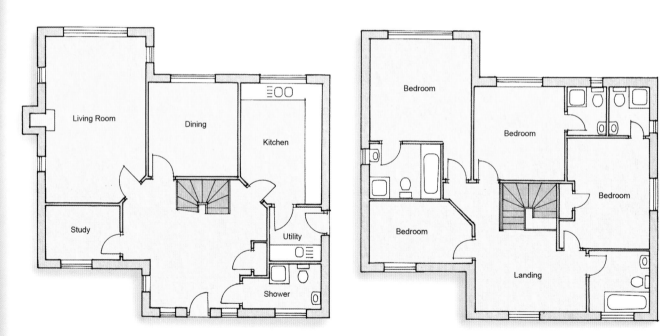

The reception rooms radiate off a large hall which is mirrored by a large landing upistairs. The reception rooms are all separate for those who prefer a more traditional layout.

Plan no. **BHP 310932**

Traditional style

Floor area

236m²

2540ft²

Bedrooms

4

Bathrooms

4

Floors

2

Key features
Separate dining room
Study
Galleried landing
Full-height hall
Porch

Garaging for
0 cars

Design
John Braid
(at Leslie R Hutt)

lhuttarchitect@btinternet.com
01463 235566

An unusual exterior design is matched by the interior. The dining room is accessed through the living room or kitchen. There are plenty of en-suite bathrooms – two of which are large enough to house corner baths.

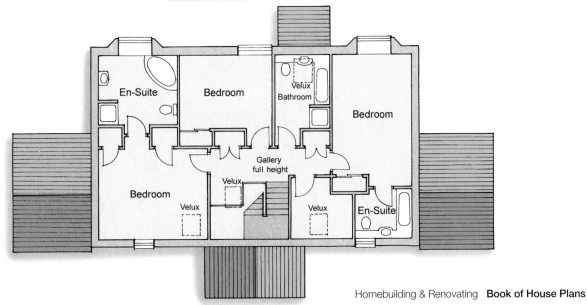

Build cost
£212,000

Design © John Braid

Traditional style

Floor area
237m²
2551ft²

Bedrooms
4

Bathrooms
2

Floors
2

Key features
Kitchen/breakfast room
Library/snug
Double-height hall
Galleried landing
Balcony

Garaging for
0 cars

Design
Jeremy Rawlings

www.periodhome.net
01884 266444

Build cost
£212,500

Design © Jeremy Rawlings

Plan no. **BHP 310647**

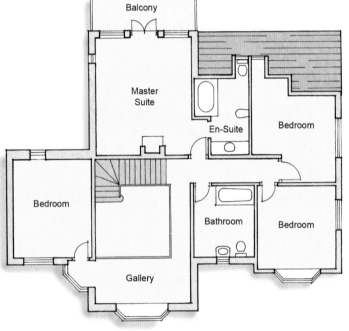

This design offers the style of a Tudor house, with its herringbone brickwork and great hall, without the angst of an older property. The ground floor is mostly open-plan which you would have with a genuine 16th century house! The galleried landing and bedroom three both have bay windows while the large master suite features its own fireplace and balcony.

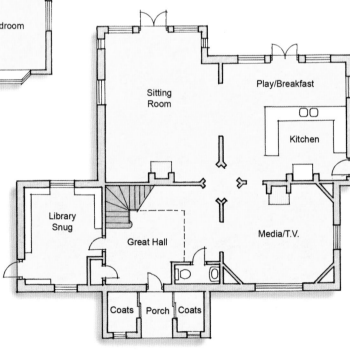

Plan no. **BHP 310893**

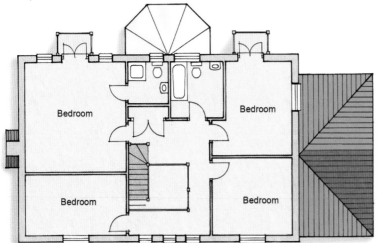

Bedroom

Bedroom

Bedroom

Bedroom

All three rear-facing reception rooms have French doors. The library, which can be accessed from both the hall and living room, leads into a conservatory. Upstairs there is a pair of balconies for the bigger bedrooms with the master having an en-suite shower room.

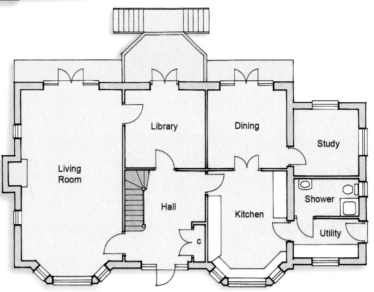

Library

Dining

Study

Living Room

Hall

Kitchen

Shower

c

Utility

Traditional style

Floor area
238m²
2562ft²

Bedrooms
4

Bathrooms
2

Floors
2

Key features
Shower room
Separate dining room
Study
Galleried landing
Conservatory

Garaging for
0 cars

Design
Custom Homes

www.customhomes.co.uk
admin@customhomes.co.uk
01787 377388

Build cost
£213,500

Design © Custom Homes

Traditional style

Floor area
238m²
2562ft²

Bedrooms
4

Bathrooms
3

Floors
2

Key features
Kitchen/breakfast room
Separate dining room
Study
Utility room
Galleried landing

Garaging for
2 cars

Design
TJ Crump
Oakwrights

www.oakwrights.co.uk
enquiries@oakwrights.co.uk
01432 353353

Build cost
£213,500

Design © TJ Crump
Oakwrights

Plan no. **BHP 310896**

This would make an exceptional family home with its generous size and well-thought-out layout. A dining hall forms the hub which all the ground floor rooms radiate from. Upstairs three of the bedrooms sit in the main body of the house while parents get some peace and quiet in a link-detached sleeping suite above the garage.

Plan no. **BHP 310632**

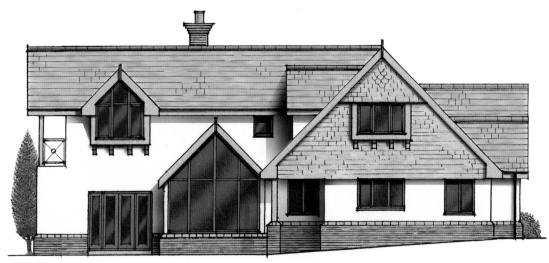

The glass-roofed family room, double-height dining hall and galleried landing provide plenty of interest while on the practical front this house also features a utility room and a bin store. The two ground floor bedrooms share a 'Jack and Jill' bathroom.

Master Bedroom

w

w

Bath

Gallery

Velux

Bedroom

Dining Hall Below

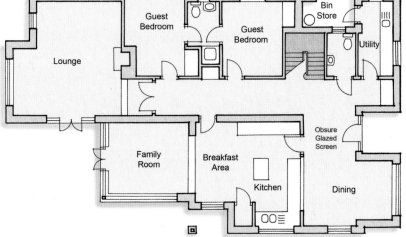

Guest Bedroom

Guest Bedroom

Bin Store

Utility

Lounge

Family Room

Breakfast Area

Kitchen

Obsure Glazed Screen

Dining

Traditional style

Floor area

238m²

2562ft²

Bedrooms

4

Bathrooms

3

Floors

2

Key features
Family room
Kitchen/breakfast room
Full-height dining hall
Galleried landing
Master en-suite

Garaging for
0 cars

Design
Design & Materials

www.designandmaterials.uk.com
enquiries@designandmaterials.
uk.com
01909 540 123

Build cost
£213,500

Design © Design &
Materials

Traditional style

Floor area
239m²
2573ft²

Bedrooms
4

Bathrooms
4

Floors
2

Key features
Kitchen/family room
Larder
Play room
Study
Living room

Garaging for
2 cars

Design
Eclipse Design

www.eclipsedesign.
copperstream.co.uk
enquiries@eclipsedesignuk.net
0845 460 4758

Build cost
£214,000

Design © Eclipse Design

Plan no. **BHP 310842**

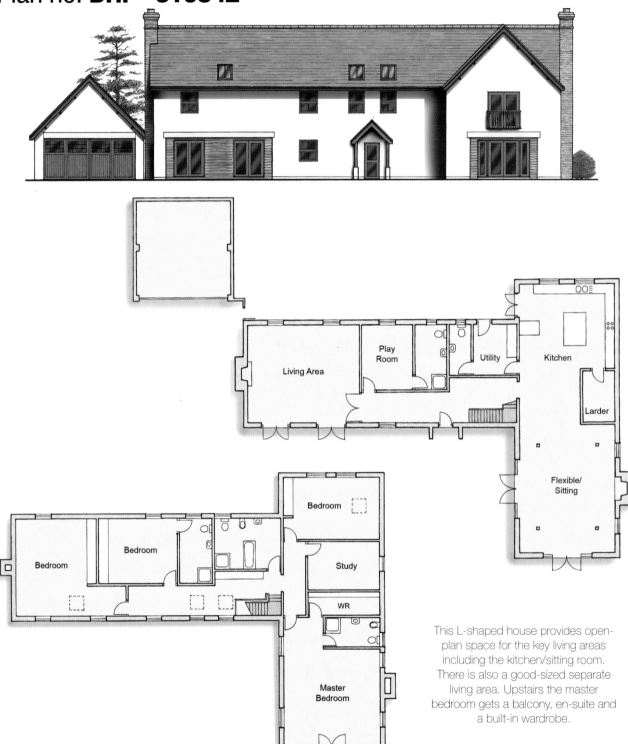

This L-shaped house provides open-plan space for the key living areas including the kitchen/sitting room. There is also a good-sized separate living area. Upstairs the master bedroom gets a balcony, en-suite and a built-in wardrobe.

Plan no. **BHP 310788**

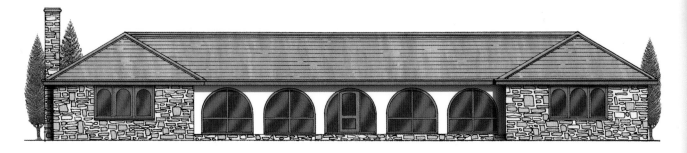

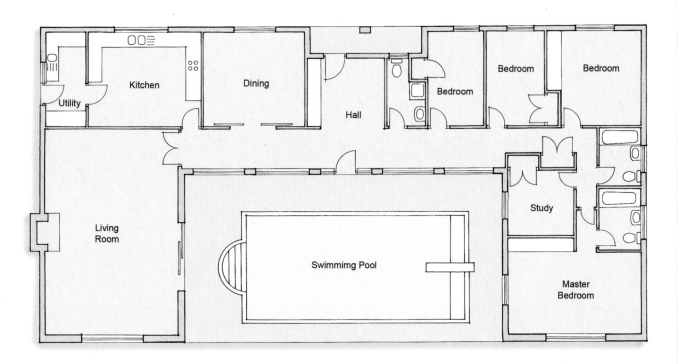

Living Room

Kitchen

Utility

Dining

Hall

Bedroom

Bedroom

Bedroom

Study

Master Bedroom

Swimmimg Pool

This is a luxury bungalow whose layout gives access to most of the rooms from a central corridor lit by five semi-circular windows. Also off the corridor is the design's centrepiece: an outside swimming pool.

Traditional style

Floor area
241m²
2594ft²

Bedrooms
4

Bathrooms
3

Floors
1

Key features
Swimming pool
Study
Separate dining room
Utility room
Master en-suite

Garaging for
0 cars

Design
The Border Design Centre

www.borderdesign.co.uk
borderdesign@btconnect.com
01578 740218

Build cost
£216,000

Design © The Border Design Centre

Traditional style

Floor area
241m²
2594ft²

Bedrooms
4

Bathrooms
2

Floors
2

Key features
Kitchen/breakfast room
Study
Utility room
Separate dining room
Master en-suite

Garaging for
0 cars

Design
Stephen Mattick

www.mattick.co.uk
mattick@mattick.co.uk
01223 891159

Build cost
£216,000

Design © Stephen Mattick

Plan no. **BHP 310875**

This traditional looking farmhouse is full of modern features including large reception rooms, an open-plan kitchen/breakfast room and separate dining and utility rooms. Upstairs there are four bedrooms – with the master en-suite.

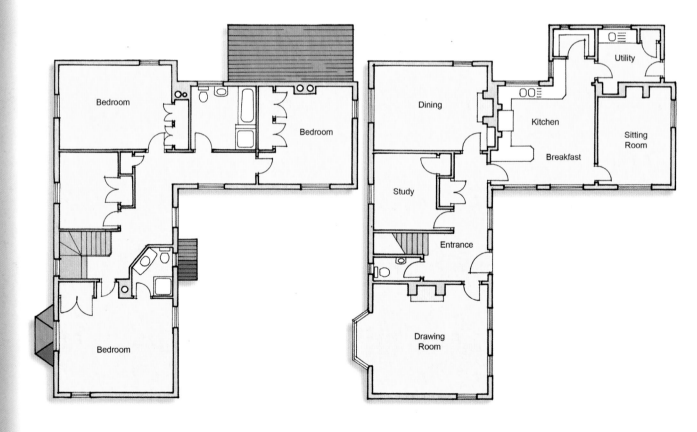

Plan no. **BHP 310323**

Plenty of external timber in ths design with its integral double garage. The gound floor features a big kitchen and living room as well as a sun room. Upstairs Velux-type rooflights provide daylight for the long access corridor.

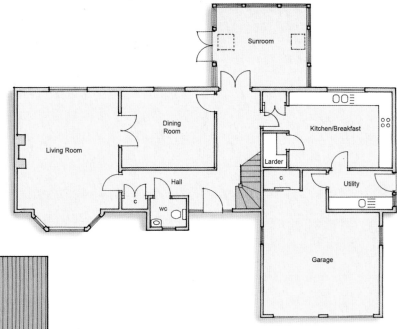

Sunroom

Dining Room

Living Room

Kitchen/Breakfast

Larder

Hall

c

Utility

c

wc

Garage

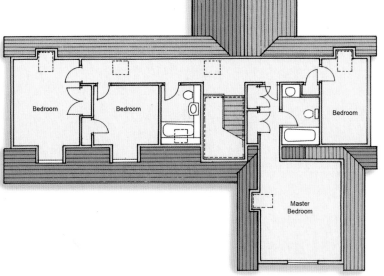

Bedroom

Bedroom

Bedroom

Master Bedroom

Traditional style

Floor area
242m²
2605ft²

Bedrooms
4

Bathrooms
2

Floors
2

Key features
Sun room
Separate dining room
Kitchen/breakfast room
Utility room
Larder

**Garaging for
2 cars**

**Design
The Border Design
Centre**

www.borderdesign.co.uk
borderdesign@btconnect.com
01578 740218

**Build cost
£217,000**

Design © The Border
Design Centre

Traditional style

Floor area
243m²
2616ft²

Bedrooms
4

Bathrooms
2

Floors
2

Key features
Kitchen/dining room
Study
Utility room
Master en-suite

Garaging for
1 car

Design
Design & Materials

www.designandmaterials.uk.com
enquiries@designandmaterials.
uk.com
01909 540 123

Build cost
£218,000

Design © Design &
Materials

Plan no. **BHP 310698**

This L-shape design has a smallish hall but manages to access all of the principal reception rooms from it. Ideal if you want to maximise space. There is a kitchen/diner, a study and a utility room. Upstairs the master bedroom suite includes a dressing room and en-suite. The second bedroom has twin-aspect windows.

Plan no. **BHP 310080**

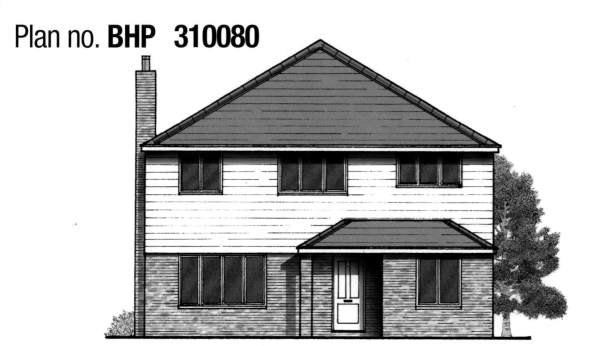

Outside you get a weatherboard and brick exterior under a tiled roof. Inside you get a kitchen with larder and utility room and a separate dining room. Upstairs two of the bedrooms are en-suite and there's a large family bathroom too.

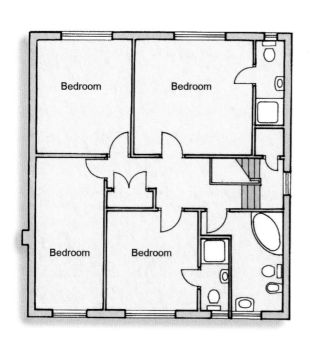

Bedroom

Bedroom

Bedroom

Bedroom

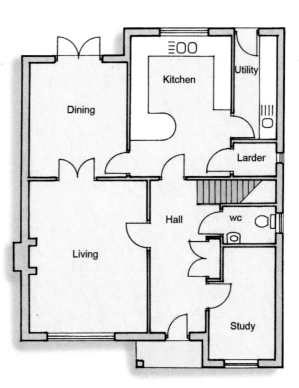

Dining

Kitchen

Utility

Larder

Hall

wc

Living

Study

Traditional style

Floor area
245m²
2637ft²

Bedrooms
4

Bathrooms
3

Floors
2

Key features
Separate dining room
Larder
Utility room
Study
Master en-suite

Garaging for
0 cars

Design
Churchill Design

www.churchilldesign.co.uk
info@churchilldesign.co.uk
01252 325701

Build cost
£220,000

Contemporary style

Floor area

248m²

2669ft²

Bedrooms

4

Bathrooms

2

Floors

2

Key features
Full-height dining hall
Family room
Study
Balconied landing
Master bedroom suite

Garaging for
0 cars

Design
John Watson

Build cost
£222,500

Plan no. **BHP 310851**

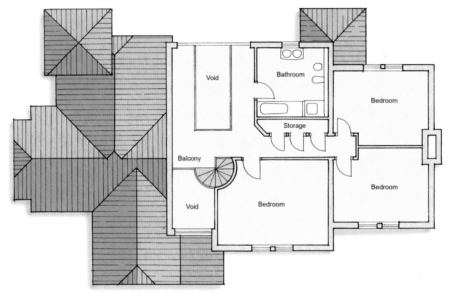

This modern take on the traditional farmhouse incorporates plenty of glass to create a bright, airy interior. Interesting architectural features include double-height rooms, a gallery and a balcony. The master bedrrom suite is particulalry luxurious.

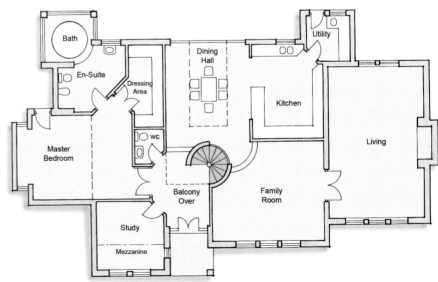

Plan no. **BHP 310128**

As traditional as this house looks from the outside the interior is designed for thoroughly modern living. That means lots of free-flowing space through the well-trod areas like the kitchen and dining room, plus a full-depth living room to relax in. The utility room is sensibly sandwiched between the main house and a garage. Sleeping space is equally generous and the galleried hall benefits from the large window on the staircase.

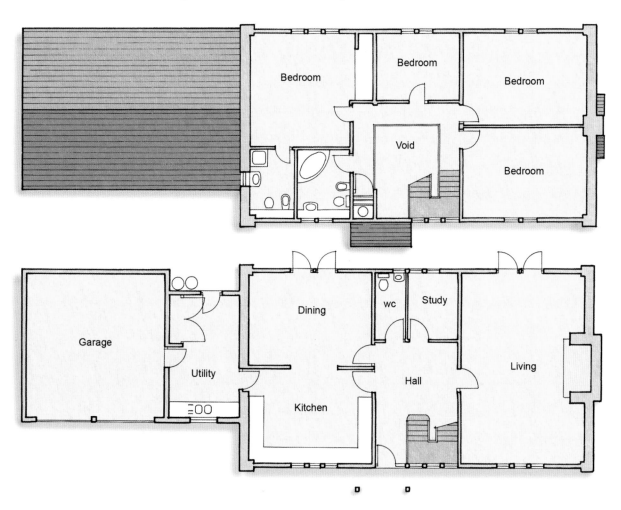

Traditional style

Floor area
248m²
2669ft²

Bedrooms
4

Bathrooms
2

Floors
2

Key features
Kitchen/dining room
Study
Utility room
Double-height hall
Galleried landing

Garaging for
2 cars

Design
Welsh Oak Frame

www.welshoakframe.com
01686 688000

Build cost
£222,500

Design © Welsh Oak Frame

Traditional style

Floor area

251m²

2702ft²

Bedrooms

4

Bathrooms

1

Floors

2

Key features
Open-plan living area
Utility room
Lobby

Garaging for
1 cars

Design
Custom Homes

www.customhomes.co.uk
admin@customhomes.co.uk
01787 377388

Build cost
£225,000

Design © Custom Homes

Plan no. **BHP 310581**

The traditional styling of this house belies a modern, open-plan interior where the hall, living room and dining room are one large space. Upstairs the four bedrooms share a single bathroom.

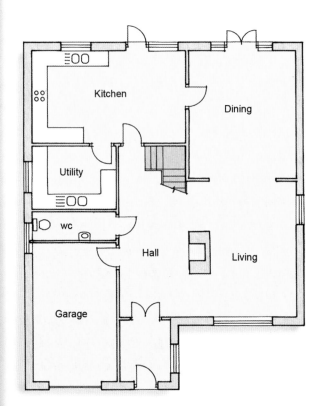

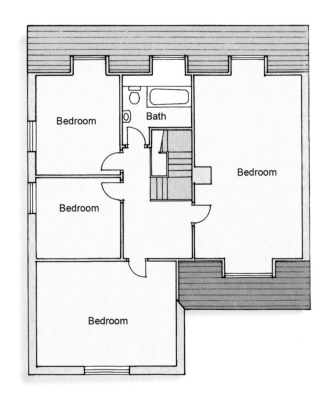

Plan no. **BHP 310884**

Traditional style

Floor area

254m²

2734ft²

Bedrooms

4

Bathrooms

3

Floors

2

Key features
Kitchen/breakfast room
Separate dining room
Study
Galleried landing
Sun lounge

Garaging for
0 cars

Design
Design & Materials

www.designandmaterials.uk.com
enquiries@designandmaterials.
uk.com
01909 540 123

Build cost
£228,000

Design © Design &
Materials

This Tudor-look house has plenty of flexible reception space. The sun room at the end of the house features triple-aspect French doors. There's a formal dining room close to the kitchen – which is complete with its own pantry and utility room. Off the galleried landing upstairs are four bedrooms, three bathrooms and stairs for accessing future attic rooms.

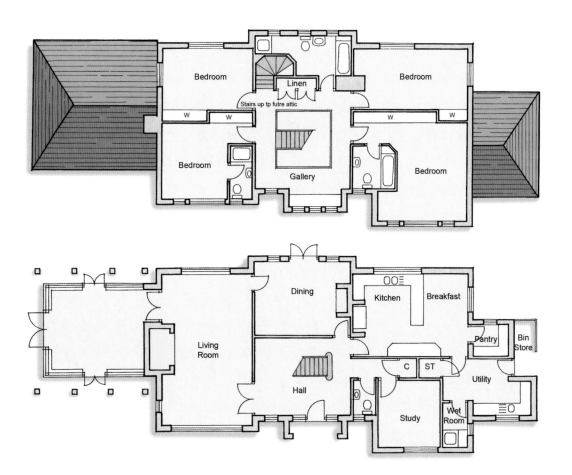

Traditional style

Floor area

255m²

2745ft²

Bedrooms

4

Bathrooms

3

Floors

2

Key features
Separate dining room
Utility room
Larder
Master en-suite

Garaging for
0 cars

Design
County Contracts

countycontractsltd@fsmail.
net
01892 785153

Build cost
£229,000

Design © County Contracts

Plan no. **BHP 310986**

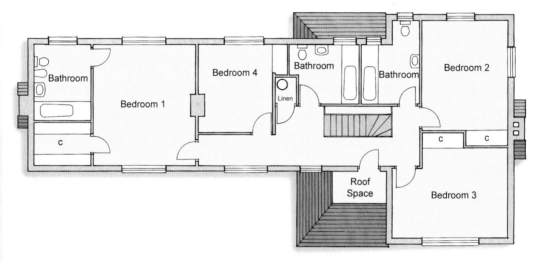

The kitchen is accessed
through the dining room but
has a utility room and larder.
Upstairs the layout is more
conventional and includes
two bathrooms as well as a
master en-suite bathroom and
walk-in wardrobe.

Plan no. **BHP 310236**

There is an open-plan living area and the ground floor comprising hall/kitchen and family room. Upstairs are four bedrooms — with the master having its own dressing room.

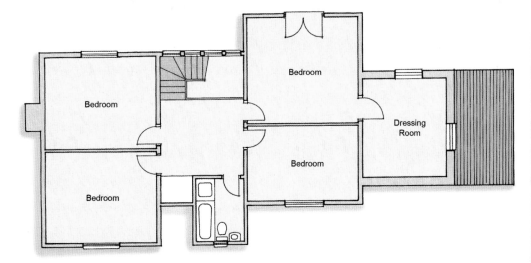

Bedroom

Bedroom

Bedroom

Bedroom

Dressing Room

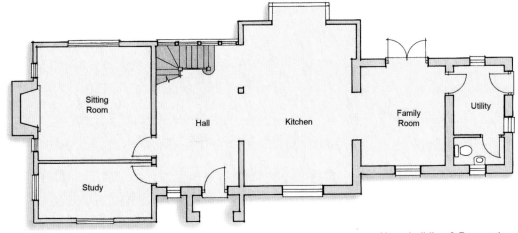

Sitting Room

Hall

Kitchen

Family Room

Utility

Study

Floor area
255m²
2745ft²

Bedrooms
4

Bathrooms
1

Floors
2

Key features
Kitchen/dining hall
Utility room
Study
Master dressing room

Garaging for
0 cars

Design
TJ Crump
Oakwrights

www.oakwrights.co.uk
enquiries@oakwrights.co.uk
01432 353353

Build cost
£229,000

Design © TJ Crump

Traditional style

Floor area
256m²
2756ft²

Bedrooms
4

Bathrooms
3

Floors
2

Key features
Kitchen/breakfast room
Separate dining room
Utility room
Study
2 beds en-suite

Garaging for
0 cars

Design
Stephen Mattick

www.mattick.co.uk
mattick@mattick.co.uk
01223 891159.

Build cost
£230,000

Design © Stephen Mattick

Plan no. **BHP 310053**

The exterior may be period but inside there are large reception rooms, a glass-roofed kitchen, four bedrooms and two en-suites.

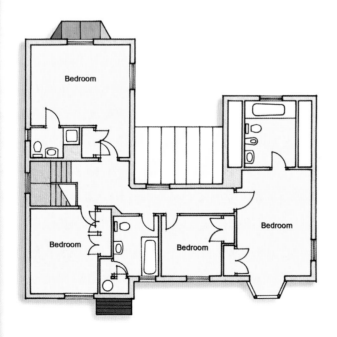

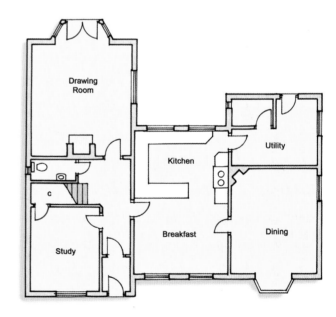

Plan no. **BHP 310659**

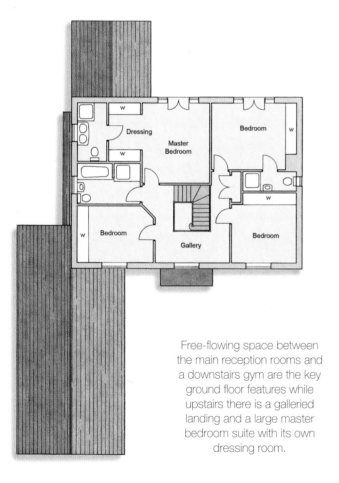

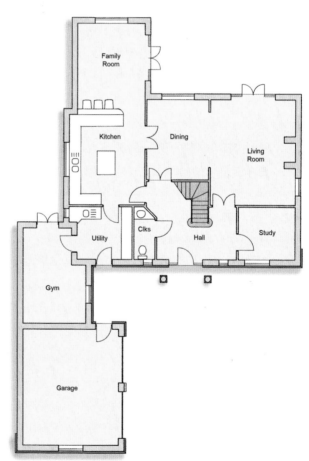

Free-flowing space between the main reception rooms and a downstairs gym are the key ground floor features while upstairs there is a galleried landing and a large master bedroom suite with its own dressing room.

Traditional style

Floor area
262m²
2820ft²

Bedrooms
4

Bathrooms
3

Floors
2

Key features
Kitchen/family room
Living/dining room
Study
Gym
Master bedroom suite

Garaging for
2 cars

Design
Design & Materials

www.designandmaterials.uk.com
enquiries@designandmaterials.
uk.com
01909 540 123

Build cost
£235,000

Design © Design &
Materials

Contemporary style

Floor area

266m²

2863ft²

Bedrooms

4

Bathrooms

3

Floors

2

Key features
Open-plan living area
Utility room
Full height hall/lounge
Master bed en-suite

Garaging for
0 cars

Design
Peter King

info@carden-king.co.uk
01367 253330

Build cost
£239,000

Design © Peter King

Plan no. **BHP 310746**

This house has flowing space inside and reflecting pools outside. The open-plan ground floor living space is a major feature. The reception rooms will feel very spacious with both the lounge and hall being two storeys high.

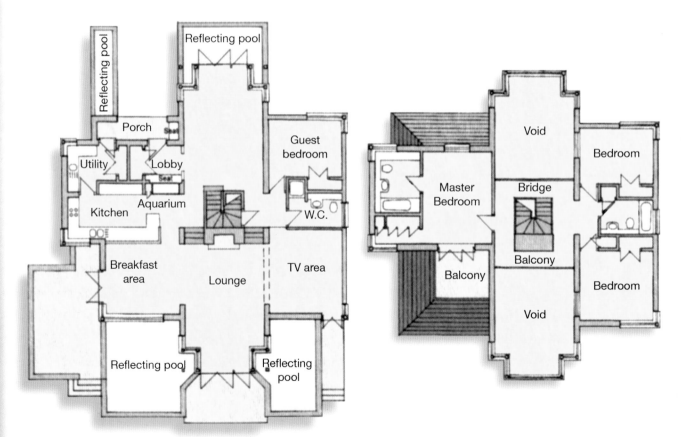

Plan no. **BHP 310599**

Basements are becoming increasingly popular, especially as land prices rise, and the garage/workshop space in this design add real value. The location of the utility room away from the kitchen is unusual but it offers plenty of storage space.

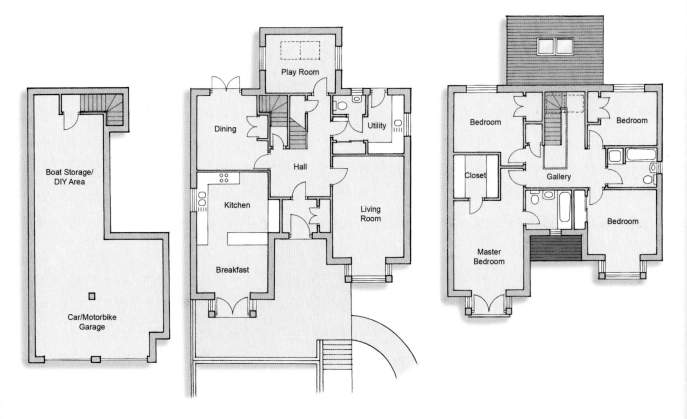

Boat Storage/ DIY Area

Car/Motorbike Garage

Play Room

Dining

Utility

Hall

Kitchen

Living Room

Breakfast

Bedroom

Bedroom

Closet

Gallery

Bedroom

Master Bedroom

Traditional style

Floor area

266m²

2863ft²

Bedrooms

4

Bathrooms

2

Floors

3

Key features
Kitchen/breakfast room
Playroom
Utility room
Master bedroom suite

Garaging for

2 cars

Design

**John Braid
(at Leslie R Hutt)**

lhuttarchitect@btinternet.com
01463 235566

Build cost
£239,000

Design © Leslie R Hutt

Traditional style

Floor area
277m²
2982ft²

Bedrooms
4

Bathrooms
3

Floors
1

Key features
Conservatory
Utility room
Dining/living room
Study
2 beds en-suite

Garaging for
2 cars

Design
Swedish House Co

www.swedishhouses.com
0870 770 0760

Build cost
£249,000

Design © Swedish House
Co

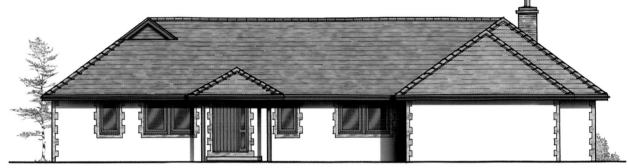

Plenty of space on one floor means a large footprint.
The living and sleeping areas are grouped together
which is often an advantage.

Plan no. **BHP 310137**

Behind the simple facade lurks a large home with sun lounge featuring a vaulted ceiling and twin-aspect lounge. The first floor rooms lead off a galleried landing and include a full-depth master suite and two further bedrooms.

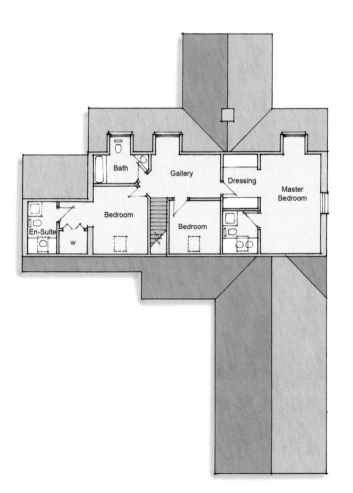

Traditional style

Floor area
278m²
2992ft²

Bedrooms
4

Bathrooms
4

Floors
2

Key features
Kitchen/breakfast room
Sun lounge
Workshop
Separate dining room
Master bedroom suite

Garaging for
2 cars

Design
Design & Materials

www.designandmaterials.uk.com
enquiries@designandmaterials.uk.com
01909 540 123

Build cost
£249,500

Design
© Design & Materials

Contemporary style

Floor area

280m²

3014ft²

Bedrooms

4

Bathrooms

3

Floors

2

Key features
Open-plan living
Workroom
study
Terraces
Master bed en-suite

Garaging for
2 cars

Design
John Shida
(Morningtide
Developments)

www.morningtide.fsnet.co.uk

johnshida@morningtide.
fsnet.co.uk

01621 815485

Build cost
£251,000

Design © John Shida

Plan no. **BHP 310920**

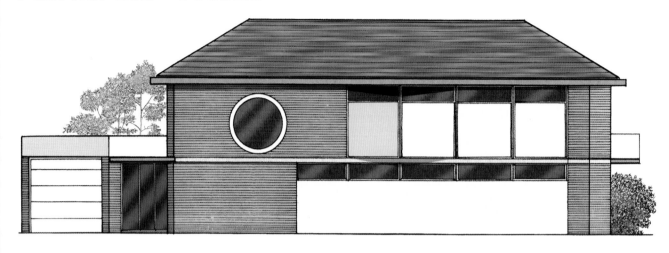

Twin terraces and a balcony would make this a good house to have orientated to make the best of the sun. Inside, the main reception rooms flow from the central family room. Upstairs, three of the four bedrooms get an en-suite bathroom.

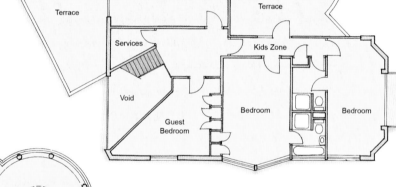

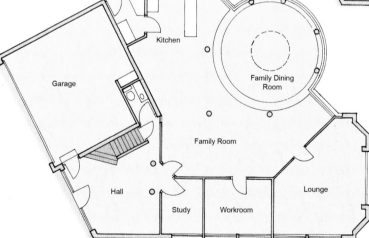

Plan no. **BHP 310074**

Traditional style

Floor area
287m²
3089ft²

Bedrooms
4

Bathrooms
3

Floors
3

Key features
Full-height conservatory
Cinema
Separate dining room
Utility room
2 en-suite beds

Garaging for
2 cars

Design
Planahome

www.planahome.uk.com
plans@planahome.uk.com
01326 373600

Build cost
£257,000

A two-storey conservatory links the main sections in this design and adds a surprisingly modern dimension to the Victorian-style house. The glazed area covers the breakfast room and kitchen, and provides an aerial walkway between the first-floor rooms. Dormer windows open up the roof space to provide two extra bedrooms on the second floor.

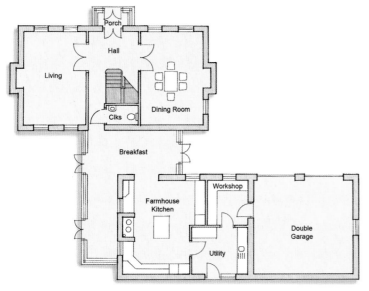

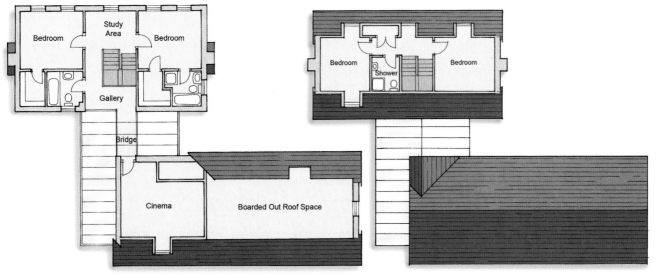

Design © Planahome

Traditional style

Floor area

290m²

3122ft²

Bedrooms

4

Bathrooms

2

Floors

2

Key features
Separate dining room
Sunroom
Utility room
Study
Master bed en-suite

Garaging for
0 cars

Design
Potton

www.potton.co.uk
contact@potton.co.uk
01767 676 400

Build cost
£259,752

Design © Potton

Plan no. **BHP 310032**

This design is ideal for those who like good-sized rooms — be they reception or bedrooms. There's an inglenook fireplace in the living area and a sun room leading off the dining room.

Plan no. **BHP 310977**

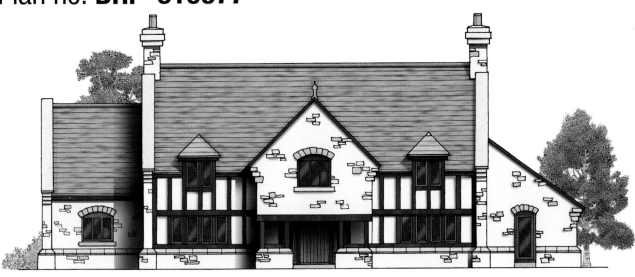

Built around the two-storey dining hall this house is deigned to impress. It features an impressive fireplace in the living room and twin doors into the library — which also features its own fireplace. Upstairs, the master bedroom comes with dressing room and en-suite bathroom.

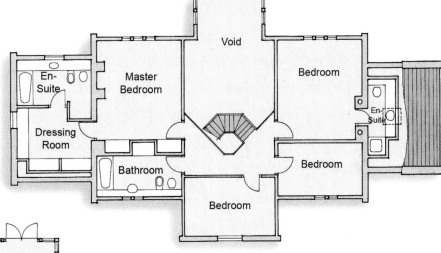

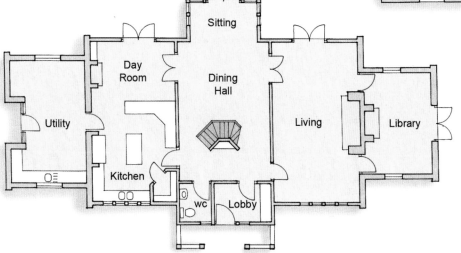

Floor area
295m²
3175ft²

Bedrooms
4

Bathrooms
3

Floors
2

Key features
Kitchen/breakfast room
Dining hall
Library
Utility room
Master bedroom suite

Garaging for
0 cars

Design
Welsh Oak Frame

www.welshoakframe.com
01686 688000

Build cost
£264,500

Traditional style

Floor area

295m²

3175ft²

Bedrooms

4

Bathrooms

2

Floors

2

Key features
Kitchen/dining room
Study
Utility room
Master bed suite

Garaging for
1 cars

Design
Welsh Oak Frame

www.welshoakframe.com
01686 688000

Build cost
£264,500

Design © Welsh Oak Frame

Plan no. **BHP 310017**

The octagonal tower is a striking feature of this design and houses the master bedroom and downstairs a study area. The utility room is open to the single garage and above it is a guest bedroom with its own access off a separate staircase from the rear entrance lobby.

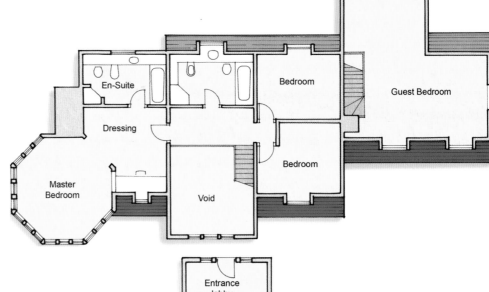

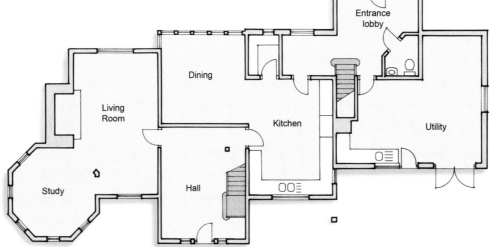

Plan no. **BHP 310242**

Once through the 'air lock' entrance porch there is an entrance hall with full gallery. Downstairs there is a big kitchen and a large living room

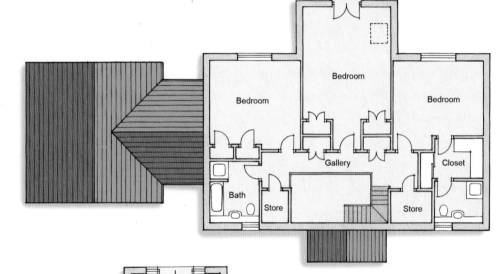

Traditional style

Floor area
297m²
3197ft²

Bedrooms
4

Bathrooms
3

Floors
2

Key features
Kitchen/dining room
Utility room
Study
Master bedroom suite

Garaging for
2 cars

Design
John Braid
(at Leslie R Hutt)

lhuttarchitect@btinternet.com
01463 235566

Build cost
£266,000

Design © Leslie R Hutt

Contemporary style

Floor area

300m²

3229ft²

Bedrooms

4

Bathrooms

3

Floors

3

Key features
Sun lounge/conservatory
Workshop
Study
Utility room
3 en-suite beds

Garaging for
2 cars

Design
**JS Building
Consultancy**

www.ukbuildingconsultancy.
co.uk
jsharples@ricsonline.org
0113 250 1303

Build cost
£269,000

Design © JS Building
Consultancy

Plan no. **BHP 310455**

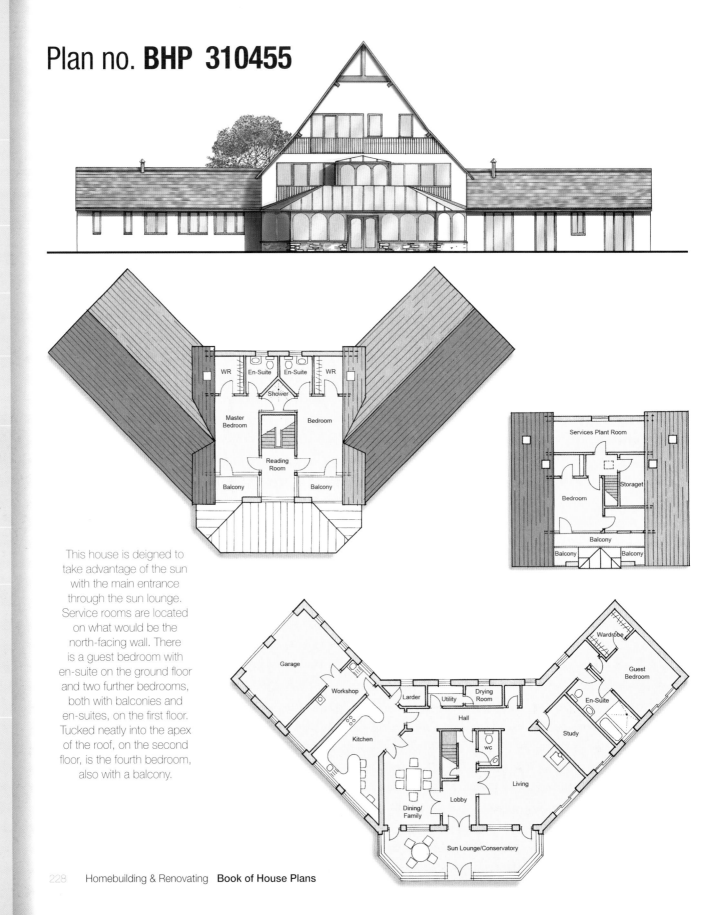

This house is deigned to take advantage of the sun with the main entrance through the sun lounge. Service rooms are located on what would be the north-facing wall. There is a guest bedroom with en-suite on the ground floor and two further bedrooms, both with balconies and en-suites, on the first floor. Tucked neatly into the apex of the roof, on the second floor, is the fourth bedroom, also with a balcony.

Plan no. **BHP 310554**

This is a house for lovers of open fires with fireplaces in the hall, lounge and den area of the large L-shaped kitchen. Upstairs the four bedrooms are all en-suite and lead off the impressive galleried landing, which itself is accessed via a grand staircase.

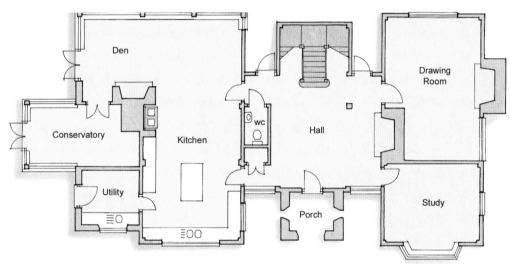

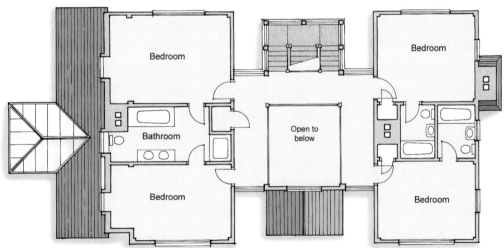

Traditional style

Floor area
300m²
3229ft²

Bedrooms
4

Bathrooms
3

Floors
2

Key features
Kitchen/dining room
Galleried hall
Study
Utility room
Conservatory

Garaging for
0 cars

Design
Border Oak

www.borderoak.com
sales@borderoak.com
01568 708752

Build cost
£269,000

Design © Border Oak

Traditional style

Floor area
301m²
3240ft²

Bedrooms
4

Bathrooms
3

Floors
2

Key features
Kitchen/breakfast room
Drawing room
separate dining room
Study
2 en-suite beds

Garaging for
3 cars

Design
Planahome

www.planahome.uk.com
plans@planahome.uk.com
01326 373600

Build cost
£270,000

Design © Planahome

Plan no. **BHP 310542**

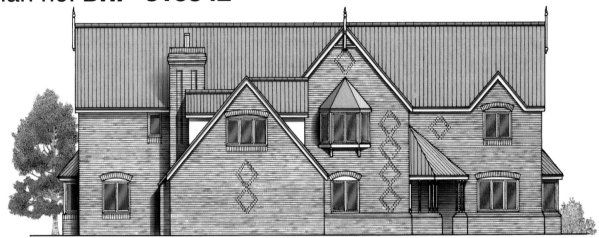

There is day-to-day flexibility in the upstairs layout of this design which features a first floor sitting room which could be used with the master bedroom or guest bedroom to form a guest suite.

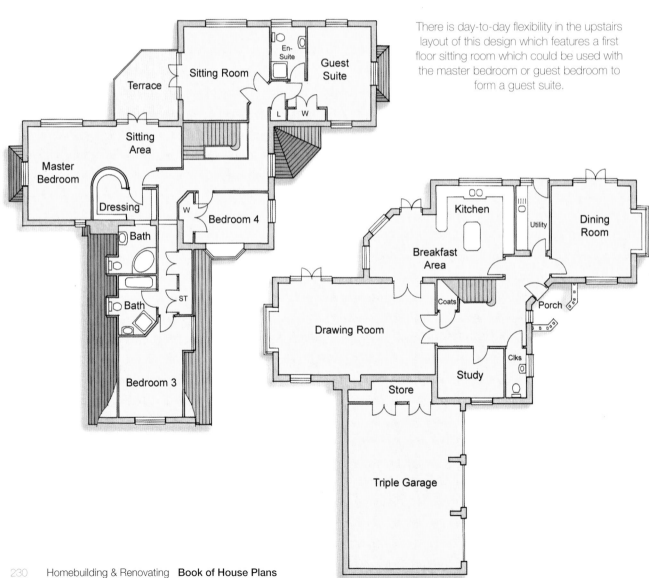

Plan no. **BHP 310635**

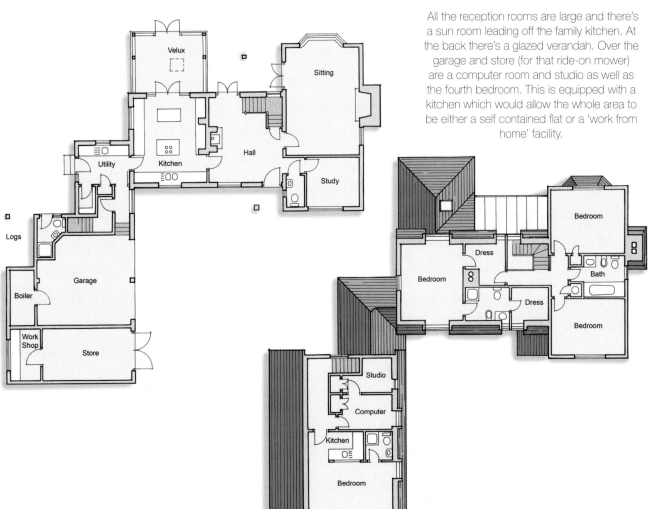

All the reception rooms are large and there's a sun room leading off the family kitchen. At the back there's a glazed verandah. Over the garage and store (for that ride-on mower) are a computer room and studio as well as the fourth bedroom. This is equipped with a kitchen which would allow the whole area to be either a self contained flat or a 'work from home' facility.

Traditional style

Floor area
302m²
3251ft²

Bedrooms
4

Bathrooms
3

Floors
2

Key features
Annexe over garage
Kitchen/diner
Study
Utility room
Master bed suite

Garaging for
2 cars

Design
Border Oak

www.borderoak.com
sales@borderoak.com
01568 708752

Build cost
£271,000

Design © Border Oak

Contemporary style

Floor area

304m²

3272ft²

Bedrooms

4

Bathrooms

3

Floors

2

Key features
Kitchen/dining room
Sun room
Twin studies
Disabled en-suite
Master bed en-suite

Garaging for

2 cars

Design

**John Shida
(Morningtide
Developments)**

www.morningtide.fsnet.co.uk
johnshida@morningtide.
fsnet.co.uk
01621 815485

Build cost
£272,500

Design © John Shida

Plan no. **BHP 310824**

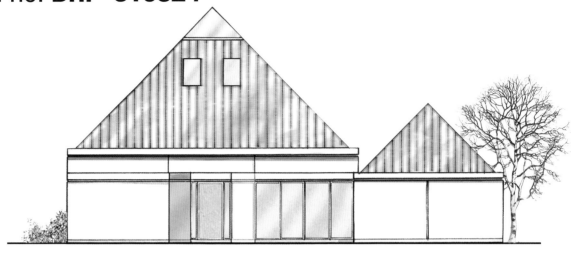

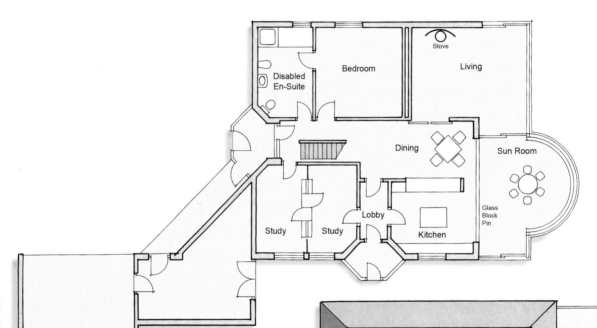

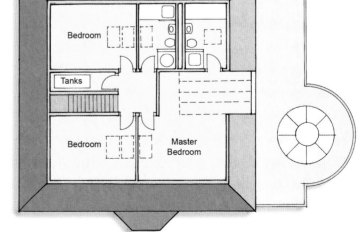

This design features twin interconnected studies
and a feature sun room. Downstairs is a bedroom
with a large en-suite — particularly suitable for
disabled use. On the first floor are three further
bedrooms and two bathrooms.

Plan no. **BHP 310995**

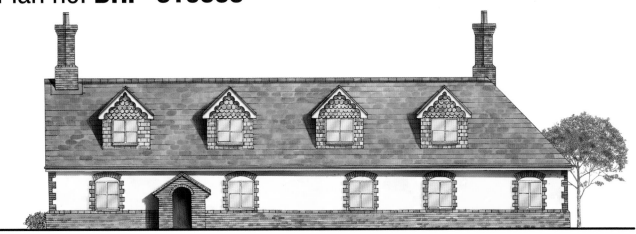

The heart of this house is the full height hall with adjacent entertaining area. Off the hall there is also a dining room which leads into the breakfast area and kitchen. The first floor has four bedrooms, including the master which has an en-suite shower room and walk-in wardrobe.

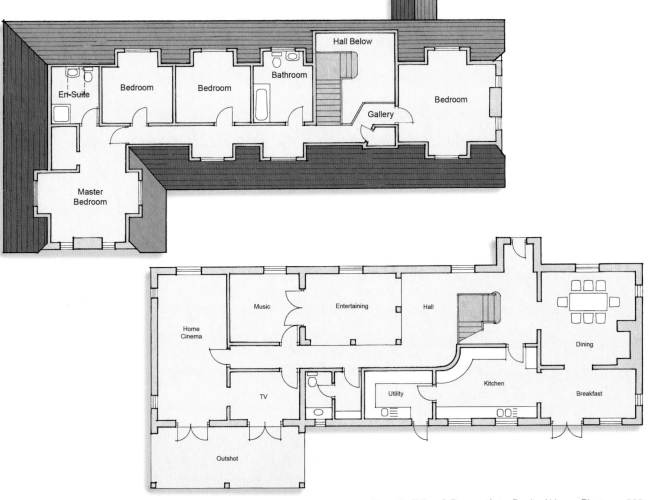

Traditional style

Floor area
306m²
3294ft²

Bedrooms
4

Bathrooms
2

Floors
2

Key features
Kitchen/breakfast room
Separate dining room
Music room
Home cinema
Master en-suite

Garaging for
0 cars

Design
Jeremy Rawlings

www.periodhome.net
01884 266444

Build cost
£274,000

Design © Jeremy Rawllings

Traditional style

Floor area

307m²

3305ft²

Bedrooms

4

Bathrooms

3

Floors

2

Key features
Kitchen/dining room
Study
Conservatory
Upper sitting room
Games room

Garaging for
2 cars

Design
Design & Materials

www.designandmaterials.uk.com
enquiries@designandmaterials.
uk.com
01909 540 123

Build cost
£275,000

Design © Design &
Materials

Plan no. **BHP 310911**

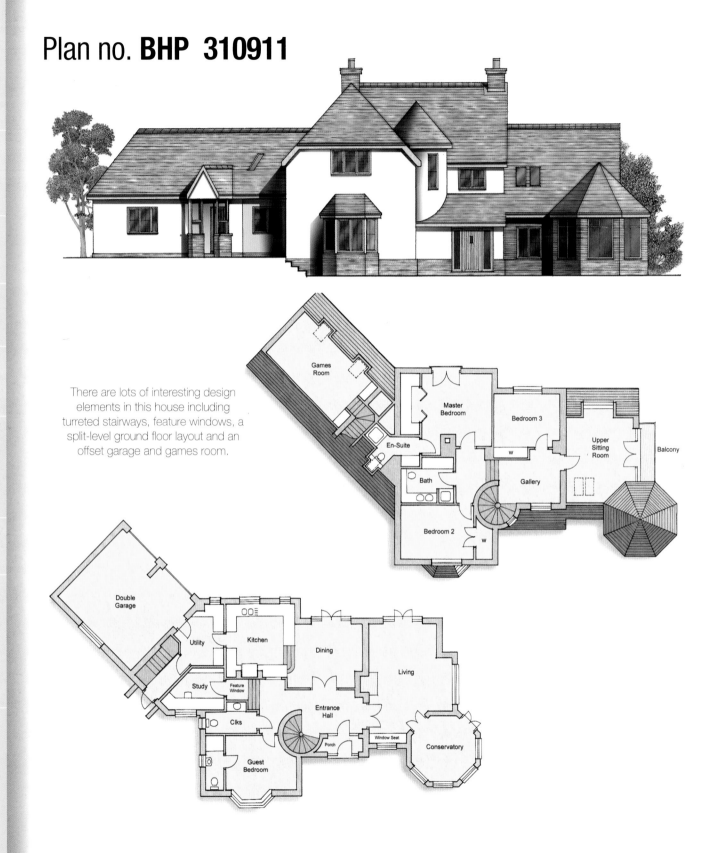

There are lots of interesting design elements in this house including turreted stairways, feature windows, a split-level ground floor layout and an offset garage and games room.

Plan no. **BHP 310311**

Back stairs from the utility room lead to a useful office space over the double garage in this interestingly styled house. Accommodation is much as you would expect for a house of this size and three of the bedrooms are en-suite.

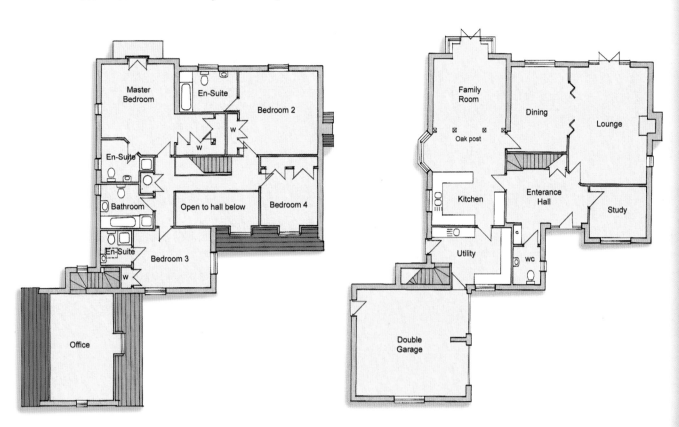

Traditional style

Floor area
309m²
3326ft²

Bedrooms
4

Bathrooms
4

Floors
2

Key features
Kitchen/family room
Lounge/dining room
Study
Office
Master bedroom suite

Garaging for
2 cars

Design
Design & Materials

www.designandmaterials.uk.com
enquiries@designandmaterials.uk.com
01909 540 123

Build cost
£277,000

Design © Design & Materials

Traditional style

Floor area
310m²
3337ft²

Bedrooms
4

Bathrooms
4

Floors
2

Key features
Kitchen/breakfast room
Garden room
Separate dining room
Study
Master bedroom suite

Garaging for
0 cars

Design
Design & Materials

www.designandmaterials.uk.com
enquiries@designandmaterials.
uk.com
01909 540 123

Build cost
£278,000

Design © Design &
Materials

Plan no. **BHP 310620**

The kitchen/garden room and living room have wide-opening doors to the garden. Upstairs the master bedroom has a vaulted ceiling, a balcony, en-suite bathroom and separate dressing room. Other features include a galleried landing with a window seat.

Plan no. **BHP 310944**

From the galleried dining hall to the conservatory this house offers high quality living space. Upstairs the master suite occupies one wing and their are three further bedrooms and two bathrooms.

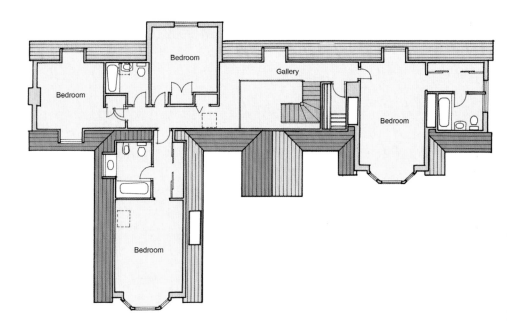

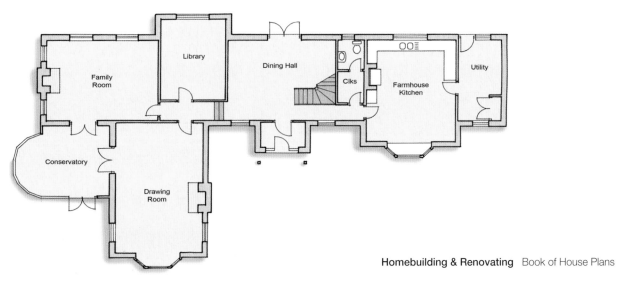

Traditional style

Floor area

310m²

3337ft²

Bedrooms

4

Bathrooms

3

Floors

2

Key features
Dining hall
Library
Conservatory
Family room
2 en-suite beds

Garaging for

0 cars

Design
The Border Design Centre

www.borderdesign.co.uk
borderdesign@btconnect.com
01578 740218

Build cost
£278,000

Design © The Border Design Centre

Traditional style

Floor area

311m²

3348ft²

Bedrooms

4

Bathrooms

3

Floors

2

Key features
Kitchen/family room
Separate dining room
Study
Playroom
Master bedroom suite

Garaging for

2 cars

Design

Churchill Design

www.churchilldesign.co.uk
info@churchilldesign.co.uk
01252 325701

Build cost

£279,000

Design © Churchill Design

Plan no. **BHP 310749**

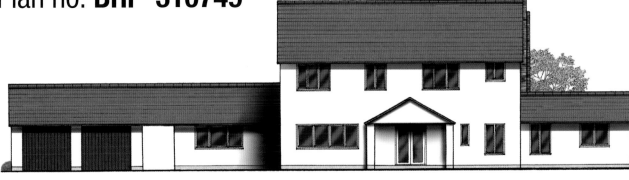

This house has a full-depth kitchen and family room with a built in larder. There is also a separate dining room and a play room with a second downstairs toilet. Upstairs there are four bedrooms — two of them en-suite.

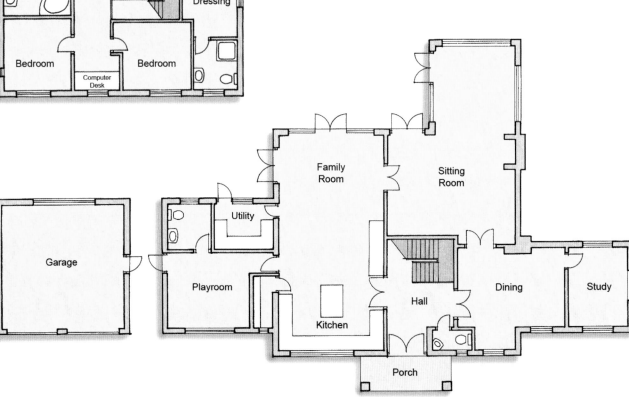

Plan no. **BHP 310488**

The fine classically-influenced frontage of this design leads through to a less formal interior. Downstairs the kitchen/breakfast room and conservatory are open-plan as are the drawing room and home cinema. The first floor features a full-depth master suite with space for luxuries including a gym.

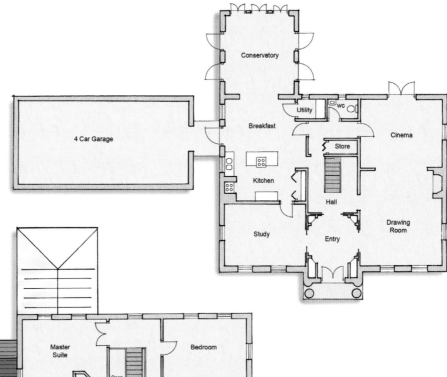

Traditional style

Floor area
314m²
3380ft²

Bedrooms
4

Bathrooms
4

Floors
2

Key features
Kitchen/breakfast room
Conservatory
Cinema
Study
Master bedroom suite

Garaging for
4 cars

Design
Jeremy Rawlings

www.periodhome.net
01884 266444

Build cost
£281,500

Design © Jeremy Rawlings

Floor area

317m²
3412ft²

Bedrooms
4

Bathrooms
4

Floors
2

Key features
Kitchen/dining room
Study
Playroom
Family room
3 en-suite beds

Garaging for

0 cars

Design
Design & Materials

www.designandmaterials.uk.com
enquiries@designandmaterials.
uk.com
01909 540 123

Build cost
£284,000

Plan no. **BHP 310113**

The Kitchen/dining area is a real feature and very much at the centre of this home. Upstairs a galleried landing leads to four bedrooms, three of which have en-suite bathrooms.

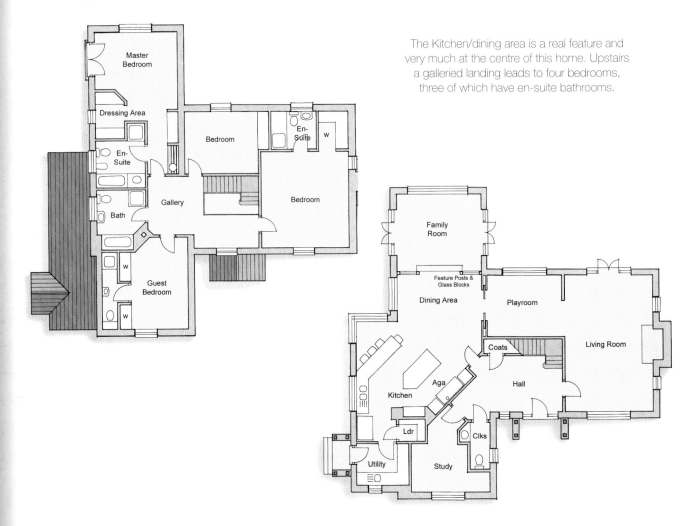

Plan no. **BHP 310602**

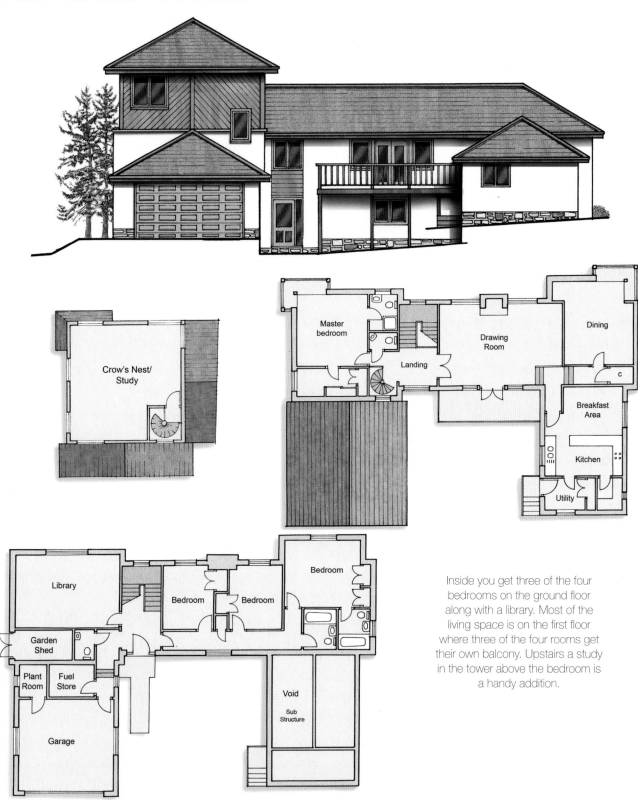

Contemporary style

Floor area
322m²
3466ft²

Bedrooms
4

Bathrooms
3

Floors
3

Key features
Kitchen/breakfast room
Separate dining room
Library
En-suite master bed
Crow's nest study

**Garaging for
2 cars**

Design
**The Border Design
Centre**

www.borderdesign.co.uk
borderdesign@btconnect.com
01578 740218

Build cost
£289,000

Inside you get three of the four bedrooms on the ground floor along with a library. Most of the living space is on the first floor where three of the four rooms get their own balcony. Upstairs a study in the tower above the bedroom is a handy addition.

Traditional style

Floor area

336m²

3617ft²

Bedrooms

4

Bathrooms

3

Floors

2

Key features
Kitchen/sun room
Galleried dining hall
Utility room
Annexe
Master bedroom suite

Garaging for
2 cars

Design
**TJ Crump
Oakwrights**

www.oakwrights.co.uk
enquiries@oakwrights.co.uk
01432 353353

Build cost
£301,000

Design © TJ Crump

Plan no. **BHP 310293**

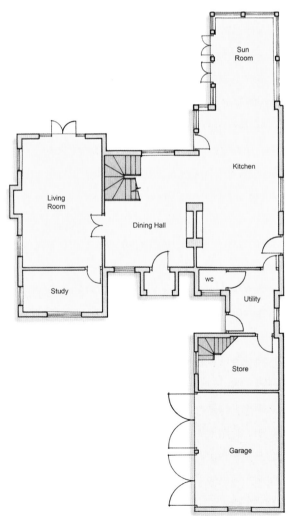

The dining hall, kitchen and sun room
are all open-plan in this elongated
house. In the main house there are four
bedrooms, two of which are en-suite
and over the garage is an annexe which
could be used as an office or as further
accommodation.

Plan no. **BHP 310470**

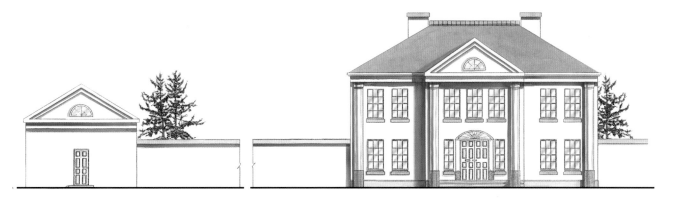

The circular entrance hall and landing in this Palladian-style house gives easy access to all of the ground and first floor rooms. These include an enormous, bay-fronted lounge as well as a symmetrical kitchen and dining spaces downstairs. Upstairs there's a master suite, a gym and three more double bedrooms.

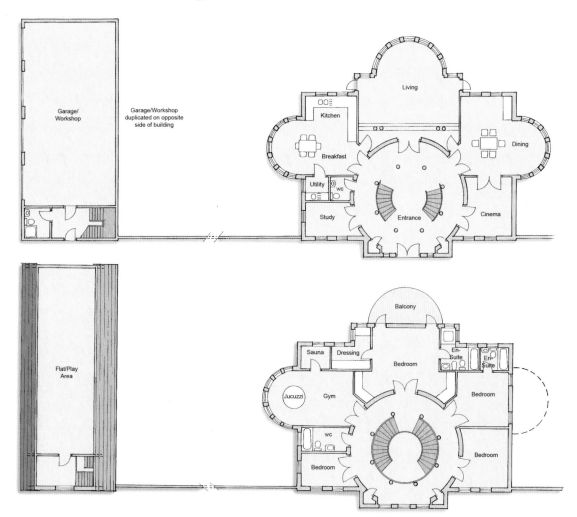

Traditional style

Floor area
340m²
3660ft²

Bedrooms
4

Bathrooms
3

Floors
2

Key features
Circular entrance hall
Kitchen/breakfast room
Cinema
Gym/Jacuzzi
Master bedroom suite

Garaging for
4 cars

Design
**Centreline
Solutions**

www.centrelinesolutions.co.uk
info@centrelinesolutions.co.uk
01383 417 509

Build cost
£305,000

Design © Centreline
Solutions

Barn style

Floor area

342m²

3681ft²

Bedrooms

4

Bathrooms

2

Floors

2

Key features
Kitchen/breakfast room
Balcony and games
room

Garaging for
0 cars

Design
**TJ Crump
Oakwrights**

www.oakwrights.co.uk
enquiries@oakwrights.co.uk
01432 353353

Build cost
£307,000

Design © TJ Crump

Plan no. **BHP 310371**

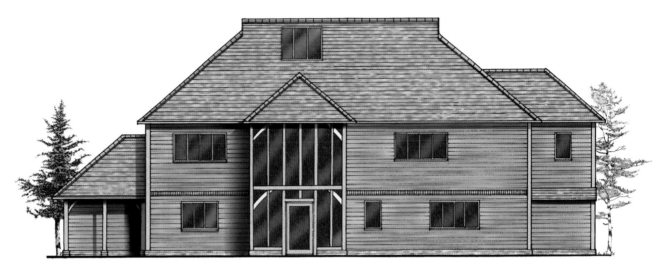

Creating a modern barn-style home offers the opportunity to use the double-height space on offer. This design does that in a number of ways. It features: a double-height gallery behind the full-height windows in the hall; a vaulted ceiling above the landing; and a balcony overlooking the garden room.

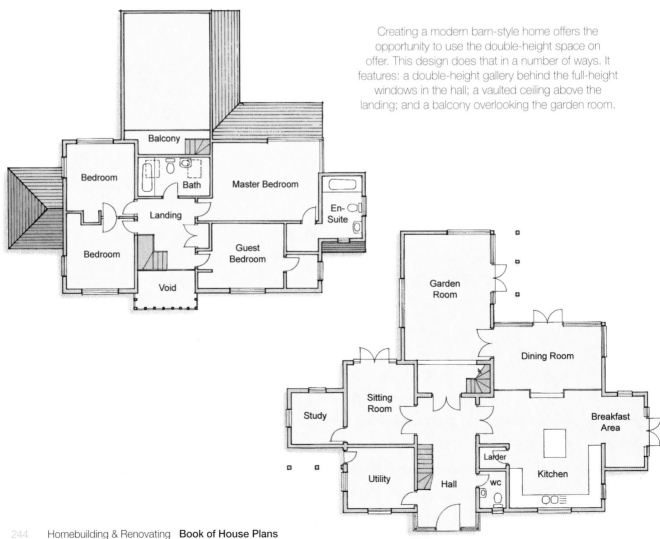

Plan no. **BHP 310434**

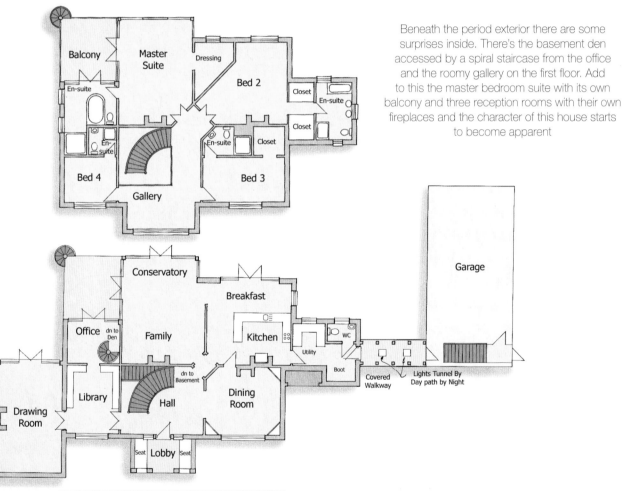

Beneath the period exterior there are some surprises inside. There's the basement den accessed by a spiral staircase from the office and the roomy gallery on the first floor. Add to this the master bedroom suite with its own balcony and three reception rooms with their own fireplaces and the character of this house starts to become apparent

(Floor plan labels, first floor:) Balcony, Master Suite, Dressing, Bed 2, Closet, En-suite, En-suite, Closet, En-suite, Closet, En-suite, Bed 4, Gallery, Bed 3

(Floor plan labels, ground floor:) Conservatory, Breakfast, Garage, Office, dn to Den, Family, Kitchen, WC, Utility, Library, dn to Basement, Hall, Boot, Covered Walkway, Lights Tunnel By Day path by Night, Drawing Room, Dining Room, Seat, Lobby, Seat

(Floor plan labels, basement:) Passage to Garage, Den, Boiler, Un Allocated, Gym

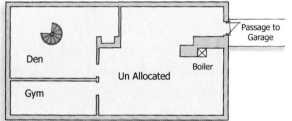

Traditional style

Floor area
350m²
3767ft²

Bedrooms
4

Bathrooms
3

Floors
3

Key features
Basement rooms
Kitchen/breakfast room
Library
Conservatory
Master bedroom suite

Garaging for
3 cars

Design
Jeremy Rawlings

www.periodhome.net
01884 266444

Build cost
£312,000

Design © Jeremy Rawlings

Traditional style

Floor area

352m²

3789ft²

Bedrooms

4

Bathrooms

2

Floors

2

Key features
Separate dining room
Reading room
Study
Utility room
Master bed en-suite

Garaging for
0 cars

Design
Chaddock Design

www.dreamspelldesign.co.uk
info@dreamspelldesign.co.uk
01789 459148

Build cost
£316,000

Plan no. **BHP 310047**

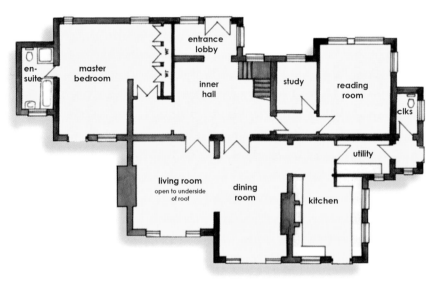

Through the large hall there's a master suite and an open-plan living and dining room. Upstairs the galleried landing overlooks the hall and downstairs living room before leading onto three bedrooms, the upstairs living room and a family bathroom.

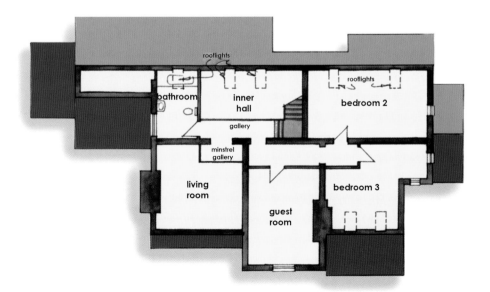

Plan no. **BHP 310170**

The half-timbered Tudor look outside leads into a modern home inside with luxury touches like an en-suite turret attached to the master bedroom, twin staircases, a big conservatory and a library.

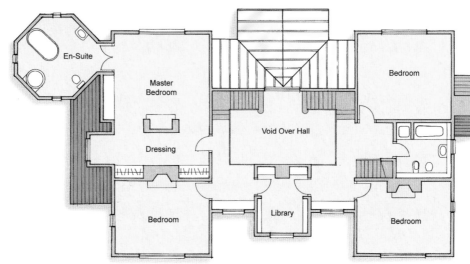

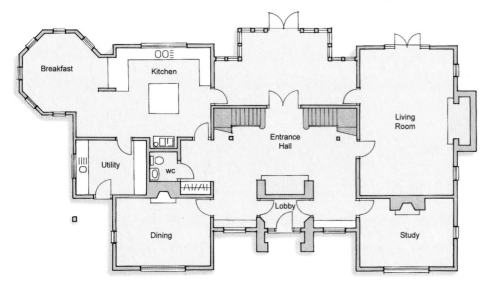

Contemporary style

Floor area
370m²
3983ft²

Bedrooms
4

Bathrooms
3

Floors
3

Key features
Family room
Breakfast room
Separate dining room
Library
Master bedroom suite

Garaging for
2 cars

Design
Chaddock Design

www.dreamspelldesign.co.uk
info@dreamspelldesign.co.uk
01789 459148

Build cost
£332,000

Design © Chaddock Design

Plan no. **BHP 310728**

The basement of this design includes a music room, gym and office together with a plant room freeing space in the rest of the house. Upstairs, beyond the galleried landing all the bedrooms are en-suite. The master includes a walk-in wardrobe and gallery overlooking the full height windows of the breakfast room.

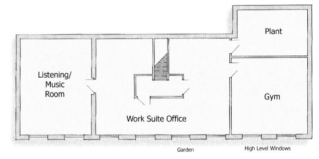

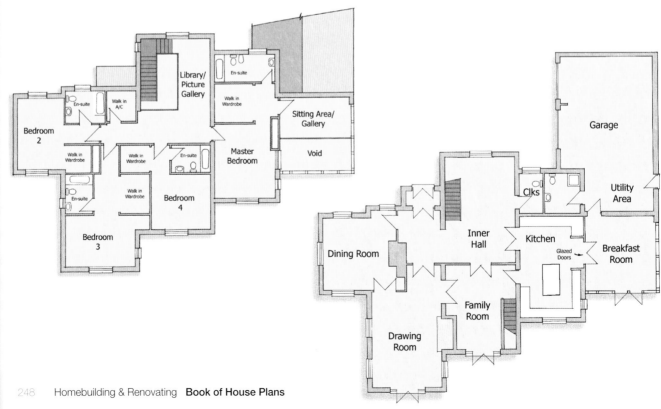

Plan no. **BHP 310827**

The galleried hall has a feature staircase leading to a fully galleried landing. There is also a large kitchen/family room, dining room and Lounge. Upstairs the four bedrooms all have their own en-suite bathrooms. There is also a laundry cupboard with a chute to the utility room below. .

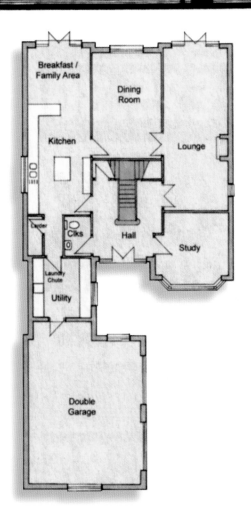

Breakfast / Family Area
Dining Room
Kitchen
Lounge
Larder
Clks
Hall
Study
Laundry Chute
Utility
Double Garage

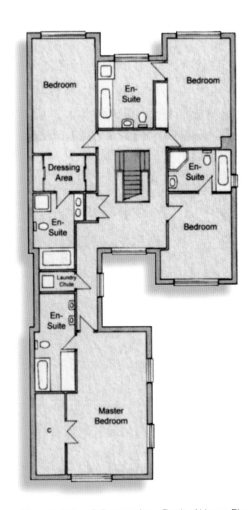

Bedroom
En-Suite
Bedroom
Dressing Area
En-Suite
Bedroom
En-Suite
Laundry Chute
En-Suite
Master Bedroom
c

Traditional style

Floor area
379m²
4080ft²

Bedrooms
4

Bathrooms
4

Floors
2

Key features
Kitchen/breakfast room
Separate dining room
Study
Utility room
All bedrooms en-suite

Garaging for
2 cars

Design
Custom Homes

www.customhomes.co.uk
admin@customhomes.co.uk
01787 377388

Build cost
£340,000

Design
© Custom Homes

Traditional style

Floor area
379m²
4080ft²

Bedrooms
4

Bathrooms
5

Floors
2

Key features
Kitchen/breakfast room
Reading room
Utility room
4 en-suite bedrooms

Garaging for
0 cars

Design
Jeremy Rawlings

www.periodhome.net
01884 266444

Build cost
£340,000

Plan no. **BHP 310467**

A central feature of this design is a double-height living room that sits centrally in the house. The kitchen/breakfast and dining rooms open onto this through double doors. Upstairs, the three bedrooms are all en-suite. The design also allows for the double-height area of the lounge to be floored over to become a fifth bedroom.

Plan no. **BHP 310122**

All the bedrooms are on the ground floor accessed off a wide hallway which means that the first floor reception rooms get access to the two large balconies and the best views in the house.

Contemporary style

Floor area
382m²
4112ft²

Bedrooms
4

Bathrooms
3

Floors
2

Key features
Kitchen/breakfast room
Family room
Study
Separate dining room
2 en-suite beds

Garaging for
0cars

Design
**John Braid
(at Leslie R Hutt)**

lhuttarchitect@btinternet.com
01463 235566

Build cost
£342,500

Contemporary style

Floor area
407m²
4381ft²

Bedrooms
4

Bathrooms
4

Floors
2

Key features
Full-height dining room
Kitchen/breakfast room
Sun room
Family room
All bedrooms en-suite

Garaging for
0 cars

Design
John Braid
(at Leslie R Hutt)

lhuttarchitect@btinternet.com
01463 235566

Build cost
£365,000

Design © Leslie R Hutt

Plan no. **BHP 310143**

Behind the ultra-contemporary look there's a pretty conventional, and ultimately flexible, layout. Features include a double-height dining room and hallway along with an large family room, kitchen and dining room.

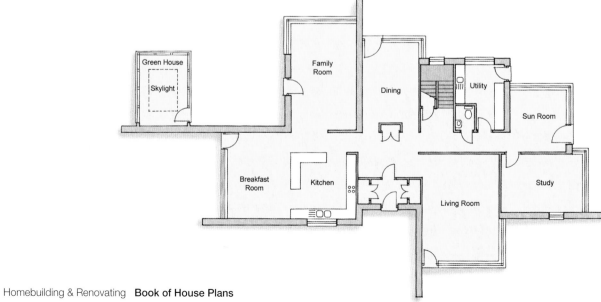

Plan no. **BHP 310509**

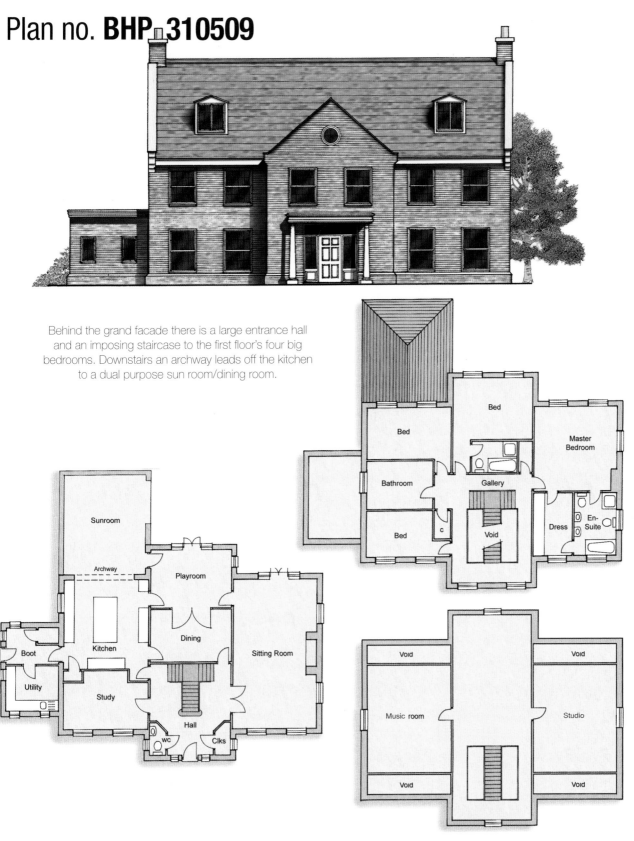

Behind the grand facade there is a large entrance hall and an imposing staircase to the first floor's four big bedrooms. Downstairs an archway leads off the kitchen to a dual purpose sun room/dining room.

Sunroom

Archway

Playroom

Kitchen

Boot

Utility

Study

Dining

Sitting Room

Hall

WC

Clks

Bed

Bed

Bathroom

Bed

c

Gallery

Void

Master Bedroom

Dress

En-Suite

Void

Void

Music room

Studio

Void

Void

Traditional style

Floor area
467m²
5027ft²

Bedrooms
4

Bathrooms
2

Floors
3

Key features
Full-height hall
Study
Playroom
Sunroom
Master bedroom suite

Garaging for
0 cars

Design
Custom Homes

www.customhomes.co.uk
admin@customhomes.co.uk
01787 377388

Build cost
£419,000

Traditional style

Floor area

480m²

5167ft²

Bedrooms

4

Bathrooms

3

Floors

2

Key features
Kitchen/breakfast room
Separate dining room
Family room
Sun room
Master bedroom suite

Garaging for

0 cars

Design

Potton

www.potton.co.uk
contact@potton.co.uk
01767 676 400

Build cost
£430,500

Design © Potton

Plan no. **BHP 310410**

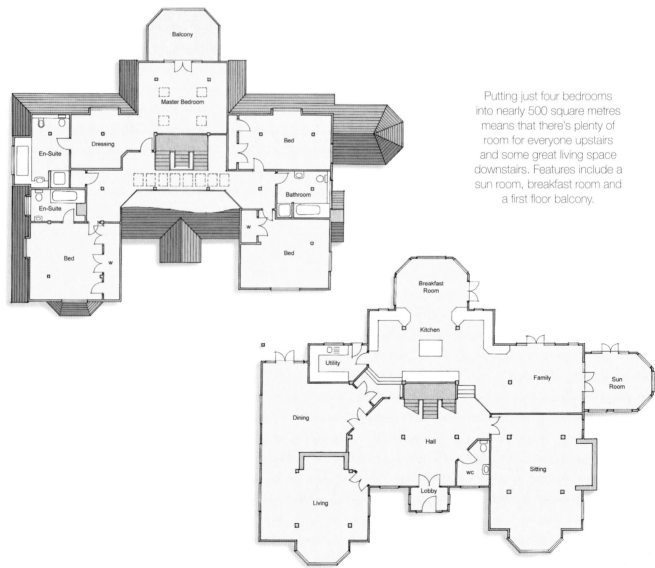

Putting just four bedrooms into nearly 500 square metres means that there's plenty of room for everyone upstairs and some great living space downstairs. Features include a sun room, breakfast room and a first floor balcony.

Plan no. **BHP 310179**

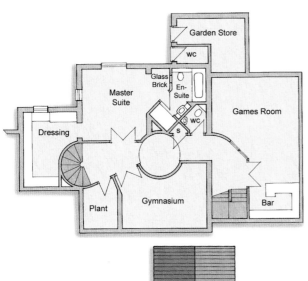

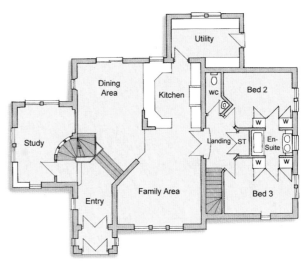

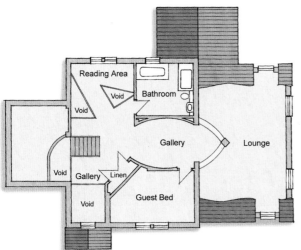

Building down as well as up gives this home some distinct space advantages over standard designs. You get room for plenty of family and guest bedrooms, lots of living space and a master suite, gym and games room below stairs.

Traditional style

Floor area

557m²

5995ft²

Bedrooms

4

Bathrooms

3

Floors

3

Key features
Gymnasium
Family area
Games room
Dressing room
Reading area

Garaging for

0 cars

Design
John Watson

Build cost
£500,000

Design © John Watson

Contemporary style

Floor area
558m²
6006ft²

Bedrooms
4

Bathrooms
3

Floors
4

Key features
Basement pool area
Kitchen/family room
Master bedroom suite
Conservatory
Roof deck

Garaging for
0 cars

Design
Angel Design and
Development

Build cost
£500,500

Plan no. **BHP 310257**

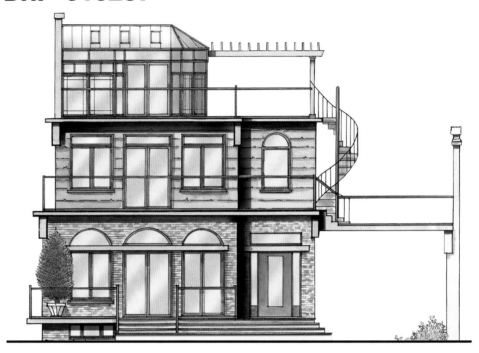

From the conservatory on the roof to the basement-level swimming pool, every floor in this townhouse is packed with exciting features. The expansive ground floor has a free-flowing family space arranged in unconventional shapes. The first floor features two double bedrooms, a study and a master suite with its own external staircase to the roof terrace.

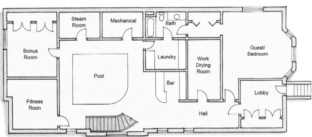

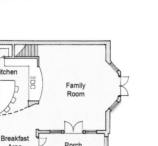

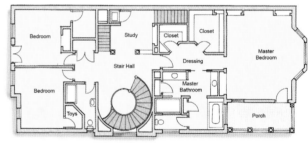

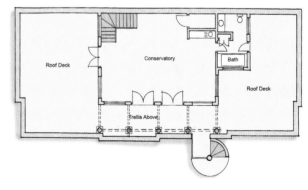

Plan no. **BHP 310011**

A basement leisure suite adds an exciting below-stairs twist to this house – complete with games room and swimming pool. A balcony links the rear-facing reception rooms – including the dining hall.

Traditional style

Floor area
619m²
6663ft²

Bedrooms
4

Bathrooms
2

Floors
3

Key features
Pool/games room
Dining hall
Study
Office
Master en-suite

Garaging for
2 cars

Design
**TJ Crump
Oakwrights**

www.oakwrights.co.uk
enquiries@oakwrights.co.uk
01432 353353

Build cost
£555,000

Design © TJ Crump

Contemporary style

Floor area
140m²
1507ft²

Bedrooms
5

Bathrooms
4

Floors
5

Key features
Kitchen/dining room
Family area
Balcony
Family room
En-suite master bed

Garaging for
0 cars

Design
Planahome

www.planahome.uk.com
plans@planahome.uk.com
01326 373600

Build cost
£129,000

Design © Planahome

Plan no. **BHP 310389**

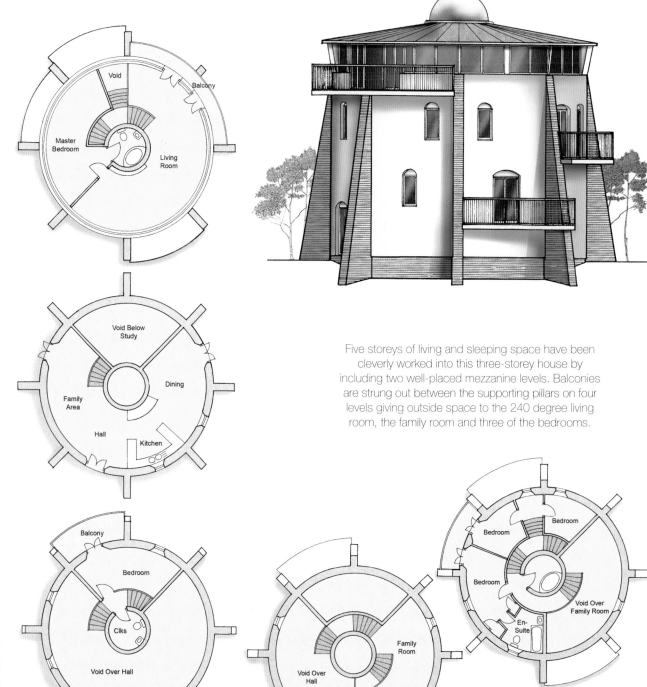

Five storeys of living and sleeping space have been cleverly worked into this three-storey house by including two well-placed mezzanine levels. Balconies are strung out between the supporting pillars on four levels giving outside space to the 240 degree living room, the family room and three of the bedrooms.

Plan no. **BHP 310869**

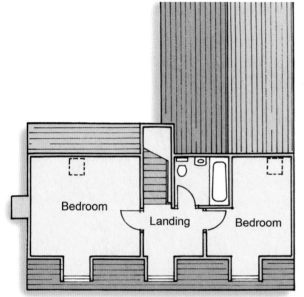

By spreading the rooms across three floors this town house design manages to fit five bedrooms and three bathrooms into a very modest footprint.

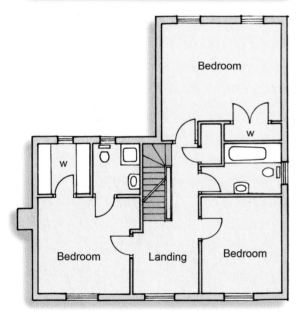

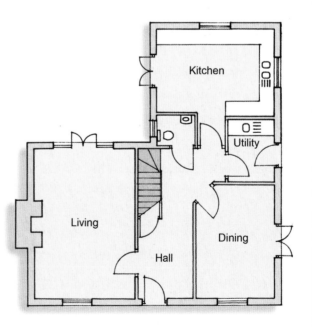

Traditional style

Floor area
152m²
1636ft²

Bedrooms
5

Bathrooms
3

Floors
3

Key features
Utility room
Master bedroom suite

Garaging for
0 cars

Design
Potton

www.potton.co.uk
contact@potton.co.uk 01767
676 400

Build cost
£140,000

Design © Potton

Traditional style

Floor area
174m²
1873ft²

Bedrooms
5

Bathrooms
3

Floors
2

Key features
Kitchen/family room
Separate dining room
Utility room
2 en-suite bedrooms

Garaging for
2 cars

Design
**The Bespoke
Design Company**

www.planahome.uk.com
plans@planahome.uk.com
01326 373600

Build cost
£160,000

Design © The Bespoke
Design Company

Plan no. **BHP 310092**

All the ground floor rooms in this design flow naturally into each other.
Upstairs the layout provides up to five bedrooms and there are walk in
wardrobes and en-suite bathrooms to two of these.

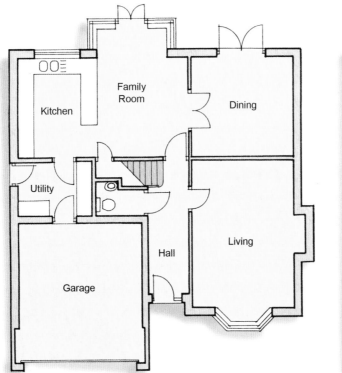

Plan no. **BHP 310536**

Traditional style

Floor area
203m²
2185ft²

Bedrooms
5

Bathrooms
3

Floors
2

Key features
Kitchen/breakfast room
Family room
Utility room
2 en-suite bedrooms

Garaging for
2 cars

Design
The Bespoke
Design Company

www.planahome.uk.com
plans@planahome.uk.com
01326 373600

Build cost
£187,000

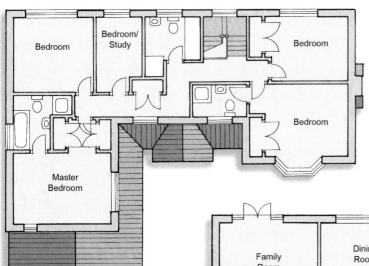

Bedroom

Bedroom/Study

Bedroom

Bedroom

Master Bedroom

The layout of reception rooms makes the most of this L-shaped design. Highlights include an interconnected family room, kitchen and breakfast room, utility room and upstairs twin en-suites.

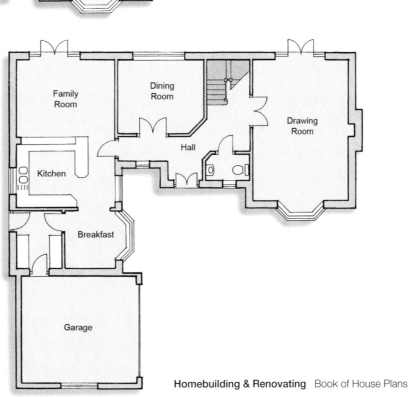

Family Room

Dining Room

Drawing Room

Kitchen

Hall

Breakfast

Garage

Traditional style

Floor area

207m²

2228ft²

Bedrooms

5

Bathrooms

3

Floors

2

Key features
Kitchen/dining room
Utility room
Study
Galleried landing
Master bedroom suite

Garaging for

2 cars

Design
Custom Homes

www.customhomes.co.uk
admin@customhomes.co.uk
01787 377388

Build cost
£190,500

Design © Custom Homes

Plan no. **BHP 310176**

Building above the garage creates a large master bedroom suite complete with dressing room. At the other end of the house is a guest room complete with en-suite.

Plan no. **BHP 310158**

The bay windows add extra space to the kitchen and family room and this design even manages to squeeze in a boot room. Upstairs the two main bedrooms get their own en-suite bathrooms.

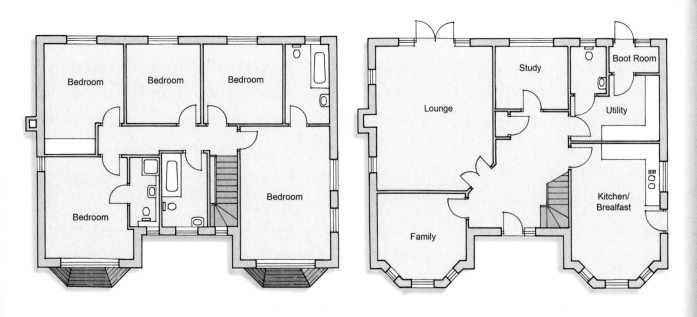

Bedroom
Bedroom
Bedroom
Bedroom
Bedroom

Study
Boot Room
Lounge
Utility
Family
Kitchen/ Breakfast

Traditional style

Floor area
208m²
2239ft²

Bedrooms
5

Bathrooms
3

Floors
2

Key features
Kitchen/breakfast room
Utility room
Study
Family room
2 en-suite bedrooms

Garaging for
0 cars

Design
Custom Homes

www.customhomes.co.uk
admin@customhomes.co.uk
01787 377388

Build cost
£191,000

Design © Custom Homes

Traditional style

Floor area

210m²

2260ft²

Bedrooms

5

Bathrooms

3

Floors

2

Key features
Kitchen/family room
Utility room
Separate dining room
Family room
Master bedroom suite

Garaging for

0 cars

Design

Planahome

www.planahome.uk.com
plans@planahome.uk.com
01326 373600

Build cost
£193,000

Design © Planahome

Plan no. **BHP 310392**

Half hips on the main roof and a bay and an oriel window add interest to the exterior. While inside there are separate dining and utility rooms. Upstairs there is a master bedroom suite with built-in dressing room, bathroom and sitting room.

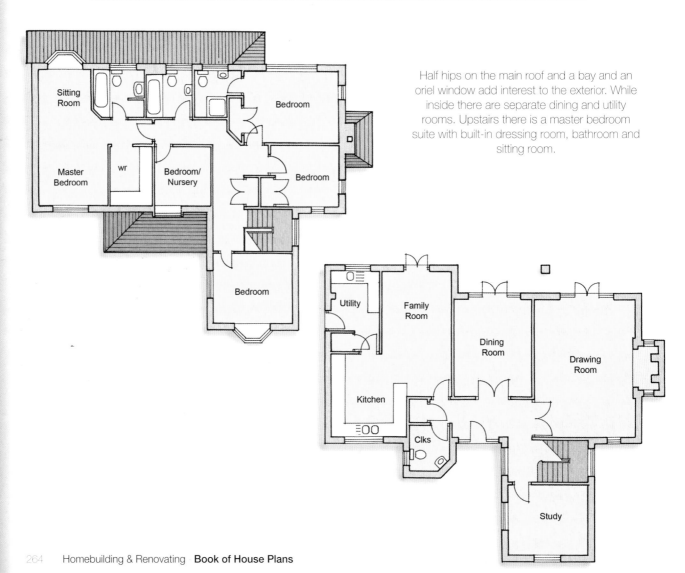

Plan no. **BHP 310428**

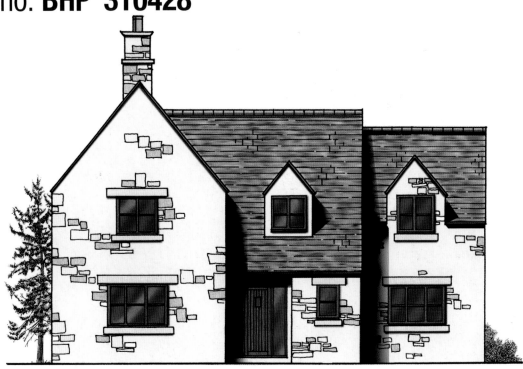

A feature fireplace divides the living room from the dining areas and conservatory beyond. Downstairs there is one bedroom with an en-suite shower room and upstairs there is a twin-aspect master bedroom with its own en-suite bathroom and three further bedrooms and a family bathroom.

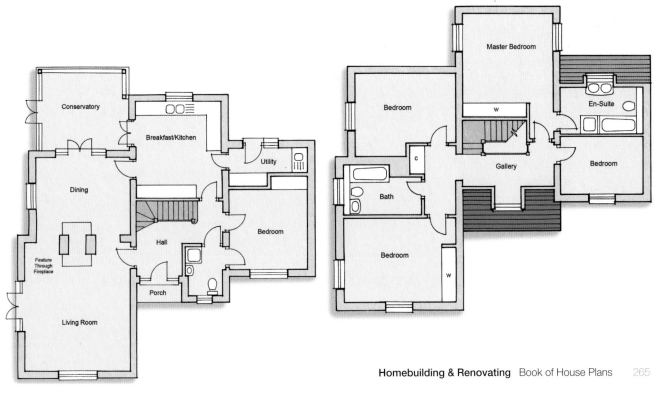

Traditional style

Floor area
213m²
2293ft²

Bedrooms
5

Bathrooms
3

Floors
2

Key features
Kitchen/breakfast room
Living/dining room
Conservatory
En-suite master bed

Garaging for
0 cars

Design
Design & Materials

www.designandmaterials.uk.com
enquiries@designandmaterials.uk.com
01909 540 123

Build cost
£196,000

Design © Design & Materials

Floor area

214m²

2303ft²

Bedrooms

5

Bathrooms

3

Floors

2

Key features
Kitchen/breakfast room
Separate dining room
Study
Utility room
Master bedroom suite

Garaging for

2 cars

Design
Stephen Mattick

www.mattick.co.uk
mattick@mattick.co.uk
01223 891159

Build cost
£197,000

Design © Stephen Mattick

Plan no. **BHP 310695**

This farmhouse combines traditional touches like the inglenook fireplace in the dining room with more modern ideas including the link-detached garage and a utility room. The link provides space for an extra bedroom and bathroom on the first floor.

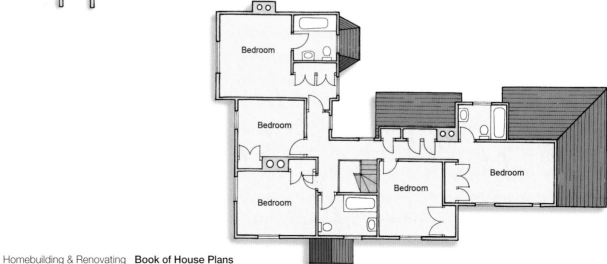

Plan no. **BHP 310422**

While this house looks fairly standard from the outside and has a conventional ground floor layout it does have the benefit of all bedrooms being en-suite.

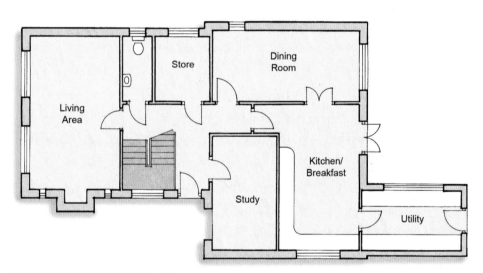

Living Area

Store

Dining Room

Study

Kitchen/ Breakfast

Utility

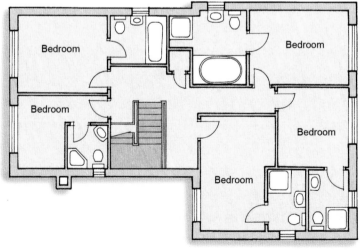

Bedroom

Bedroom

Bedroom

Bedroom

Bedroom

Traditional style

Floor area
215m²
2314ft²

Bedrooms
5

Bathrooms
5

Floors
2

Key features
Kitchen/breakfast room
Separate dining room
Study
Utility room
All bedrooms en-suite

Garaging for
0 cars

Design
Custom Homes

www.customhomes.co.uk
admin@customhomes.co.uk
01787 377388

Build cost
£198,000

Traditional style

Floor area
223m²
2400ft²

Bedrooms
5

Bathrooms
4

Floors
3

Key features
Kitchen/breakfast room
Dining room
Study
Games room
Master en-suite

Garaging for
2 cars

Design
Potton

www.potton.co.uk
contact@potton.co.uk
01767 676 400

Build cost
£200,000

Design © Potton

Plan no. **BHP 310182**

Building on three levels makes great use of a plot and creates space
for two floors of bedrooms and a separate L-shaped games room. The
ground floor has a full-depth living room and a dining space both with
access to the garden.

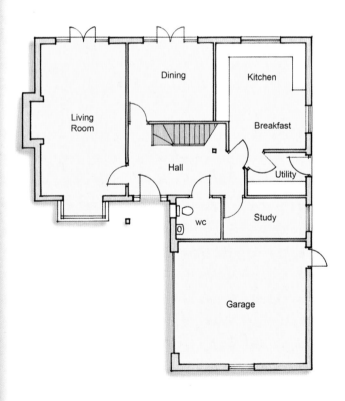

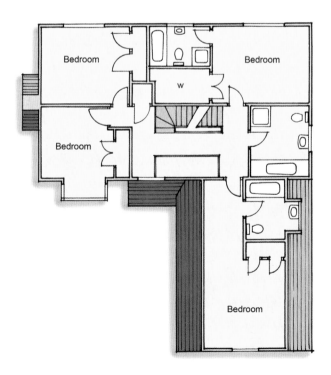

Plan no. **BHP 310719**

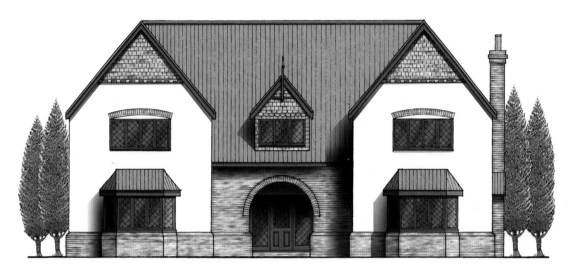

The three bay windows maximise space and light in the reception rooms and bedroom 4. Both the guest suite and master bedroom have en-suite facilities and the latter has use of the rear balcony.

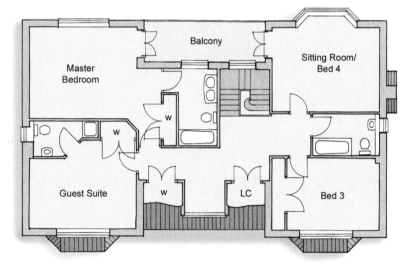

Balcony

Master Bedroom

Sitting Room/ Bed 4

w

w

Guest Suite

w

LC

Bed 3

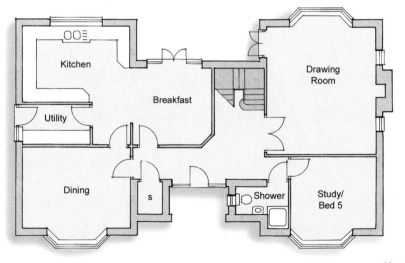

Kitchen

Drawing Room

Breakfast

Utility

Dining

s

Shower

Study/ Bed 5

Traditional style

Floor area
235m²
2530ft²

Bedrooms
5

Bathrooms
4

Floors
2

Key features
Kitchen/breakfast room
Utility room
Separate dining room
Master bed en-suite
Balcony

Garaging for
0 cars

Design
Planahome

www.planahome.uk.com
plans@planahome.uk.com
01326 373600

Build cost
£211,000

Design © Planahome

Traditional style

Floor area

240m²

2583ft²

Bedrooms

5

Bathrooms

4

Floors

2

Key features
Kitchen/family room
Dining hall
Study
Balcony
Master dressing area

Garaging for

0 cars

Design
Design & Materials

www.designandmaterials.uk.com
enquiries@designandmaterials.
uk.com
01909 540 123

Build cost
£215,000

Design © Design &
Materials

Plan no. **BHP 310947**

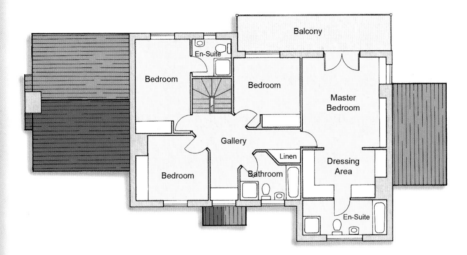

Designed to suit modern living
the kitchen, breakfast area and
family room flow together to form
a living space. Outside there's
a verandah that runs along
the whole back of the house.
Upstairs the master bedroom
suite includes a dressing area,
en-suite bathroom and a balcony.

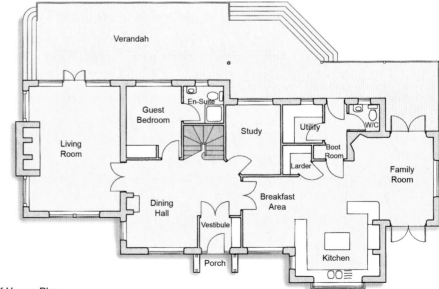

Plan no. **BHP 310962**

For its volume this house is reasonably narrow and with few side windows it would sit well on an average building plot. Yet it still offers five bedrooms, three bathrooms a family room, utility room and study.

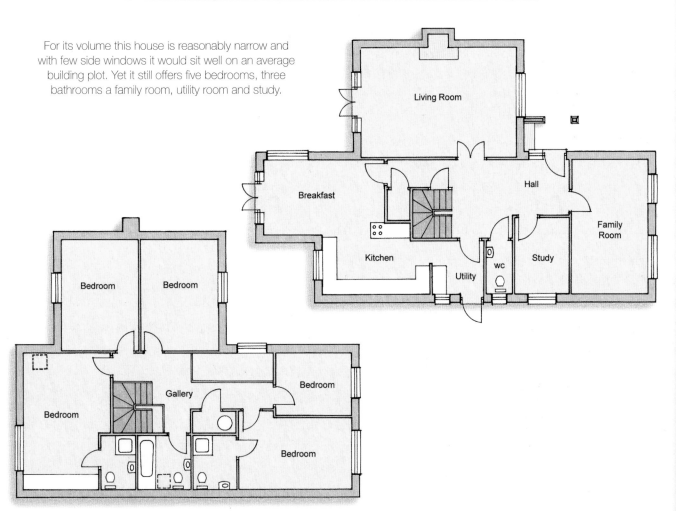

Living Room

Breakfast

Hall

Kitchen

Family Room

Study

WC

Utility

Bedroom

Bedroom

Bedroom

Gallery

Bedroom

Bedroom

Traditional style

Floor area
241m²
2594ft²

Bedrooms
5

Bathrooms
3

Floors
2

Key features
Kitchen/breakfast room
Family room
Study
2 bedrooms en-suite

Garaging for
0 cars

Design
Custom Homes

www.customhomes.co.uk
admin@customhomes.co.uk
01787 377388

Build cost
£216,000

Design © Custom Homes

Traditional style

Floor area

255m²

2745ft²

Bedrooms

5

Bathrooms

3

Floors

3

Key features
Kitchen/breakfast room
Separate dining room
Sun room
Music room
Master en-suite

Garaging for

0 cars

Design
Churchill Design

www.churchilldesign.co.uk
info@churchilldesign.co.uk
01252 325701

Build cost
£229,000

Design © Churchill Design

Plan no. **BHP 310227**

Dormer windows on each elevation of this design help light the second floor. Below there are another three bedrooms and an L-shaped master suite. On the ground floor there is a sun lounge, a twin-aspect dining room and a combined kitchen and breakfast room.

Kitchen/Breakfast

Utility

Study

wc

Hall

Clks

Sitting

Dining

Sun Room

Lobby

Music Room

Bedroom

Shower Room

Dressing

En-Suite

Master Bedroom

Gallery

Bedroom

Bedroom

Bath

Bedroom

Plan no. **BHP 310983**

From the sunroom on the first floor the galleried landing leads on to four bedrooms and a self-contained guest suite. Downstairs there is an L-shaped family and dining room and two further reception rooms.

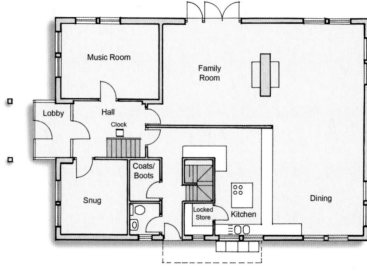

Music Room

Family Room

Lobby

Hall

Clock

Coats/ Boots

Snug

Locked Store

Kitchen

Dining

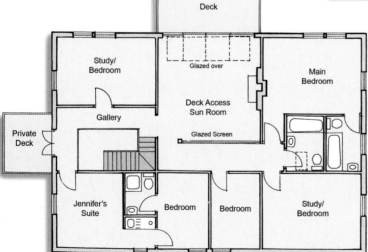

Deck

Study/ Bedroom

Glazed over

Main Bedroom

Deck Access Sun Room

Gallery

Glazed Screen

Private Deck

Jennifer's Suite

Bedroom

Bedroom

Study/ Bedroom

Contemporary style

Floor area
262m²
2820ft²

Bedrooms
5

Bathrooms
3

Floors
2

Key features
Open-plan living
Music room
Snug
Sun room
Self-contained suite

Garaging for
0 cars

Design
**John Shida
(Morningtide
Developments)**
www.morningtide.fsnet.co.uk
johnshida@morningtide.fsnet.
co.uk
01621 815485

Build cost
£235,000

Design © John Shida

Traditional style

Floor area

263m²

2831ft²

Bedrooms

5

Bathrooms

2

Floors

2

Key features
Sitting room
Study
Separate dining room
Galleried landing
Master bed en-suite

Garaging for
2 cars

Design
Architecture Plus

www.architecture-plus.co.uk
01934 416416

Build cost
£236,000

Design © Architecture Plus

Plan no. **BHP 310278**

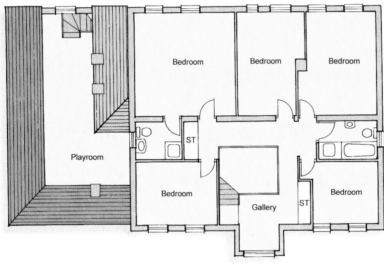

Hidden over the garage is a playroom that's accessed by a staircase leading up from the kitchen. There are three more reception rooms and a study on the ground floor. Upstairs, a galleried landing leads to the five bedrooms and two bathrooms.

Plan no. **BHP 310077**

A very modern layout hides behind the leaded windows of this traditional design. The big kitchen is flooded with natural light from the glazed lantern in the ceiling and the French windows that open out onto an enclosed patio. The lounge also features French doors to the patio. Upstairs there are five good-sized bedrooms off a galleried landing.

Traditional style

Floor area
270m²
2906ft²

Bedrooms
5

Bathrooms
2

Floors
2

Key features
Kitchen/dining room
Utility room
Study
Separate dining room
En-suite master bed

Garaging for
0 cars

Design
JS Building Consultancy

www.ukbuildingconsultancy.
co.uk jsharples@ricsonline.org
0113 250 1303

Build cost
£242,000

Design © JS Building Consultancy

Traditional style

Floor area

272m²

2928ft²

Bedrooms

5

Bathrooms

3

Floors

2

Key features
Kitchen/family room
Study
Dining room
Utility room
2 beds en-suite

Garaging for
3 cars

Design
Custom Homes

www.customhomes.co.uk
admin@customhomes.co.uk
01787 377388

Build cost
£244,000

Design © Custom Homes

Plan no. **BHP 310413**

Rotating the garage through 45 degrees adds interest to the exterior. Inside, the house has a spacious family room and kitchen and a large hall and landing.

Plan no. **BHP 310452**

The hall of this house has added interest due to the angling of the dining room and living room walls. Upstairs the galleried landing is more conventionally-shaped – but still generously proportioned. To the back of the house is the kitchen and utility area with the master bedroom, en-suite and family bathroom above.

Bed 1

En-Suite

Bathroom

Bed 4

Bed 5

Landing

Bed 2

Bed 3

Kitchen

Breakfast

L

C

Utility

WC

Study

Hall

Living

Dining

c

Lobby

Traditional style

Floor area

279m²

3003ft²

Bedrooms

5

Bathrooms

3

Floors

2

Key features
Family room
2 beds en-suite

Garaging for
0 cars

Design
Border Oak

www.borderoak.com
sales@borderoak.com
01568 708752

Build cost
£250,000

Design © Border Oak

Plan no. **BHP 310779**

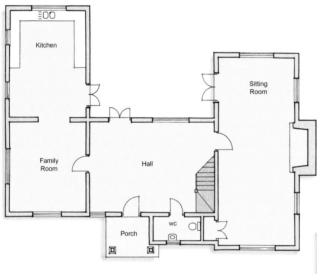

This house delivers size of rooms rather than quantity. There are just two receptions plus kitchen and hall. Upstairs as well as a galleried landing and five bedrooms their are two en-suites and a family bathroom.

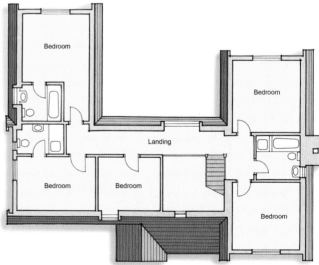

Plan no. **BHP 310131**

At first sight a reasonably standard modern house but on further inspection it is has many interesting touches: an oriel window for the front facing bedroom; a gablet and half-hip over both the dining room and drawing room wings to cover the square glazed bays.

Guest Suite

Master Bedroom

Terrace

Bedroom

Gallery

Sitting Room/ Bedroom

Bedroom

Triple Garage

Utility

Kitchen

S   L

Breakfast

ST

Study

Hall

Drawing Room

Porch

Dining

Traditional style

Floor area

284m²

3057ft²

Bedrooms

5

Bathrooms

3

Floors

3

Key features
Conservatory
Utility room
Separate dining room
Master bedroom suite

Garaging for
2 cars

Design
**JS Building
Consultancy**

www.ukbuildingconsultancy.
co.uk
jsharples@ricsonline.org
0113 250 1303

Build cost
£255,000

Design © JS Building
Consultancy

Plan no. **BHP 310665**

The double garage is tucked at the back of the house, behind the conservatory. Because the available space is divided between three floors there is only room for living room, dining room, kitchen and utility room on the ground floor. But the room over the garage could be sacrificed as a bedroom and used alternatively as a music room or study.

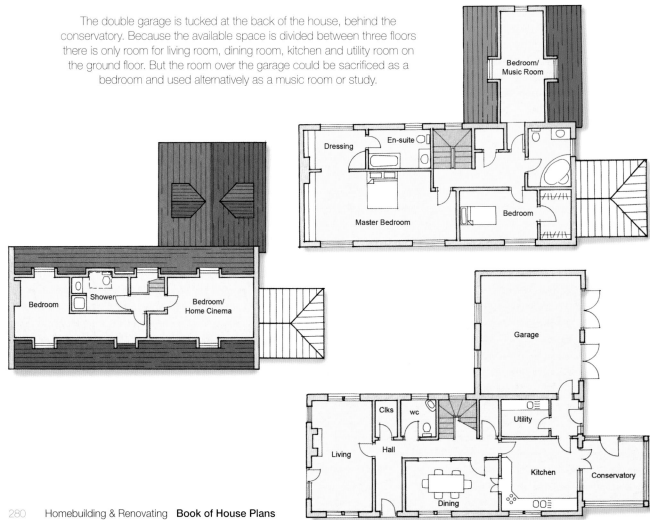

Plan no. **BHP 310722**

Traditional style

Floor area
290m²
3122ft²

Bedrooms
5

Bathrooms
4

Floors
3

Key features
Bedrooms with
vaulted ceilings

Garaging for
0 cars

Design
Design & Materials

www.designandmaterials.uk.com
enquiries@designandmaterials.
uk.com
01909 540 123

Build cost
£260,000

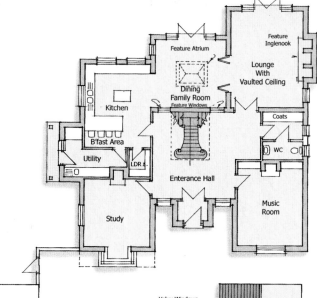

A feature staircase leads up from the large entrance hall to a galleried landing/upper sitting area. Linking the lounge and kitchen is an atrium which features a large square skylight. Upstairs there's space for four bedrooms on the first floor and a further bedroom, playroom or studio on the second floor.

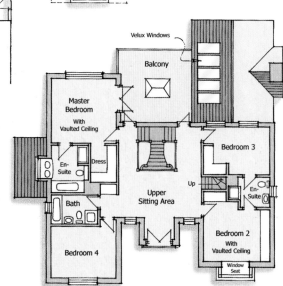

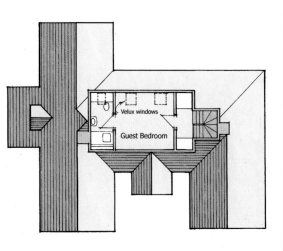

Contemporary style

Floor area
290m²
3122ft²

Bedrooms
5

Bathrooms
2

Floors
3

Key features
Kitchen/dining room
Utility room
Workshop
Study
Master bed en-suite

Garaging for
2 cars

Design
The Border Design Centre

www.borderdesign.co.uk
borderdesign@btconnect.com
01578 740218

Build cost
£259,000

Design © The Border
Design Centre

Plan no. **BHP 310734**

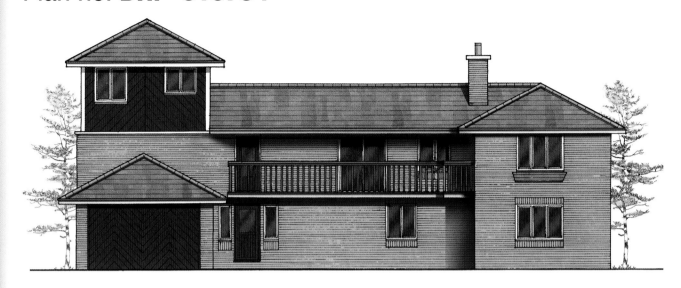

The study sits above the rest of the house on the second floor and in the right location could take advantage of views – as could the balcony which leads off the large first floor living room in this upside-down house. The master bedroom is also on the first floor with the remaining bedrooms and utility room located on the ground floor.

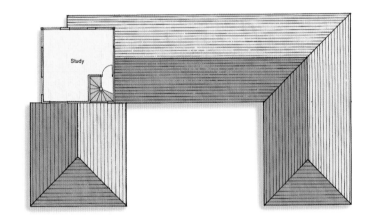

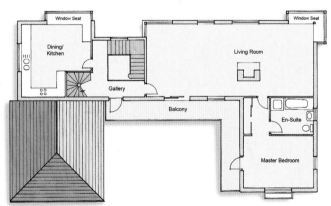

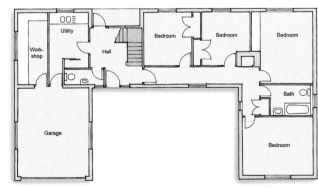

Plan no. **BHP 310902**

Large wooden barns are enduringly popular, but increasingly scarce. So, building your own is a realistic option – complete with the trademark double-height accommodation usually associated with big barn conversions. This one is no different with a double height lounge overlooked by a large gallery.

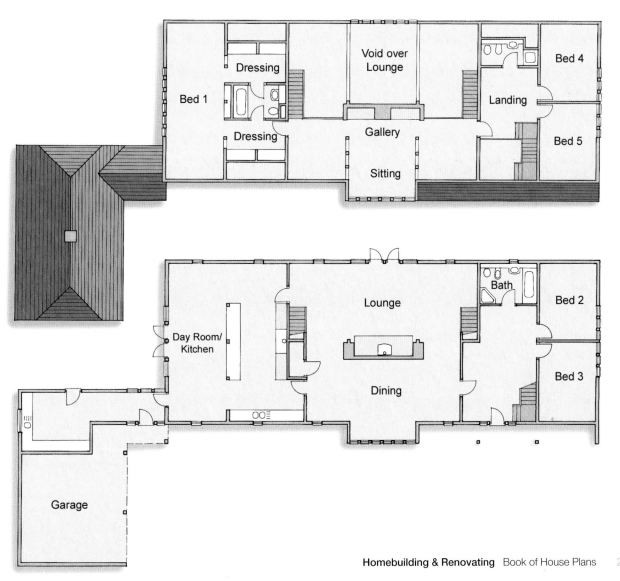

Barn style

Floor area
293m²
3154ft²

Bedrooms
5

Bathrooms
3

Floors
2

Key features
Kitchen/breakfast room
Lounge/dining room
Utility room
Galleried sitting room
Master bedroom suite

Garaging for
2 cars

Design
Welsh Oak Frame

www.welshoakframe.com
01686 688000

Build cost
£262,000

Design © Wesh Oak Frame

Traditional style

Floor area

295m²

3175ft²

Bedrooms

5

Bathrooms

4

Floors

3

Key features
Kitchen/family room
Vaulted sitting room
Snug
Study
Vaulted master bed suite

Garaging for
2 cars

Design
Planahome

www.planahome.uk.com
plans@planahome.uk.com
01326 373600

Build cost
£264,500

Design © Planahome

Plan no. **BHP 310050**

This home has a large inglenook fireplace in the hall and a sitting room with a vaulted ceiling. The first floor has three bedrooms including the master suite and on the second floor is a guest sitting gallery and two further bedrooms.

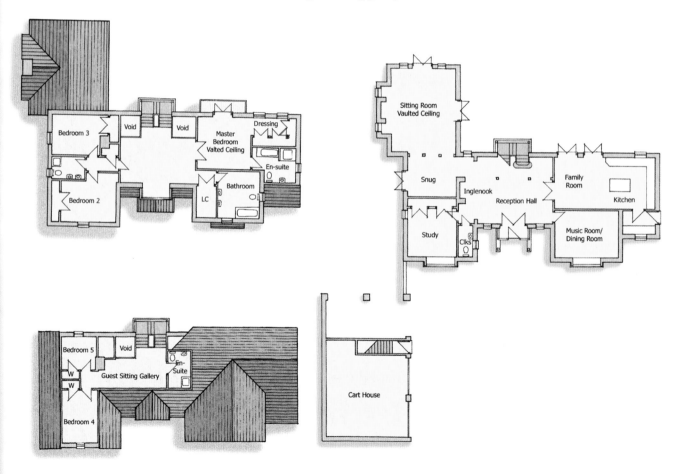

Plan no. **BHP 310953**

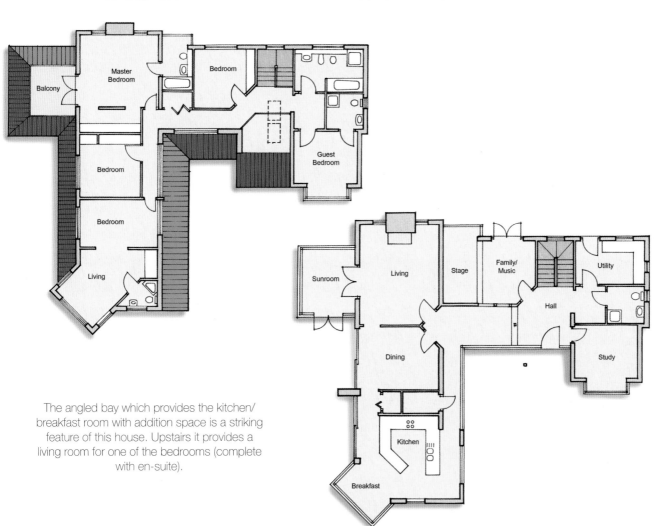

The angled bay which provides the kitchen/breakfast room with addition space is a striking feature of this house. Upstairs it provides a living room for one of the bedrooms (complete with en-suite).

Contemporary style

Floor area
296m²
3186ft²

Bedrooms
5

Bathrooms
4

Floors
2

Key features
Kitchen/breakfast room
Family room
Study
Sunroom
3 en-suite bedrooms

Garaging for
0 cars

Design
Fine Modern Homes (R.Robins)

www.finemodernhomes.co.uk
01225 777727

Build cost
£265,500

Design
© Fine Modern Homes

Traditional style

Floor area

300m²

3229ft²

Bedrooms

5

Bathrooms

3

Floors

4

Key features
Breakfast room
Dining room
Library
Basement
2 en-suite beds

Garaging for
2 cars

Design
**Ian Gow
(Sierra Designs)**

www.sierradesigns.co.uk
01977 621 360

Build cost
£269,000

Design © Sierra Designs

Plan no. **BHP 310524**

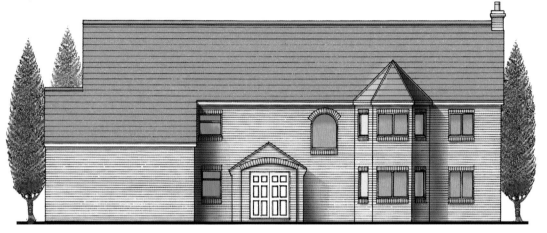

The large hall with angled staircase gives access to the kitchen, dining room, conservatory, lounge, library and study on the ground floor. Upstairs there are two bedrooms with en-suites and dressing rooms and three further bedrooms and a reading area off the large landing.

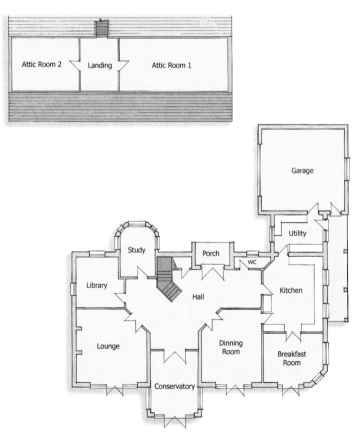

Plan no. **BHP 310296**

This is an ideal design for a building plot with views. On the first floor there is a twin-balconied lounge and there's also a balcony for the master bedroom and two further bedrooms. The remaining bedrooms, kitchen/dining room, study and music room are all on the ground floor.

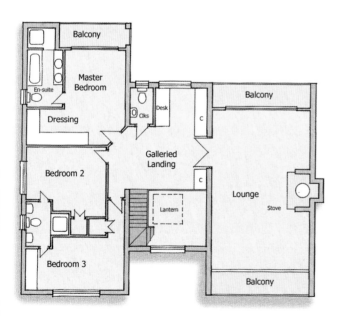

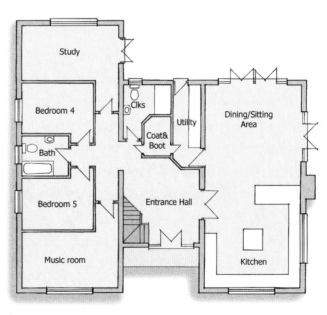

Traditional style

Floor area

300m²

3229ft²

Bedrooms

5

Bathrooms

3

Floors

2

Key features
Kitchen/dining room
Utilty room
Study
Music room
Master bedroom suite

Garaging for
0 cars

Design
Churchill Design

www.churchilldesign.co.uk
info@churchilldesign.co.uk
01252 325701

Build cost
£269,000

Design © Churchill Design

Traditional style

Floor area

300m²

3229ft²

Bedrooms

5

Bathrooms

3

Floors

2

Key features
Kitchen/breakfast room
Dining room
Family room
Study
2en-suite beds

Garaging for
2 cars

Design
Design & Materials

www.designandmaterials.uk.com
enquiries@designandmaterials.
uk.com
01909 540 123

Build cost
£269,000

Design © Design &
Materials

Plan no. **BHP 310332**

The angled garage block adds interest to this design and creates the opportunity to squeeze in a study next to the utility room. Downstairs are living room, dining room and conservatory and on the first floor there is an upper sitting room with its own balcony.

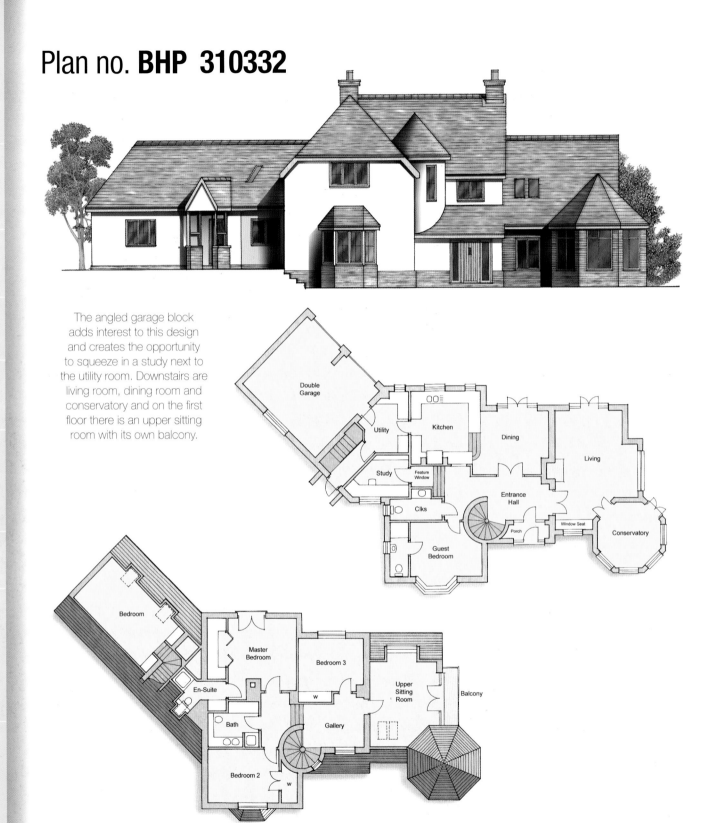

Plan no. **BHP 310206**

On the ground floor one wing of this H-shaped house contains the sitting room and the other the kitchen/ utility room. The two are linked by a large hall with its own fireplace. Upstairs, there's a galleried landing and five bedrooms, two of them en-suite. The family bathroom sits in the extension over the front porch.

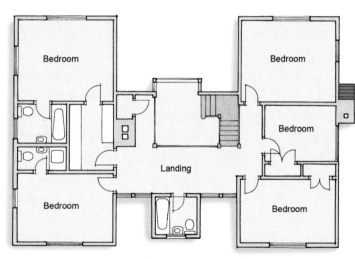

Bedroom

Bedroom

Bedroom

Bedroom

Landing

Bedroom

Bedroom

Sitting

Kitchen

Hall

Utility

Porch

Traditional style

Floor area
302m²
3251ft²

Bedrooms
5

Bathrooms
3

Floors
2

Key features
Kitchen/dining room
Utility room
Galleried landing
2 en-suite bedrrooms

Garaging for
0 cars

Design
Border Oak

www.borderoak.com
sales@borderoak.com
01568 708752

Build cost
£271,000

Design © Border Oak

Traditional style

Floor area

305m²

3283ft²

Bedrooms

5

Bathrooms

3

Floors

2

Key features
Open-plan living area
Living room
Utility room
Galleried landing
2 en-suite beds

Garaging for

0 cars

Design

Welsh Oak Frame

www.welshoakframe.com
01686 688000

Build cost

£273,500

Design © Welsh Oak Frame

Plan no. **BHP 310923**

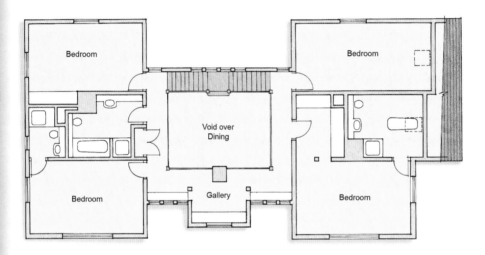

Open-plan living space stretched from the dining hall through to the kitchen and breakfast room. There's a big gallery, approached by a twin staircases, over the dining hall. On the ground floor there is also a large living room and the fifth bedroom.

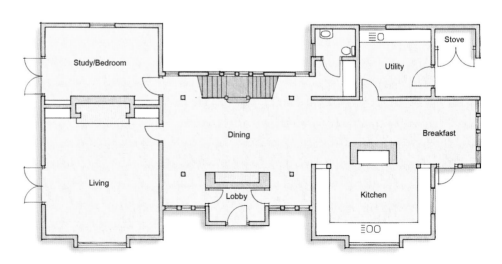

Plan no. **BHP 310140**

The two-storey conservatory gives a clue that behind the traditional exterior of this design hides a contemporary home with interesting curved walls. You enter the house through a sweeping hallway that leads into a full-depth lounge and two large reception rooms. From here you can go downstairs to the basement gym and an fifth bedroom. Head upwards and you can enjoy the comfort of the first floor lounge with its glazed gallery.

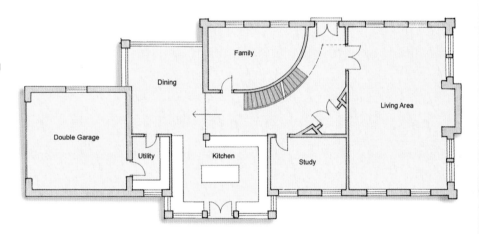

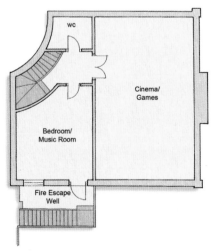

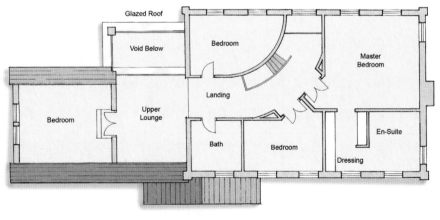

Traditional style

Floor area
310m²
3337ft²

Bedrooms
5

Bathrooms
2

Floors
3

Key features
Family room
Study
Utility room
Cinema/games room
Master bed en-suite

Garaging for
2 cars

Design
John Watson

Build cost
£278,000

Design © John Watson

Traditional style

Floor area

310m²

3337ft²

Bedrooms

5

Bathrooms

3

Floors

2

Key features
Kitchen/breakfast room
Utility room
Two studies
TV room
2 en-suite beds

Garaging for

0 cars

Design
Potton

www.potton.co.uk
contact@potton.co.uk
01767 676 400

Build cost
£278,000

Plan no. **BHP 310839**

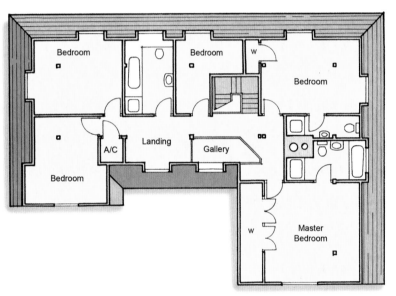

There's a large inglenook fireplace in the living room and space for another in the large TV room. There are also twin studies and a kitchen/dining room.

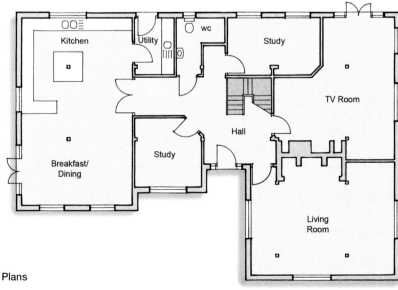

Plan no. **BHP 310926**

The conservatory can be accessed from both the family room and dining room and the three rooms together could be used as a large linked space. Upstairs there are five bedrooms – two of which are en-suite.

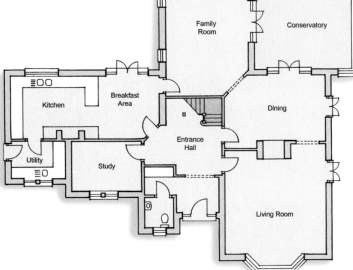

Traditional style

Floor area

317m²

3412ft²

Bedrooms

5

Bathrooms

3

Floors

2

Key features
Kitchen/breakfast room
Conservatory
Family room
Study
2 en-suite bedrooms

Garaging for

0 cars

Design
Design & Materials

www.designandmaterials.uk.com
enquiries@designandmaterials.
uk.com
01909 540 123

Build cost
£284,000

Contemporary style

Floor area

320m²

3444ft²

Bedrooms

5

Bathrooms

4

Floors

2

Key features
Kitchen/dining room
Studio
Spiral staircase
4 beds en-suite

Garaging for

0 cars

Design
John Shida
(Morningtide Developments)
www.morningtide.fsnet.co.uk
johnshida@morningtide.
fsnet.co.uk
01621 815485

Build cost
£287,000

Design © John Shida

Plan no. **BHP 310023**

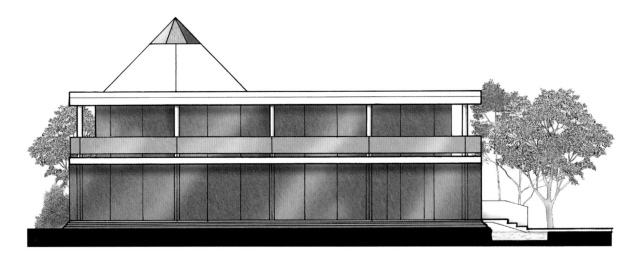

People who live in this glass house will certainly enjoy views and plenty of natural light. The emphasis is on uncluttered space - provided by the open-plan living area on the ground floor.

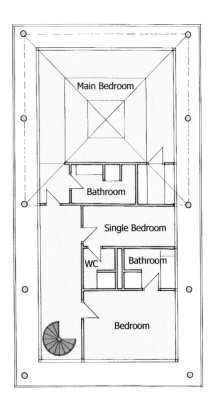

Main Bedroom

Bathroom

Single Bedroom

WC

Bathroom

Bedroom

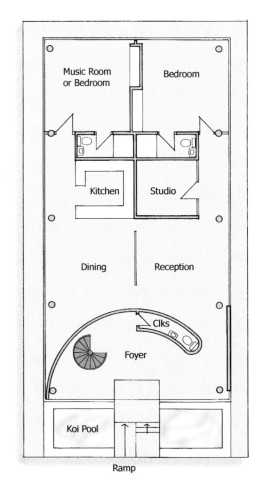

Music Room or Bedroom

Bedroom

Kitchen

Studio

Dining

Reception

Clks

Foyer

Koi Pool

Ramp

Plan no. **BHP 310689**

An upper lounge looks down into the living room below and also has access onto a balcony. There is a dining room between the living room and kitchen and a large family room/breakfast area.

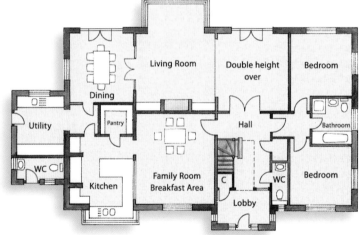

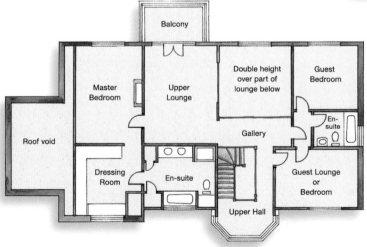

Floor area
321m²
3455ft²

Bedrooms
5

Bathrooms
3

Floors
2

Key features
Family room
Galleried lounge
Separate dining room
Utility room
Master bedroom suite

Garaging for
0 cars

Design
Opus Architecture and Design

01252 861759

Build cost
£288,000

Plan no. **BHP 310878**

The master bedroom is on the ground floor but with a guest suite, including a guest sitting room complete with a balcony, on the first floor it may be worth considering swapping these over. There is also a two storey lounge overlooked from the galleried landing.

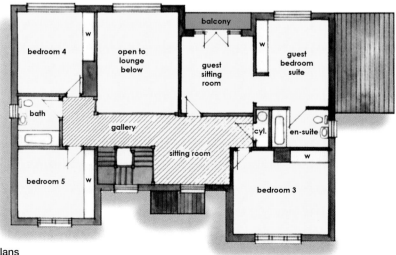

Plan no. **BHP 310308**

If you are looking for a period-style house the exterior detailing here is of a very high quality. Inside there are plenty of fireplaces and a back staircase from the family room to the galleried landing.

Family Room

Dining Room

Lobby

WC

WC

Utility

Kitchen

Hall

Sitting Room

Porch

Bedroom

Bedroom

SH

Bathroom

Bedroom

Bedroom

C

Gallery

Bedroom

SH

Dress Room

Bathroom

Bathroom

Bedroom

Study

Traditional style

Floor area
327m²
3520ft²

Bedrooms
5

Bathrooms
5

Floors
2

Key features
Kitchen/family room
Utility room
Dining room
Master bedroom suite
All bedrooms en-suite

**Garaging for
0 cars**

**Design
Border Oak**

www.borderoak.com
sales@borderoak.com
01568 708752

**Build cost
£293,000**

Design © Border Oak

Traditional style

Floor area
334m²
3595ft²

Bedrooms
5

Bathrooms
3

Floors
2

Exceptional features
Kitchen/breakfast room
Full height lounge
Study
Family room
Master bedrrom suite

Garaging for
2 cars

Design
Design & Materials

www.designandmaterials.uk.com
enquiries@designandmaterials.
uk.com
01909 540 123

Build cost
£299,500

Design © Design &
Materials

Plan no. **BHP 310629**

The single-storey living room has a vaulted ceiling and is overlooked from the galleried landing. The separate dining room is accessed directly from both the hall and kitchen/breakfast room. There is also a workshop behind the garage with direct access through to the utility room.

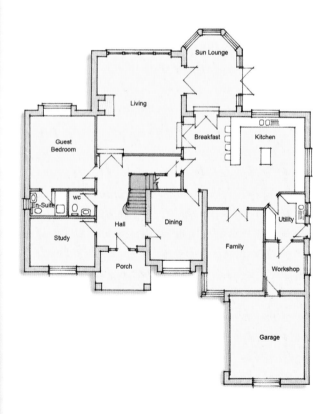

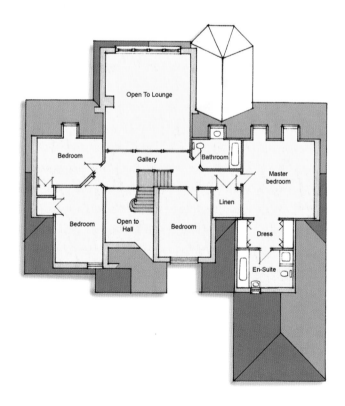

Plan no. **BHP 310890**

The ground floor includes an integral sun lounge and open-plan kitchen and breakfast area and up to four further reception rooms. Off the galleried landing on the first floor there are five bedrooms and stairs to a useful attic space.

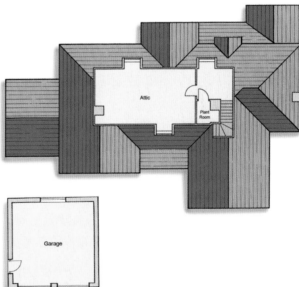

Traditional style

Floor area
335m²
3606ft²

Bedrooms
5

Bathrooms
5

Floors
3

Key features
Kitchen/breakfast room
Sun lounge
Family room
Separate dining room
All bedrooms en-suite

Garaging for
2 cars

Design
Design & Materials

www.designandmaterials.uk.com
enquiries@designandmaterials.uk.com
01909 540 123

Build cost
£300,000

Design © Design & Materials

Traditional style

Floor area

340m²

3660ft²

Bedrooms

5

Bathrooms

4

Floors

2

Key features
Grand entrance hall
Cinema
Kitchen/breakfast room
Conservatory
Gym

**Garaging for
4 cars**

**Design
Design & Materials**

www.designandmaterials.uk.com
enquiries@designandmaterials.
uk.com
01909 540 123

**Build cost
£305,000**

Design © Design &
Materials

Plan no. **BHP 310917**

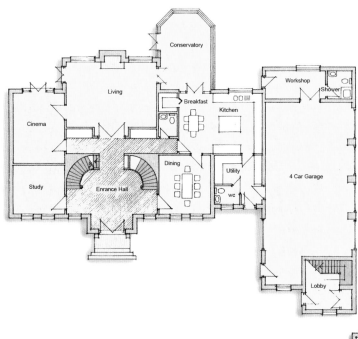

Twin sweeping staircases in a double-height entrance hall set the scene for this impressive house. Beyond the entrance hall through double doors is a big living room which offers access to the home cinema and large conservatory. The first floor rooms radiate out from galleried landing and include a master suite with balcony and space for a Jack and Jill gym. Over the garage is a self-contained annexe with its own entrance.

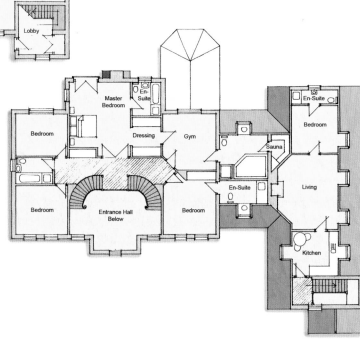

Plan no. **BHP 310008**

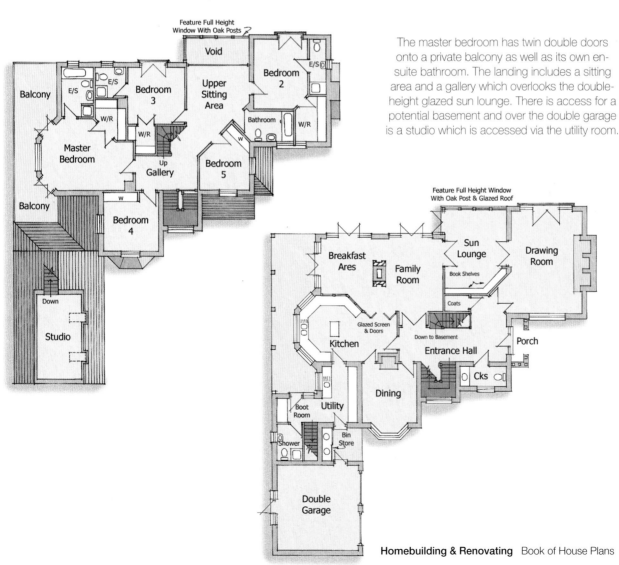

Feature Full Height
Window With Oak Posts

Void

Bedroom 3

E/S

E/S

Balcony

Upper Sitting Area

Bedroom 2

E/S

Bathroom

W/R

W/R

Master Bedroom

W/R

Up

Gallery

Bedroom 5

W

Balcony

W

Bedroom 4

Down

Studio

The master bedroom has twin double doors onto a private balcony as well as its own en-suite bathroom. The landing includes a sitting area and a gallery which overlooks the double-height glazed sun lounge. There is access for a potential basement and over the double garage is a studio which is accessed via the utility room.

Feature Full Height Window
With Oak Post & Glazed Roof

Breakfast Ares

Family Room

Sun Lounge

Drawing Room

Book Shelves

Coats

Glazed Screen & Doors

Kitchen

Down to Basement

Entrance Hall

Porch

Dining

Cks

Boot Room

Utility

Shower

Bin Store

Double Garage

Traditional style

Floor area
345m²
3714ft²

Bedrooms
5

Bathrooms
5

Floors
2

Key features
Kitchen/family room
Sun lounge
Studio
Separate dining room
3 bedrooms en-suite

Garaging for
2 cars

Design
Design & Materials

www.designandmaterials.uk.com
enquiries@designandmaterials.
uk.com
01909 540 123

Build cost
£309,500

Design © Design &
Materials

Contemporary style

Floor area

347m²

3735ft²

Bedrooms

5

Bathrooms

3

Floors

4

Key features
Basement gym
Study
Vaulted family room
Utility room
Vaulted master suite

Garaging for
2 cars

Design
Design & Materials

www.designandmaterials.uk.com
enquiries@designandmaterials.
uk.com
01909 540 123

Build cost
£311,000

Design © Deaign &
Materials

Plan no. **BHP 310701**

This design offers high levels of space on a relatively narrow footprint. But in spite of this it still offers plenty of features including vaulted ceilings in the family room, master bedroom and second bedroom. There is also an underground gym.

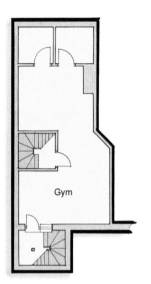

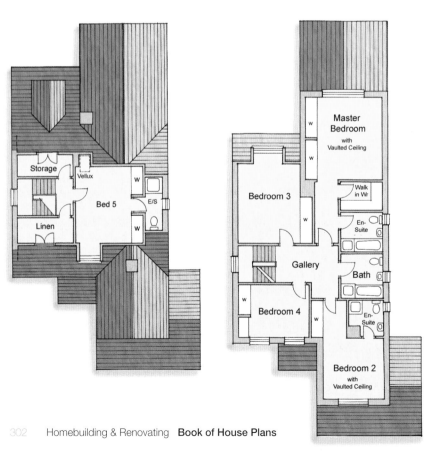

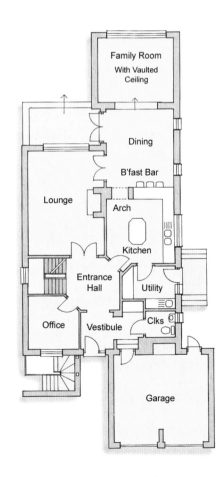

Plan no. **BHP 310290**

Traditional style

Floor area
344m²
3703ft²

Bedrooms
5

Bathrooms
3

Floors
2

Designed for family living
the snooker room, study
and sun lounge are all
accessed from the family
room while the dining room
is reached via the kitchen
or living room.

Balcony

Bathroom

Open to
Below

Bedroom 1

Sitting
Area

Master
Bedroom

En-
Suite

Bedroom 4

ST

Bedroom 2

Bedroom 3

En-
Suite

Living Room

Dining Room

Sun Lounge

Study

Utility

B'Fast
Area

Kitchen

Family
Room

Snooker
Room

Garage

Key features
Kitchen/breakfast room
Family room
Snooker room
Separate dining room
2 bedrrooms en-suite

Garaging for
2 cars

Design
John Braid
(at Leslie R Hutt)

lhuttarchitect@btinternet.com
01463 235566

Build cost
£308,500

Design © Leslie R Hutt

Traditional style

Floor area
363m²
3907ft²

Bedrooms
5

Bathrooms
4

Floors
2

Key features
Kitchen/breakfast room
Utility room
Guest/granny annexe
3 bedrooms en-suite

Garaging for
0 cars

Design
Swedish House Co

www.swedishhouses.com
0870 770 0760

Build cost
£325,500

Plan no. **BHP 310776**

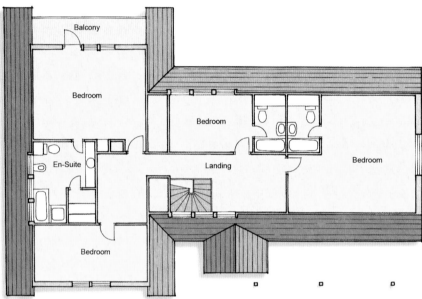

Big rooms offer plenty of space in this house which has its own ground floor guest suite that is separated by two doors in an 'air lock' arrangement. Upstairs, there is a balcony off the main bedroom which has its own spacious en-suite bathroom.

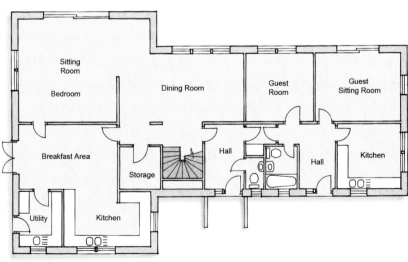

Plan no. **BHP 310527**

A classical exterior here hides an interior which offers the opportunity for open-plan living. The feature conservatory stretches almost the full width of the house. On the first floor, the master bedroom suite includes a balcony that overlooks the conservatory.

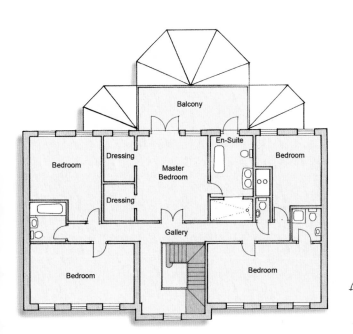

Bedroom · Dressing · Master Bedroom · Balcony · En-Suite · Bedroom · Dressing · Gallery · Bedroom · Bedroom

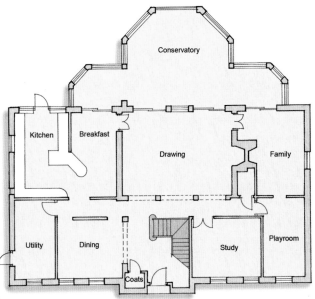

Kitchen · Breakfast · Conservatory · Drawing · Family · Utility · Dining · Coats · Study · Playroom

Traditional style

Floor area
364m²
3918ft²

Bedrooms
5

Bathrooms
3

Floors
2

Key features
Conservatory
Kitchen/breakfast room
Family room
Playroom
2 en-suite beds

Garaging for
0 cars

Design
Jeremy Rawlings

www.periodhome.net
01884 266444

Build cost
£326,500

Traditional style

Floor area

380m²

4090ft²

Bedrooms

5

Bathrooms

3

Floors

2

Key features
Separate dining room
Reading room
2 en-suite bedrooms

Garaging for
2 cars

Design
ICD Dzine

www.icd-dzine.com
01638 610117

Build cost
£341,000

Design © X

Plan no. **BHP 310500**

The formal layout in this design provides space for four large rooms and a full-width lounge on the ground floor. Upstairs four equal-sized bedrooms, one with en-suite, are accessed from a landing and a bridge that overlooks the lounge space.

Plan no. **BHP 310437**

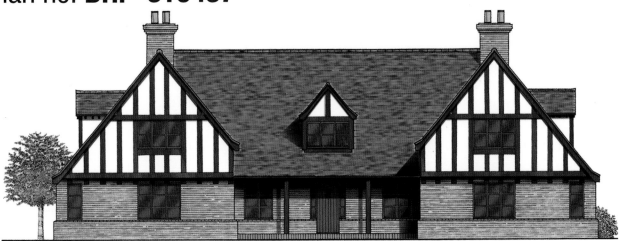

Through the entrance hall and straight down a small flight of stairs is the indoor pool. There's an inglenook fireplace in the family room and another open fire in the living room. Upstairs vaulted ceilings are key features in the front bedrooms while a large balcony leads off the two rear bedrooms.

Balcony

Bedroom

Bedroom

Bedroom

Gallery

Landing

Gallery

Bedroom
(Vaulted)

Bedroom
(Vaulted)

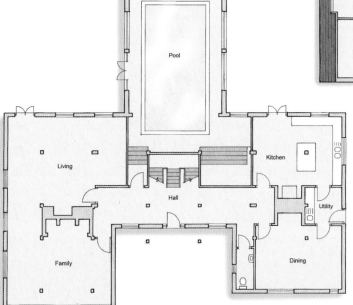

Pool

Living

Kitchen

Hall

Utility

Family

Dining

Traditional style

Floor area
383m²
4123ft²

Bedrooms
5

Bathrooms
3

Floors
2

Key features
Indoor swimming pool
Family room
Separate diniing room
Galleried landing
2 en-suite bedrooms

Garaging for
0 cars

Design
Potton

www.potton.co.uk
contact@potton.co.uk
01767 676 400

Build cost
£343,500

Design © Potton

Traditional style

Floor area

390m²

4198ft²

Bedrooms

6

Bathrooms

6

Floors

2

Key features
Kitchen/living room
Granny annexe
Bedsit over garage
2 en-suite beds

Garaging for
2 cars

Design
Design & Materials

www.designandmaterials.uk.com
enquiries@designandmaterials.
uk.com
01909 540 123

Build cost
£350,000

Design © Design &
Materials

Plan no. **BHP 310578**

This design provides five
bedrooms in the main
house and a self-contained
annexe above the garage.
Other touches include a
master bedroom suite and
a galleried landing.

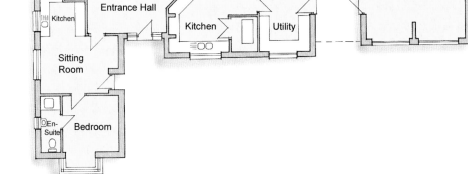

Plan no. **BHP 310254**

This house offers plenty of variety in the roof lines, tile-hung gables and single-storey wings. At the back is a conservatory which provides light for the full-depth hall.

Traditional style

Floor area
399m²
4295ft²

Bedrooms
5

Bathrooms
4

Floors
2

Key features
Kitchen/family room
Snooker room
separate dining room
Conservatory
3 en-suite bedrooms

Garaging for
3 cars

Design
Planahome

www.planahome.uk.com
plans@planahome.uk.com
01326 373600

Build cost
£358,000

Design
© Planahome

Traditional style

Floor area
400m²
4306ft²

Bedrooms
5

Bathrooms
5

Floors
2

Key features
Kitchen/breakfast
room
Sparate dining room
Family room
4 beds en-suite

Garaging for
0 cars

Design
**John Braid
(at Leslie R Hutt)**

lhuttarchitect@btinternet.com
01463 235566

Build cost
£359,000

Design © Leslie R Hutt

Plan no. **BHP 310317**

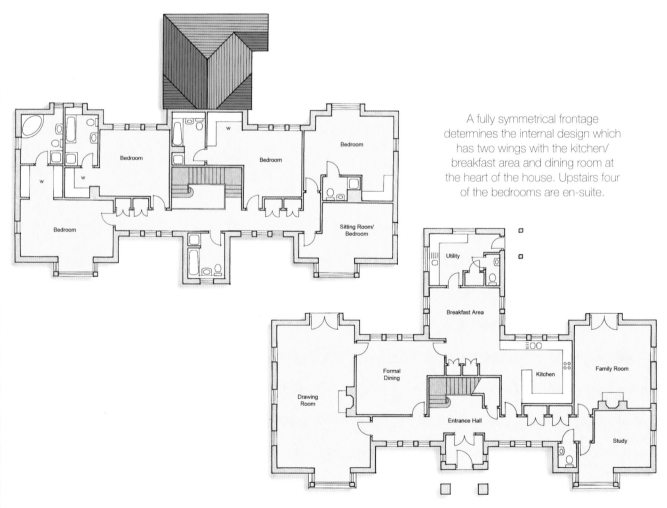

A fully symmetrical frontage
determines the internal design which
has two wings with the kitchen/
breakfast area and dining room at
the heart of the house. Upstairs four
of the bedrooms are en-suite.

Plan no. **BHP 310644**

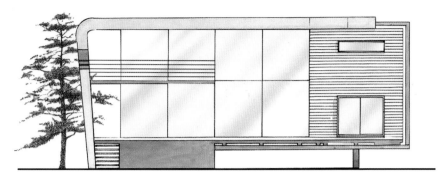

This design aims to take full advantage of a beautiful view with large areas of glass breaking down the barriers between the inside and outside. The ground floor features lots of open space but this can be changed quickly by sliding dividing screens into place. The master bedroom on the first floor features a twin aspect balcony, and is joined by another four double bedrooms.

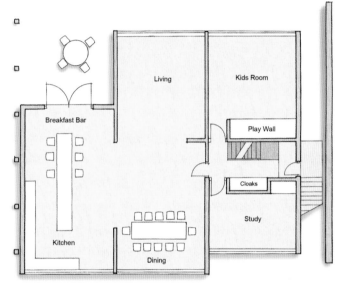

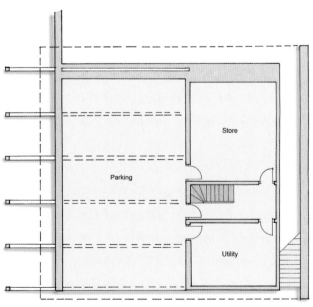

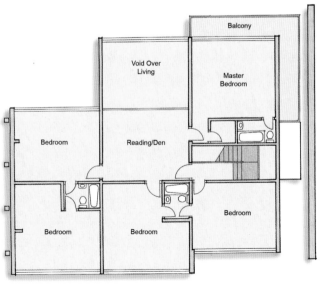

Contemporary style

Floor area
402m²
4327ft²

Bedrooms
5

Bathrooms
3

Floors
3

Key features
Open-plan living
Utility room
Play room
Study
En-suite master bed

Garaging for
5 cars

Design
Spacelab UK

www.spacelabuk.com
info@spacelab.co.uk
0207 684 5392

Build cost
£360,500

Design
© Spacelab UK

Traditional style

Floor area

404m²

4349ft²

Bedrooms

5

Bathrooms

4

Floors

4

Key features
Kitchen/breakfast room
Utility room
Family room
Study
Master bedroom suite

Garaging for
2 cars

Design
Design & Materials

www.designandmaterials.uk.com
enquiries@designandmaterials.
uk.com
01909 540 123

Build cost
£363,000

Design
© Design & Materials

Plan no. **BHP 310056**

A sloping site doesn't mean you have to compromise on your build. The basement provides a double garage and covered parking for two cars along with an external and internal store. The ground and first floors provide ample living and sleeping space while there is a self-contained suite on the top floor.

Plan no. **BHP 310641**

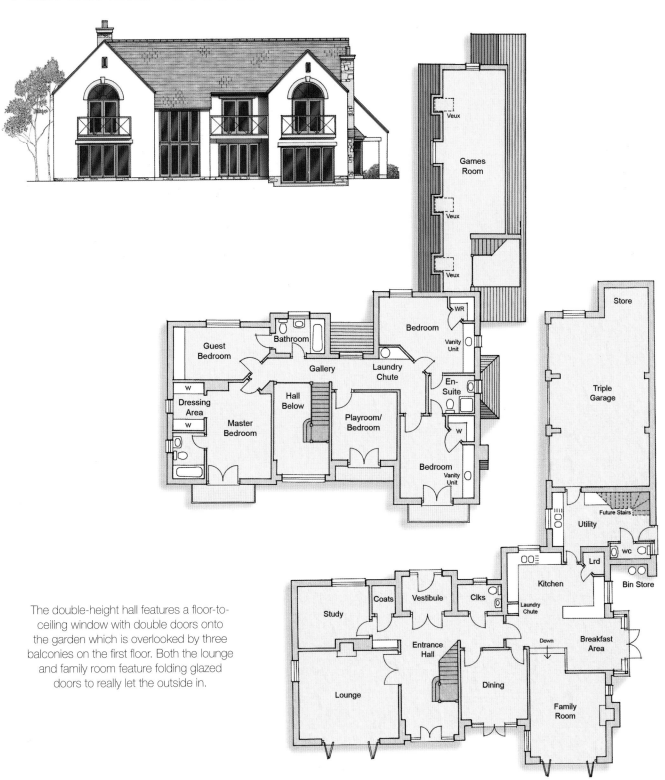

The double-height hall features a floor-to-ceiling window with double doors onto the garden which is overlooked by three balconies on the first floor. Both the lounge and family room feature folding glazed doors to really let the outside in.

Contemporary style

Floor area
425m²
4575ft²

Bedrooms
5

Bathrooms
3

Floors
2

Key features
Kitchen/breakfast room
Family room
Study
Games Room
Master bed suite

Garaging for
3 cars

Design
Design & Materials

www.designandmaterials.uk.com
enquiries@designandmaterials.uk.com
01909 540 123

Build cost
£381,000

Contemporary style

Floor area
430m²
4628ft²

Bedrooms
5

Bathrooms
5

Floors
2

Key features
Open-plan living area
Swimming pool
Music room
Conservatory
Master bedroom suite

Garaging for
2 cars

Design
Design 62

01484 300843

Build cost
£386,000

Design © Design 62

Plan no. **BHP 310068**

The indoor swimming pool is located in a conservatory that wraps around the back of this house which includes a second conservatory and a soundproofed music room.

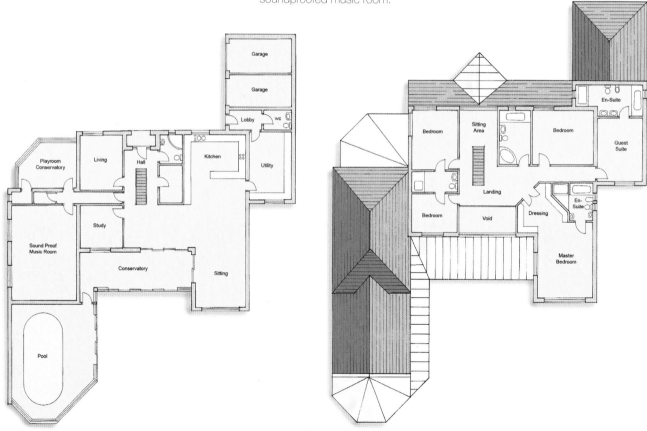

Plan no. **BHP** **310338**

Two bedrooms benefit from the twin first floor balcony structures at the rear of this house. Downstairs there is a vaulted hall complete with impressive double-flight staircase.

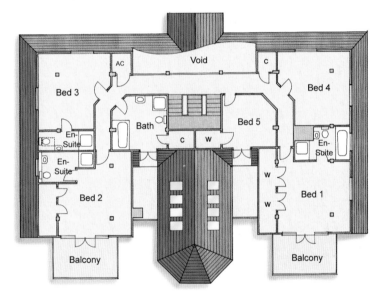

Traditional style

Floor area
450m²
4844ft²

Bedrooms
5

Bathrooms
4

Floors
2

Key features
Vaulted hall
Games Room
Full height living area
Study
3 bedrooms en-suite

Garaging for
0 cars

Design
Potton

www.potton.co.uk
contact@potton.co.uk
01767 676 400

Build cost
£404,000

Design © Potton

Traditional style

Floor area
465m²
5005ft²

Bedrooms
5

Bathrooms
3

Floors
2

Key features
Kitchen/dining room
Play room
Music room
Conservatory
Master bedroom suite

Garaging for
2 cars

Design
Design & Materials

www.designandmaterials.uk.com
enquiries@designandmaterials.
uk.com
01909 540 123

Build cost
£417,000

Design © Design &
Materials

Plan no. **BHP 310485**

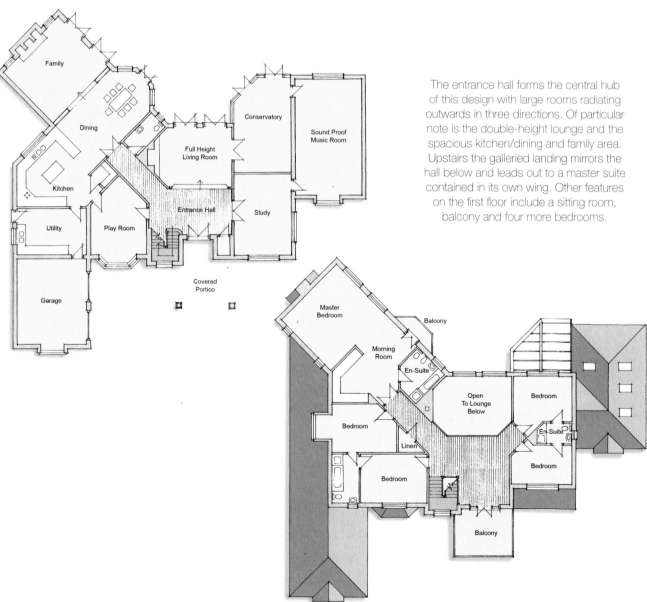

The entrance hall forms the central hub of this design with large rooms radiating outwards in three directions. Of particular note is the double-height lounge and the spacious kitchen/dining and family area. Upstairs the galleried landing mirrors the hall below and leads out to a master suite contained in its own wing. Other features on the first floor include a sitting room, balcony and four more bedrooms.

Plan no. **BHP 310320**

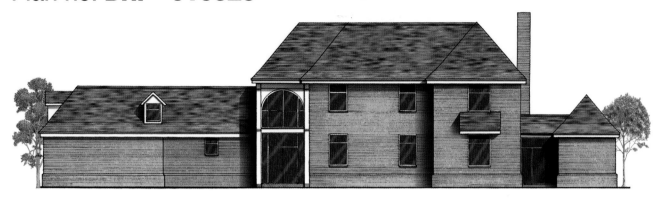

This is a house of big reception rooms – many of them interlinked. The first floor games room is a striking feature and is approached via a galleried walkway overlooking the foyer.

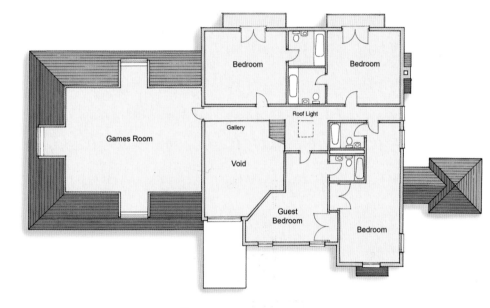

Bedroom

Bedroom

Roof Light

Games Room

Gallery

Void

Guest Bedroom

Bedroom

Garage

Main Brdroom

Living

Family

ST

ST

Clks

Kitchen

Bath

Foyer

Den

Laund'

Family Dining

Boots

Wash

Contemporary style

Floor area

506m²

5447ft²

Bedrooms

5

Bathrooms

5

Floors

2

Key features
Kitchen/dining room
Open-plan living area
Games room
Galleried landing
All bedrooms en-suite

Garaging for
3 cars

Design
**John Shida
(Morningtide
Developments)**

www.morningtide.fsnet.co.uk
johnshida@morningtide.
fsnet.co.uk
01621 815485

Build cost
£454,000

Design © John Shida

Traditional style

Floor area

521m²

5608ft²

Bedrooms

5

Bathrooms

5

Floors

4

Key features
Kitchen/breakfast room
Feature staircase
Basement games room
Conservatory
Master bedroom suite

Garaging for
2 cars

Design
**TJ Crump
Oakwrights**

www.oakwrights.co.uk
enquiries@oakwrights.co.uk
01432 353353

Build cost
£467,000

Design © TJ Crump

Plan no. **BHP 310692**

This design features accommodation on four levels. Above the basement garage complex is a large kitchen and an equally generous living room. On the first floor are four bedrooms with the fifth, the master bedroom suite, occupying the whole of the second floor

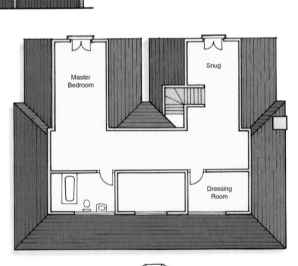

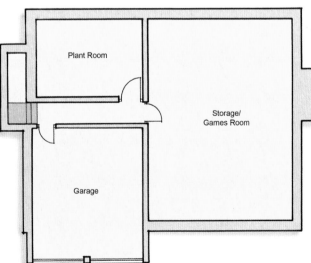

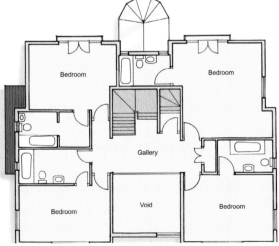

Plan no. **BHP 310815**

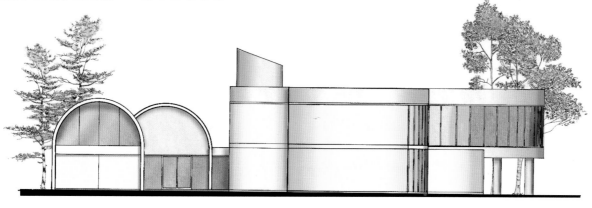

The ultimate in open-plan living? The main living space is completely open-plan with only the dining room and studio separate. Up the spiral stairs are five bedrooms off a central walkway.

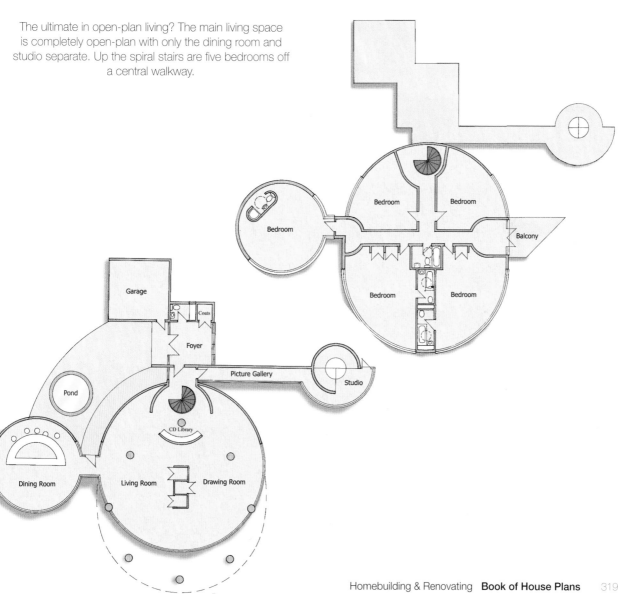

Bedroom

Bedroom

Bedroom

Bedroom

Balcony

Bedroom

Bedroom

Garage

Coats

Foyer

Picture Gallery

Studio

Pond

CD Library

Dining Room

Living Room

Drawing Room

Contemporary style

Floor area

538m²

5791ft²

Bedrooms

5

Bathrooms

4

Floors

2

Key features
Kitchen/dining room
Open-plan living area
Studio
Picture gallery
2 en-suite beds

Garaging for

0 cars

Design
**John Shida
(Morningtide
Developments)**

www.morningtide.fsnet.co.uk

johnshida@morningtide.
fsnet.co.uk

01621 815485

Build cost
£482,500

Design © John Shida

Traditional style

Floor area

620m²

6674ft²

Bedrooms

5

Bathrooms

3

Floors

2

Key features
Kitchen/dining room
Music room
Internal courtyard
Study
All bedrooms en-suite

Garaging for
2 cars

Design
**JS Building
Consultancy**

www.ukbuildingconsultancy.
co.uk
jsharples@ricsonline.org
0113 250 1303

Build cost
£556,000

Design © JS Building
Consultancy

Plan no. **BHP 310386**

This house is a hollow square with a central courtyard that acts as a light well. There's a feature curved staircase in the galleried hall – which also has a vaulted ceiling. At the back of the house the living room, dining room and kitchen lead onto a deep terrace, the latter via a conservatory.

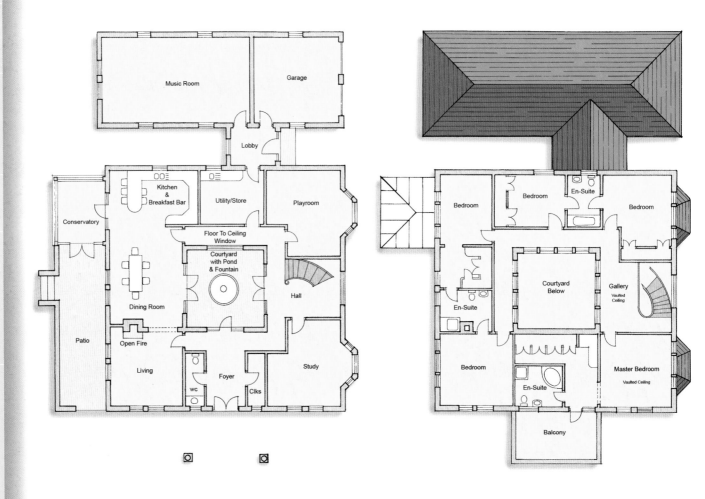

Plan no. **BHP 310161**

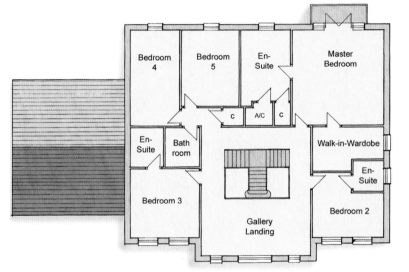

Bedroom 4 · Bedroom 5 · En-Suite · Master Bedroom · c · A/C · c · En-Suite · Bath room · Walk-in-Wardobe · En-Suite · Bedroom 3 · Bedroom 2 · Gallery Landing

With an underground pool and sauna complex this house offers high-level features including a galleried hall, separate dining room and large master bedroom suite with walk-in wardrobe.

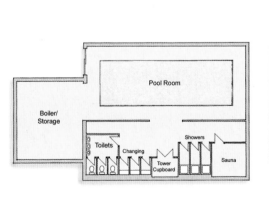

Pool Room · Boiler/ Storage · Toilets · Changing · Showers · Tower Cupboard · Sauna

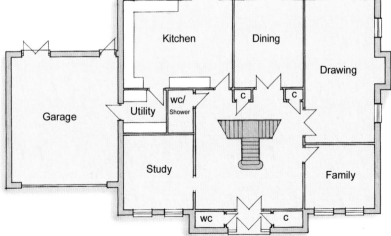

Garage · Kitchen · Dining · Drawing · Utility · WC/ Shower · c · c · Study · Family · WC · c

Traditional style

Floor area
668m²
7190ft²

Bedrooms
5

Bathrooms
4

Floors
3

Key features
Basement pool/sauna
Kitchen/breakfast room
Study
Separate dining room
3 bedrooms en-suite

Garaging for
2 cars

Design
Custom Homes

www.customhomes.co.uk
admin@customhomes.co.uk
01787 377388

Build cost
£599,000

Design © Custom Homes

Traditional style

Floor area

698m²

7513ft²

Bedrooms

5

Bathrooms

5

Floors

2

Key features
Family room
Separate dining room
Study
Galleried landing
All bedrooms en-suite

Garaging for

0 cars

Design

Border Oak

www.borderoak.com
sales@borderoak.com
01568 708752

Build cost
£626,000

Design © Border Oak

Plan no. **BHP 310188**

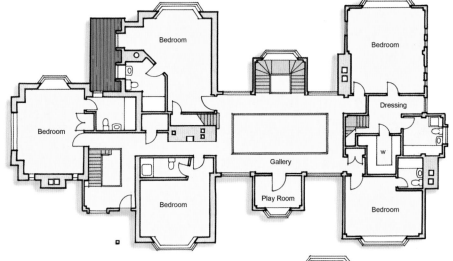

There's a grand entrance this
house which is designed to
impress. The hall features
a full galleried landing with
matching staircase leading
to five en-suite bedrooms.
There is also a service
staircase tucked behind the
kitchen/utility room.

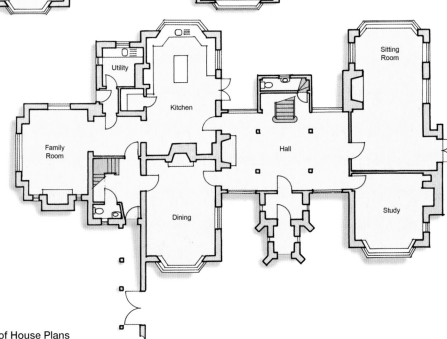

Plan no. **BHP 310971**

There's a sunken patio to allow natural light into the swimming pool/sitting area of the basement – which covers most of footprint of this house. Upstairs there's a very high specification home including a billiard room capable of housing a full-sized table.

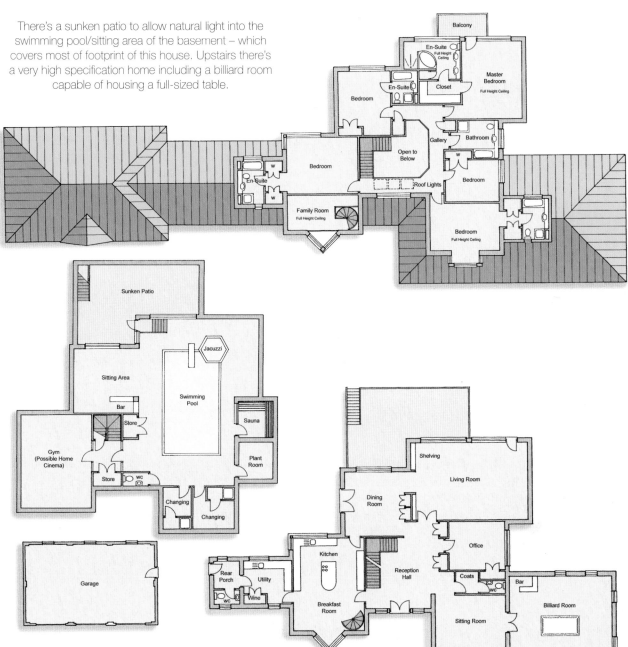

Floor area

850m²

9149ft²

Bedrooms

5

Bathrooms

5

Floors

3

Key features
Basement pool/gym
Kitchen/breakfast room
Billiard room
Family room
Master bedroom suite

Garaging for
3 cars

Design
**John Braid
(at Leslie R Hutt)**

lhuttarchitect@btinternet.com
01463 235566

Build cost
£762,000

Design © Leslie R Hutt

Contemporary style

Floor area

218m²

2347ft²

Bedrooms

6

Bathrooms

5

Floors

2

Key features
Kitchen/dining room
Music room
Study
Larder
4 bedrooms en-suite

Garaging for
2 cars

Design
Eclipse Design

www.eclipsedesign.
copperstream.co.uk
enquiries@eclipsedesignuk.
net 0845 460 4758

Build cost
£200,500

Design © Eclipse Design

Plan no. **BHP 310881**

This contemporary-styled house doesn't disappoint inside with an open-plan hall/living room and kitchen/dining area. Upstairs there's a large balcony, six bedrooms and five bathrooms.

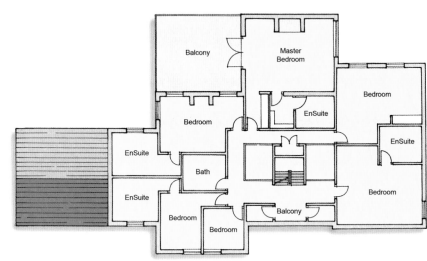

Plan no. **BHP 310773**

The ground floor offers a free-flowing design from the kitchen and dining room leading out to a covered outdoor eating area – this loggia can also be accessed from the drawing room. Upstairs there's a rear-facing balcony that leads off two bedrooms, a separate dressing room and a luxurious seating/viewing area off the landing.

Traditional style

Floor area

312m²

3358ft²

Bedrooms

6

Bathrooms

4

Floors

2

Key features
Kitchen/breakfast room
Family room
Separate dining room
Utility room
En-suite master bed

Garaging for
2 cars

Design
**The Bespoke
Design Company**

www.planahome.uk.com
plans@planahome.uk.com
01326 373600

Build cost
£280,000

Contemporary style

Floor area
320m²
3444ft²

Bedrooms
6

Bathrooms
4

Floors
2

Key features
Kitchen/dining room
Twin studies
Conservatory
Guest suite
Master bedroom suite

Garaging for
2 cars

Design
John Watson

Build cost
£287,000

Design © John Watson

Plan no. **BHP 310533**

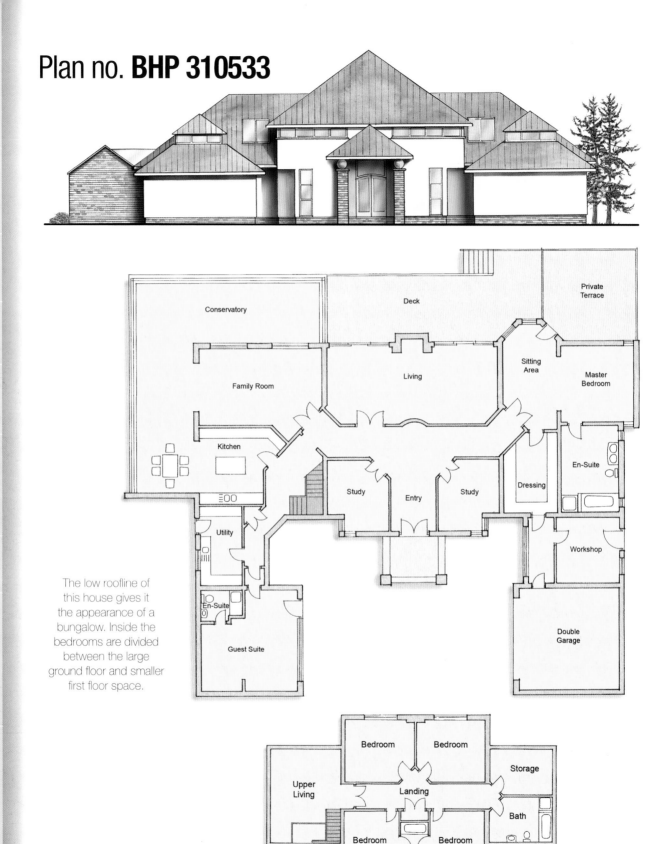

The low roofline of this house gives it the appearance of a bungalow. Inside the bedrooms are divided between the large ground floor and smaller first floor space.

Plan no. **BHP 310929**

The large galleried family room with stairs to the first floor is at the very centre of the house but is not the entrance hall. like many Victorian homes the rooms in which visitors might be entertained are accessible without entering the 'private' family areas.

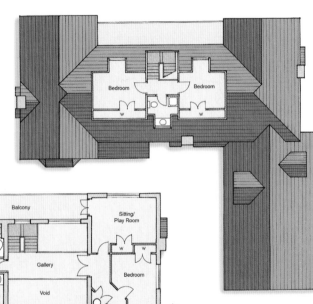

Traditional style

Floor area
336m²
3617ft²

Bedrooms
6

Bathrooms
4

Floors
3

Key features
Kitchen breakfast room
Family room
Study
Playroom
Master bed en-suite

Garaging for
3 cars

Design
Planahome

www.planahome.uk.com
plans@planahome.uk.com
01326 373600

Build cost
£301,000

Design © Planahome

Traditional style

Floor area
340m²
3660ft²

Bedrooms
6

Bathrooms
3

Floors
2

Key features
Kitchen/breakfast room
Snooker room
Family room
Sun lounge
2 bedrooms en-suite

Garaging for
2 cars

Design
**John Braid
(at Leslie R Hutt)**

lhuttarchitect@btinternet.com
01463 235566

Build cost
£305,000

Design © Leslie R Hutt

Plan no. **BHP 310095**

Among this house's luxury touches are an inset balcony for the master bedroom suite's sitting room, a double-height sun lounge to relax in and a snooker room.

Plan no. **BHP 310998**

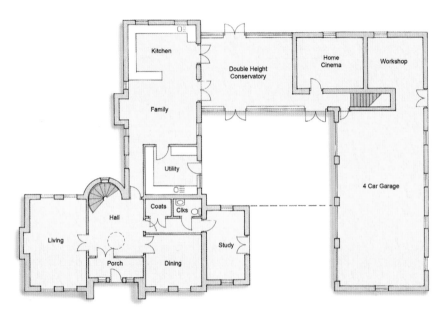

Through the archway which leads to the four-car garage can be glimpsed the double-height conservatory which features a raised walkway to access the gym and self-contained apartment. To the other side of the conservatory is a large kitchen and family room.

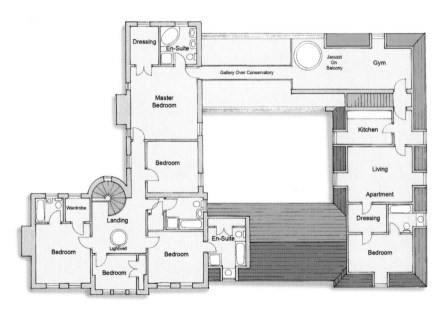

Traditional style

Floor area
350m²
3767ft²

Bedrooms
6

Bathrooms
5

Floors
2

Key features
Kitchen/family room
Conservatory
Study
Gym/Jacuzzi
Master bedroom suite

Garaging for
4 cars

Design
Planahome

www.planahome.uk.com
plans@planahome.uk.com
01326 373600

Build cost
£312,000

Design © Planahome

Traditional style

Floor area
436m²
4693ft²

Bedrooms
6

Bathrooms
5

Floors
2

Key features
Kitchen/family room
Conservatory
Cinema
Gym/Jacuzzi
Self-contained flat

Garaging for
4 cars

Design
Planahome

www.planahome.uk.com
plans@planahome.uk.com
01326 373600

Build cost
£391,000

Design © Planahome

Plan no. **BHP 310302**

This plan is unusual as the garage is positioned behind the house which would probably lead to the laundry/utility, left hand conservatory and kitchen overlooking a sweeping drive. Over the garage is a grand master bedroom – complete with open fireplace.

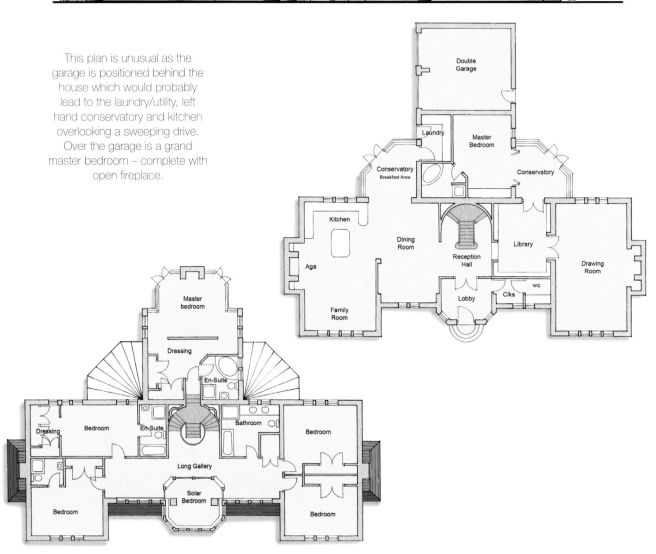

Plan no. **BHP 310785**

The exterior design of this house is conventional but one unusual feature is the large sun lounge – which can be accessed from both the kitchen and drawing room. Upstairs there are six bedrooms and five en-suite bathrooms.

Floor plan labels (upper floor):
Bedroom, Bedroom, Bedroom, Bedroom, A/C, Galleried Landing, Bedroom, Bedroom

Floor plan labels (ground floor):
Sunlounge, Utility, WC, Larder, Boot Room, Kitchen, Drawing Room, Wine Store, Dining, Family Room, WC, Study

Traditional style

Floor area
515m²
5543ft²

Bedrooms
6

Bathrooms
5

Floors
2

Key features
Sun lounge
Study
Family room
Separate dining room
All bedrooms en-suite

Garaging for
0 cars

Design
Custom Homes

www.customhomes.co.uk
admin@customhomes.co.uk
01787 377388

Build cost
£464,500

Design © Custom Homes

Contemporary style

Floor area

550m²

5920ft²

Bedrooms

6

Bathrooms

5

Floors

3

Key features
Pool and sauna
Sun lounge
Separate dining room
Library area
Master bedroom suite

Garaging for
2 cars

Design
Design 62

01484 300843

Build cost
£493,000

Design © Design 62

Plan no. **BHP 310821**

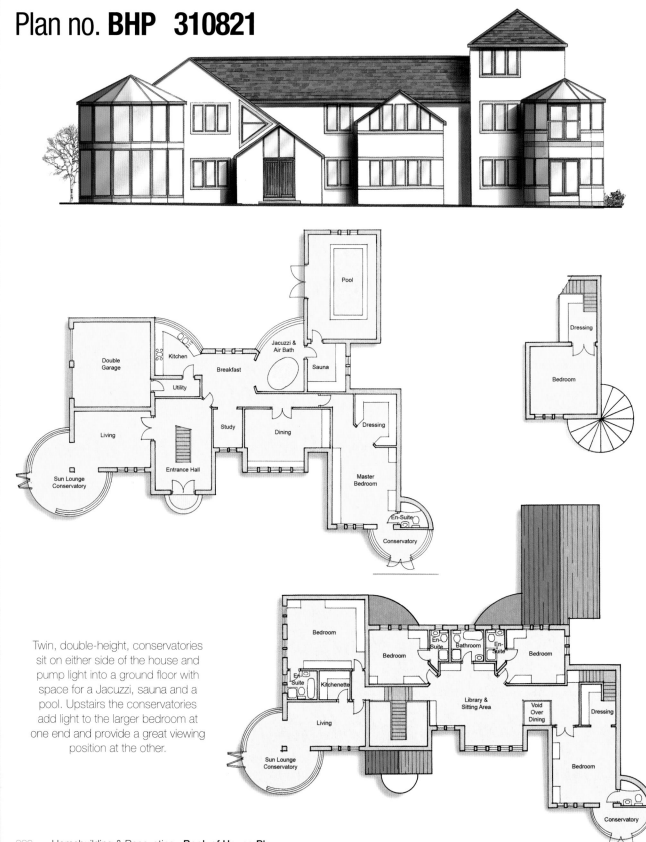

Twin, double-height, conservatories sit on either side of the house and pump light into a ground floor with space for a Jacuzzi, sauna and a pool. Upstairs the conservatories add light to the larger bedroom at one end and provide a great viewing position at the other.

Plan no. **BHP 310125**

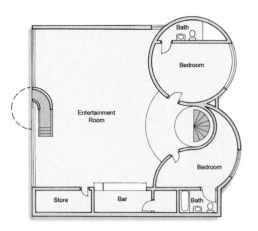

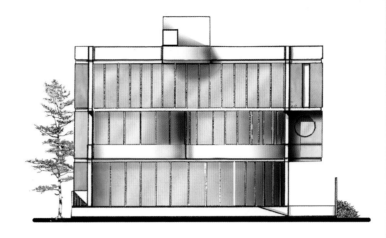

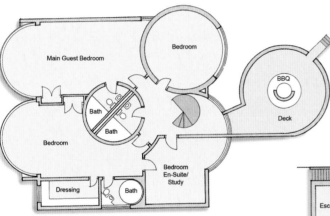

Almost a leisure complex, this home has its' entire basement taken up by a swimming pool, gym and Jacuzzi. Upstairs the ground floor features a playroom along with an open-plan living and dining area. The leisure theme continues on the first floor with its dedicated, full-depth, entertainment room and ends with a flourish on the second floor's circular deck.

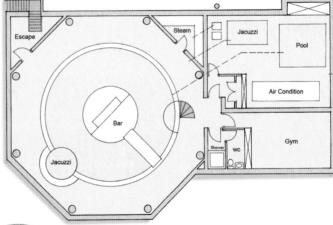

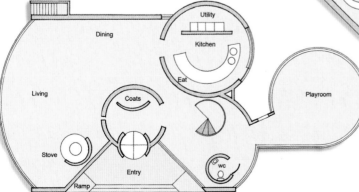

Contemporary style

Floor area
888m²
9558ft²

Bedrooms
6

Bathrooms
5

Floors
4

Key features
Swimming pool/gym
Open-plan living area
Entertainment room
BBQ deck
Playroom

Garaging for
0 cars

Design
**John Shida
(Morningtide
Developments)**

www.morningtide.fsnet.co.uk
johnshida@morningtide.
fsnet.co.uk
01621 815485

Build cost
£796,000

Design © John Shida

Traditional style

Floor area

236m²

2540ft²

Bedrooms

7

Bathrooms

4

Floors

3

Key features
Kitchen/breakfast room
Conservatory
Separate dining room
Games room
3 en-suites

Garaging for
0 cars

Design
Potton

www.potton.co.uk
contact@potton.co.uk
01767 676 400

Build cost
£212,000

Design © Potton

Plan no. **BHP 310185**

This house packs seven bedrooms into three floors and still offers a large kitchen/family room, separate dining room and study – all in a relatively modest 236 square metres.

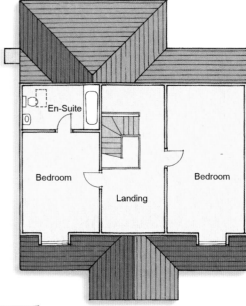

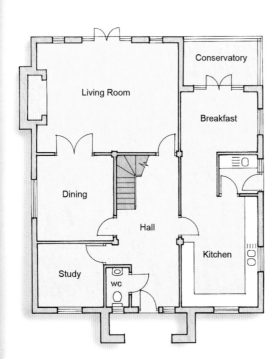

Plan no. **BHP 310440**

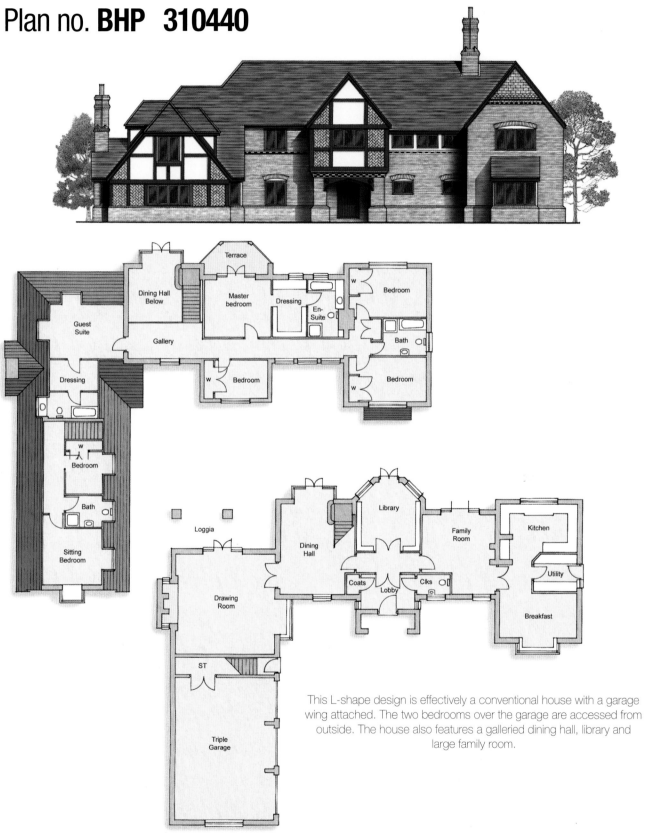

This L-shape design is effectively a conventional house with a garage wing attached. The two bedrooms over the garage are accessed from outside. The house also features a galleried dining hall, library and large family room.

Traditional style

Floor area
332m²
3574ft²

Bedrooms
7

Bathrooms
4

Floors
2

Key features
Kitchen/breakfast room
Dining hall
Family room
Utility room
Master bedroom suite

Garaging for
3 cars

Design
Planahome

www.planahome.uk.com
plans@planahome.uk.com
01326 373600

Build cost
£298,000

Design © Planahome

Traditional style

Floor area
354m²
3810ft²

Bedrooms
7

Bathrooms
4

Floors
3

Key features
Kitchen/breakfast room
Family room
Separate dining room
Library
Master bedroom suite

Garaging for
2 cars

Design
Planahome

www.planahome.uk.com
plans@planahome.uk.com
01326 373600

Build cost
£317,500

Design © Planahome

Plan no. **BHP 310305**

The varied roof lines, bay windows and dormers create an interesting exterior to this well-specified family home.

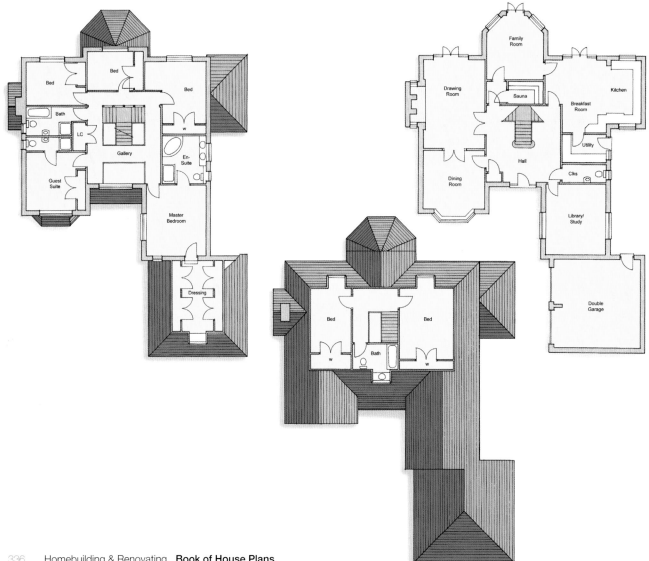

Plan no. **BHP 310848**

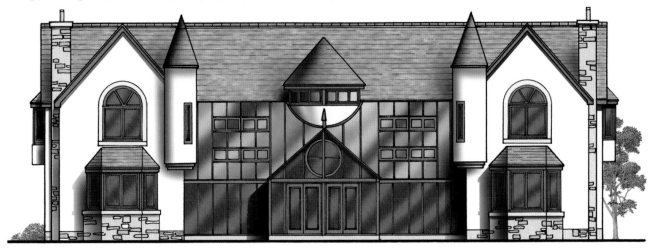

This house has stables, integral garaging and an indoor swimming pool in an enormous conservatory. Upstairs is similarly luxurious with a galleried landing and a substantial master bedroom suite with separate study and snug.

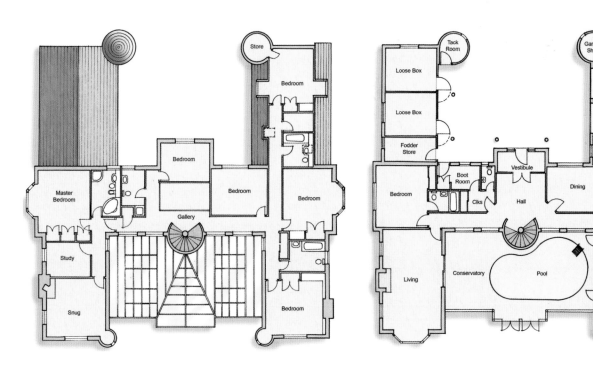

Traditional style

Floor area
438m²
4715ft²

Bedrooms
7

Bathrooms
5

Floors
2

Key features
Pool conservatory
Stable block
Family room
Separate dining room
Master bedroom suite

Garaging for
2 cars

Design
The Border Design Centre

www.borderdesign.co.uk
borderdesign@btconnect.com
01578 740218

Build cost
£393,000

Design © The Border
Design Centre

Contemporary style

Floor area

454m²

4887ft²

Bedrooms

6

Bathrooms

7

Floors

1

Key features
Swimming pool
Open-plan living area
Conservatory
Library
5 bedrooms en-suite

Garaging for
2 cars

Design
Architecture Plus

www.architecture-plus.co.uk
01934 416416

Build cost
£407,000

Design © Architecture Plus

Plan no. **BHP 310344**

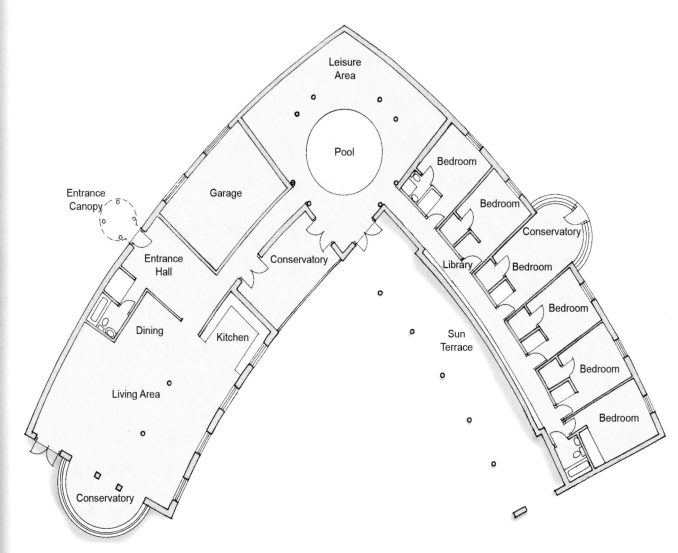

The pool area forms the central hub of the house and leads off to six en-suite bedrooms and a sun terrace to starboard and an open-plan kitchen/dining area on the port side. Three conservatories are included in the design to take advantage of morning, midday and afternoon sun.

Plan no. **BHP 310674**

Bedroom

Bedroom

Bedroom

En-Suite

Bath

Gallery

En-Suite

Linen

Feature Window

Bedroom

Dressing Room

Master Bedroom

Balcony

Bar

Pool

Sitting Area

Plant Room

Shower

Steam Room

Gym

Breakfast Area

Family

Kitchen

Utility

Hall

wc

Dining

Living

Bedroom

Study

En-Suite

Bedroom

En-Suite

Bar

Window Seat

Window Seat

Entertaining Room

Balcony

The compact footprint of this house and the use of a basement initially hides the fact that it offers a massive 511 sq m of living space – allowing for seven bedrooms as well as swimming pool and gym.

Contemporary style

Floor area
511m²
5500ft²

Bedrooms
7

Bathrooms
6

Floors
4

Key features
Swimming pool/gym
Kitchen/breakfast room
Living/dining room
Study
4 bedrooms en-suite

Garaging for
0 cars

Design
Design & Materials

www.designandmaterials.uk.com
enquiries@designandmaterials.uk.com
01909 540 123

Build cost
£458,000

Design © Design & Materials

Traditional style

Floor area

545m²

5866ft²

Bedrooms

7

Bathrooms

7

Floors

2

Key features
Full height 'Great Hall'
Kitchen/breakfast room
Family room
Library
All bedrooms en-suite

Garaging for
0 cars

Design
Jeremy Rawlings

www.periodhome.net
01884 266444

Build cost
£489,000

Design © Jeremy Rawlings

Plan no. **BHP 310611**

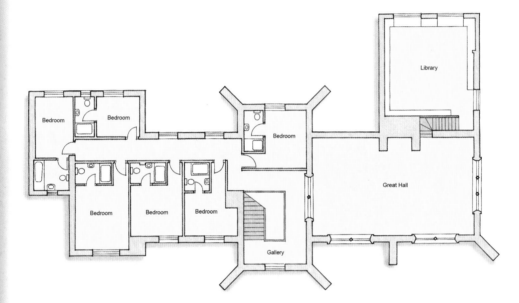

There's an ecclesiastical air to this design thanks to its mullioned windows and grand, arched entrance. Inside, things are less church-like with a large conservatory off the Great Hall. This is also accessed from the sitting area of the master bedroom suite which is on the ground floor. Upstairs are six further bedrooms.

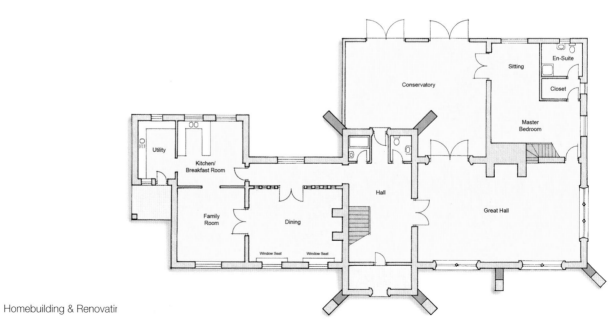

Plan no. **BHP 310638**

The kitchen, conservatory and breakfast room provide plenty of useful space and the utility room offers direct access to the built-in garage. Luxury is provided in the form of an indoor swimming pool with vaulted ceiling and a home gym. Upstairs there are balconies for three of the bedrooms, a galleried landing and a vaulted-ceiling sitting area.

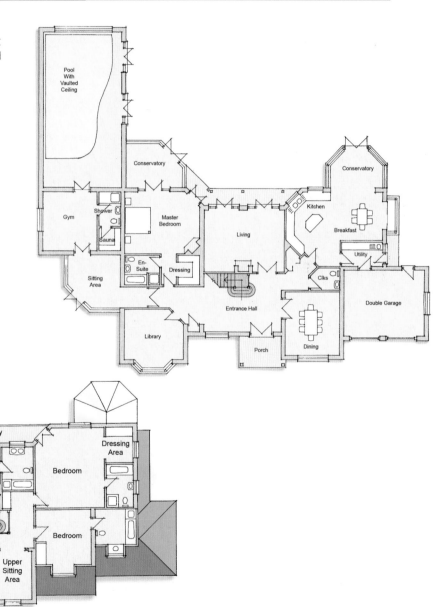

Traditional style

Floor area

576m²

6200ft²

Bedrooms

7

Bathrooms

6

Floors

2

Key features
Kitchen dining room
Conservatory
Playroom
Vaulted sitting room
Self-contained flat

Garaging for
3 cars

Design
Design & Materials

www.designandmaterials.uk.com
enquiries@designandmaterials.
uk.com

01909 540 123

Build cost

£516,500

Design © Design &
Materials

Plan no. **BHP 310287**

The design offers a large family room with folding doors which can be linked to the kitchen/dining area. The drawing room has a vaulted ceiling and there is a conservatory, study, playroom and large utility room as well. Upstairs has an annexe with its own access over the triple garage.

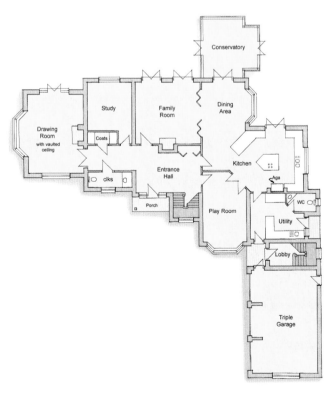

Plan no. **BHP 310119**

The layout is based around a central light well which is surrounded by a gallery and a staircase rising between levels. The first and second floors have access to balconies and the open-plan ground floor lounge features a splendid semi-circular bay window.

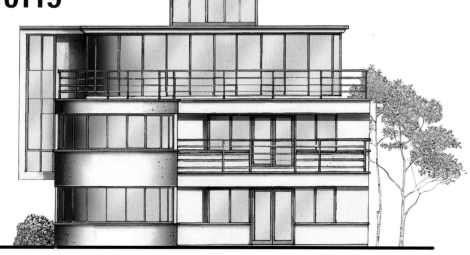

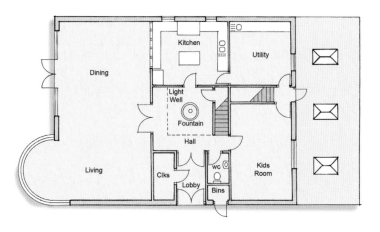

Kitchen

Utility

Dining

Light Well

Fountain

Hall

Living

Clks

Lobby

wc

Bins

Kids Room

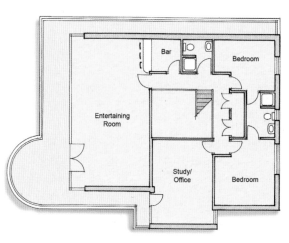

Bar

Bedroom

Entertaining Room

Study/Office

Bedroom

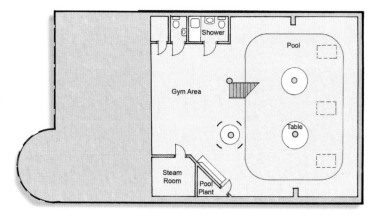

Shower

Pool

Gym Area

Table

Steam Room

Pool Plant

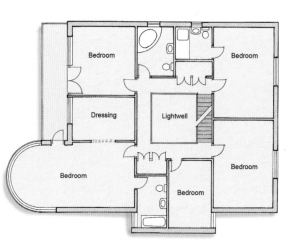

Bedroom

Bedroom

Dressing

Lightwell

Bedroom

Bedroom

Bedroom

Contemporary style

Floor area
635m²
6835ft²

Bedrooms
7

Bathrooms
6

Floors
4

Key features
Swimming pool/gym
Open-plan living area
Entertaining room
Study
Master bedroom suite

Garaging for
0 cars

Design
Architecture Plus

www.architecture-plus.co.uk
01934 416416

Build cost
£569,500

Design © Architecture Plus

Contemporary style

Floor area

700m²

7535ft²

Bedrooms

7

Bathrooms

5

Floors

4

Key features
Swimming pool/gym
Entertaining room
Living/dining room
Playroom
Master bedroom suite

Garaging for
0 cars

Design
Jeremy Rawlings

www.periodhome.net
01884 266444

Build cost
£628,000

Design
© Jeremy Rawlings

Plan no. **BHP 310335**

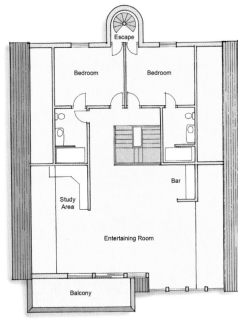

A dramatic cantilevered first floor adds to the drama of this modern design which offers a full-width deck on the ground floor and offset balconies on the first and second floors. Below ground is a gym, steam room and swimming pool complex.

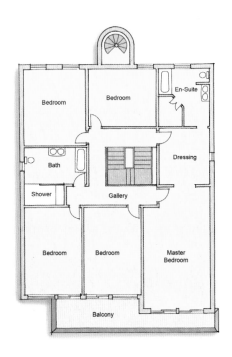

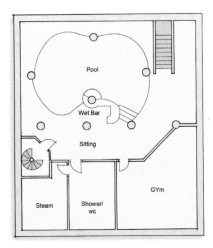

Plan no. **BHP 310299**

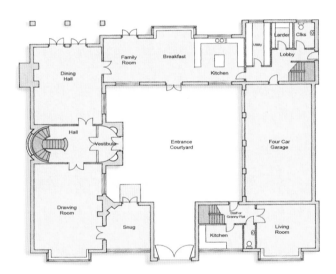

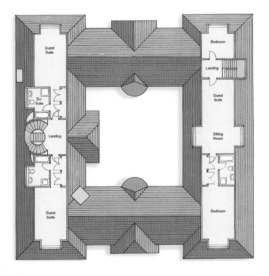

Traditional style

Floor area
880m²
9472ft²

Bedrooms
12

Bathrooms
8

Floors
3

Key features
Entrance courtyard
Kitchen/family room
Dining hall
Guest bedroom suite
Master bedroom suite

**Garaging for
4 cars**

Design
**The Bespoke
Design Company**

www.planahome.uk.com
plans@planahome.uk.com
01326 373600

**Build cost
£789,000**

The four wings of this house are formed around a central courtyard accessed through an archway with double gates. Inside there are three separate staircases to take you to the first floor with its bedrooms, bathrooms, gallery and study. The central staircase spirals upwards to the second floor landing's guest suites. On the opposite side of the house there's another guest suite and two further bedrooms.

ARCHITECTURE
Plus

As an independent architectural consultant I seek to work with my clients on projects that will engage and challenge me whilst helping you to achieve your goal of a dream home.

Architecture plus was created to provide accessible architectural design input that is flexible in approach, I seek to provide an architectural design service for individual clients and tailor my services accordingly. There are many people who can draw plans but fewer who can 'design' homes.

If you have a dream or a perfect plot that is challenging you or you are sitting on a plot and want to realise the potential then that is a good reason to contact Architecture plus.

T 01934 416416 • **F** 01934 622583 • **E** info@architectureplus.co.uk • **www.architectureplus.co.uk**
Architecture Plus • 5 Dunkery Road • Weston Super Mare • Somerset • BS23 2TD

A Member of the
Chartered Institute of
Architectural Technologists

cottages · farmhouses · manor houses · contemporary barns · garages · outbuildings ·

award winning bespoke oak framed structures

BORDER OAK

Border Oak Design & Construction Ltd
Kingsland Sawmills, Kingsland, Leominster, Herefordshire, HR6 9SF
Tel 01568 708 752 Fax 01568 708 295
www.borderoak.com

A Member of UKTFA

Realising your dream

Building your new home is a demanding and exciting project, but if you involve Maple Timber Frame right from the very beginning it need not be a daunting one. Call us now and let our design team help you realise your dream.

Maple Timber Frame of Langley
Manufacturers of Fine Timber Frame Homes
Tarnacre Hall Business Park, St Michaels
PR3 0SZ Telephone: 01995 679444
Email: enquiry@mapletimberframe.com
Website: www.mapletimberframe.com

Design :: Materials

We'll turn your dream home

into your real home

Design & Materials reputation is built on four decades expertise creating bespoke brick and block homes that are quiet, warm and solid. Our individually tailored service covers.

- Bespoke design, or choose one of our existing house plans
- Planning and Building Regulations
- Sourcing and supplying materials
- National network of contractors and industry experts

From North to South from start to finish, from cottages to mansions, from traditional layout to contemporary open plan and from 'hands-on' to 'hands-off' Design & Materials has everything you need to build your own home.

www.designandmaterials.uk.com

or call **01909 540 123**

or email enquiries@designandmaterials.uk.com

Design :: Materials
CREATING BESPOKE HOMES

Truly exceptional windows and doors. Only Marvin.

Marvin Windows and Doors are made for you. So they fit to your exact specifications, style, size and lifestyle. All handcrafted of beautiful wood, durable clad and a meticulous attention to every last detail. See the difference Marvin makes.

Made for you.®

www.marvin.com

To see what Marvin can do for you, visit one of our showrooms or our website at www.marvin-architectural.com. Contact us by phone or e-mail today.

Marvin Architectural of UK	Marvin Architectural of Ireland	N. I: Window Crafters
Canal House, Catherine Wheel Road	Stephen Street	Omagh Enterprise Centre
Brentford, Middlesex TW8 8BD	Dunlavin, Co. Wicklow	Great Northern Road, Omagh BT78 5LU
Phone: 0208 5698222	Phone: 00353 45 401000	Phone: 028 8225 1300
E-mail: sales@marvinuk.com	E-mail: sales@marvin-architectural.com	E-mail: info@windowcrafters.co.uk

FLOORWARMING ^{UK}

Floorwarming (UK) Limited
Warwick Mill Business Centre
Warwick Bridge
Carlisle
Cumbria CA4 8RR

Floorwarming UK leads the way in quality underfloor heating systems.

Providing comfort, space and style to any home or office, our individually-tailored systems are designed to complement today's busy lifestyle – while maintaining traditional standards of workmanship and service.

From concept to installation our specialist teams of engineers provide an unrivalled level of expertise, with an after-care service to ensure you get the very best from your system.

- Renewable Energy Specialists
- Nationwide Installation service
- Insulation
- Screed
- Technical support 24/7

For full details about Floorwarming UK's range of services and products, or a Personal Quotation including bespoke design, system specifications and all relevant components, contact us on:

t: 0870 8506660

or alternatively email us at info@floorwarming.co.uk

DESIGN

SUPPLY

INSTALL

UNDERFLOOR HEATING SPECIALISTS

YOU STAND ON OUR REPUTATION

Come Home to Welsh Oak Frame

If your desire is for the timeless beauty of a traditional oak framed home, we want to help you turn your dream home into a reality. Come home to a Welsh Oak Frame.

Discover the beauty of oak for your home.

Welsh Oak Frame, Belmont Yard, Station Road, Caersws, Powys, SY17 5EQ
Tel: 01686 688000 Fax: 01686 688139
email: info@welshoakframe.com website; www.welshoakframe.com

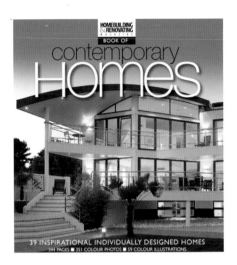

NEW EDITION OF CONTEMPORARY HOMES It's bigger and better than ever before - and completely redesigned, featuring 351 colour pictures, contact details of designers, builders and key suppliers. Enjoy reading about 39 of the most innovative houses to be built in the UK in the past five years. This book is both inspiring and practical, explaining the stories of how the houses were conceived and built.

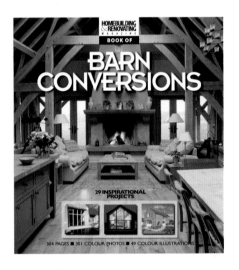

BRAND NEW SELECTION OF BARN CONVERSIONS This new collection is illustrated with hundreds of beautiful photographs and has the full story of each conversion as well as design, building and supplier contact details, providing you with inspiration and practical guidance. An essential companion for anyone serious about turning an old barn into a dream new home.

HOW TO RENOVATE A HOUSE IN FRANCE Whether you are buying an old house, worrying about damp stone walls, struggling to understand lime render, shopping for partition walling, hunting for builders, doing your own plumbing, trying to get planning permission... in short, if you are involved in any way with a renovation project in France, this book will be essential reading.

HOW TO CREATE A JARDIN PAYSAN This is a book about creating a traditional, rural French-style garden which will have a timeless charm. It's an antidote to the garden makeover, to suburban-style manicured lawns, or ranch fencing and tarmac driveways.

AVAILABLE NOW
INSPIRATION AND ADVICE

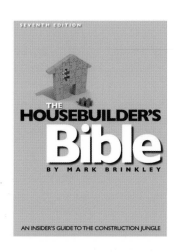

THE HOUSEBUILDER'S BIBLE This is the best-selling book on construction for builders and selfbuilders containing information, advice and yardstick costings. It is fully updated and is compliant with the latest building regs. It also includes an expanded green section, more information on extensions and a new snagging list.

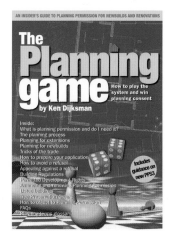

THE PLANNING GAME It's a guide to planning permission for newbuilds and extensions aimed at anyone who intends to do anything which will require planning permission. It provides a clear no-nonsense description of how the system works and what you will need to do to maximise your chances of success.

ORDER TODAY
VIEW our wide selection of self-build and renovation books online

VISIT www.homebuilding.co.uk/bookshop or call 01527 834437